the Book of

psalms

for singing

25th anniversary edition

David . . . in the book of Psalms . . . calls Him "Lord."

—Luke 20:42-44

Let the word of Christ richly dwell within you . . . with psalms and hymns and spiritual songs . . .

—Colossians 3:16

. . . Be filled with the Spirit . . . singing and making melody with your heart to the Lord.

—Ephesians 5:18, 19

C&C
For Christ's Crown and Covenant
PUBLICATIONS

FIRST PRINTING, 1973
SECOND PRINTING, 1975
THIRD PRINTING, 1978
FOURTH PRINTING, 1980
FIFTH PRINTING, 1983
SIXTH PRINTING, 1987
SEVENTH PRINTING, 1991
EIGHTH PRINTING, 1995
NINTH PRINTING, 1998
TENTH PRINTING, 1999

The Board of Education and Publication
Reformed Presbyterian Church of North America
7408 Penn Avenue
Pittsburgh, Pennsylvania 15208

Printed in the United States of America.

Every effort has been made to trace composers and original sources of the music in this volume and to record these in the alphabetical index of tunes. Permission for the use of copyrighted tunes or harmonizations has been acknowledged on the page with the music. If in any instance proper credit has not been given, the publishers will welcome notice that can lead to the removal of inaccuracies in future printings or editions.

ISBN 1-884527-00-0 (clothbound)
ISBN 1-884577-01-9 (vinyl ringbound)
ISBN 1-884527-02-7 (cloth ringbound)
ISBN 1-884527-08-6 (large-print)

INTRODUCTION

DESCRIPTION AND PURPOSE

As the title indicates, this volume contains English versions of the Psalms in musical settings designed for singing in public and private worship. Most of the versions are in rhymed meter in the tradition of the Genevan and Scottish Psalters of the early 1600's and of many later Psalmbooks. In an effort to capture further the meaning and force of the Hebrew poetry, some Psalms have been translated into unrhymed or irregular meters. The words from the Authorized Version of the Bible have been used for the chants and for a number of other musical settings.

TITLE

The collection of inspired songs in the Scriptures was designated by ancient Hebrew manuscripts as SEPHER TEHILLIM (Book of Praises). In quotations from Ephesians and Colossians on the title page of this volume, Paul described them as "psalms and hymns and songs of the Spirit," using terms from various headings and opening words found in the Greek version of the Scriptures which was familiar in his day. It seemed appropriate for this present publication, however, to use the title found in most English Bibles, the very words by which Jesus described the collection (Luke 24:42) when He said, "David himself says in the Book of Psalms."

IDENTIFICATION OF SELECTIONS

The 150 Psalms are clearly identified by the numbers used in the Hebrew Masoretic text, which has been followed by most English translations of Scripture. Divisions, alternate tunes, or different versions are indicated by a letter following this Psalm number, as 1A, 1B, or 119L, 119M, 119N.

VERSES AND STANZAS

Each selection is introduced by a title consisting of the Psalm number, followed by the verses which are included if the Psalm has been divided. The verses are further identified by small superscript numbers at the beginning of each. Stanzas are numbered according to the requirement of the music used, but from the beginning to the end of the Psalm, rather than within each selection. The worshipper is thus made aware of the continuity of each Psalm, even though he may be singing only a portion of it.

DIVISION OF PSALMS

Much effort has been devoted to insuring that every Psalm is available in divisions of singable length. With few exceptions, dividing has conformed to the strophes in the Hebrew text. Every Psalm is translated throughout in the same version, or in each of two versions, as in Psalm 18 A-F and G-L. The only exceptions to this rule are 68A, where only verses 1-6 of the Psalm are in five-line stanzas; 102B, in which verses 12-22 of the Psalm are in four-line stanzas; and 41C, 72D, 89I, and 106G, in which the final verse of the Psalm is presented in a unique musical setting.

MUSIC

The basis for choosing all of the music has been appropriateness for congregational singing without instrumental accompaniment. Most tunes are familiar, having strong melodies within average voice range, together with harmonizations that are interesting yet easily learned. Some alternate tunes, and some assigned to alternate versions, will require training and practice by leaders and singers alike. None, however, should be beyond the musical ability of those willing to prepare for singing praise to God. All have been selected with a view toward expressing the thought and mood of the words.

REFERENCE TO DEITY

To help the worshipper appreciate the names and titles of God inspired by the Holy Spirit in the Psalms, those preparing the versions for this volume have followed two rules: (1) use these names and titles whenever, but only when, they occur in the ancient texts; (2) distinguish consistently among them.

The Personal Name of God, spelled "JHWH" in English letters, occurs so frequently in the Psalms that a brief explanation is appropriate. For centuries before Christ, this Name was considered so sacred by the Hebrews that they would not pronounce it, and when reading or chanting they substituted the title ADONAI (Lord), which also occurs frequently in the Psalms. Most English translators have followed the ancient Greeks in using "Lord" to translate both the Name and the title of God but have usually distinguished between them by capitals, "LORD," for the Personal name and by conventional lettering, "Lord," for the title.

Here listed are three principal references to God in the order of the frequency with which they occur in the Psalms. Following each, also in the order of frequency, are the translations used in this volume:

JHWH: The LORD, LORD, Jehovah, GOD, THEE, HE, HIS.

ELOHIM: God.

ADONAI: The Lord, Lord, my Lord, Jehovah.

In a number of versions, "you" and its corresponding forms have replaced "thou" forms in addressing God and man, and in most others, "thou" forms (as in the Authorized Version) are used for both Deity and humanity. In a few versions the pattern has been that of several modern English translations of Scripture which address men as "you" and God as "Thou."

Care has been exercised in the capitalization of pronouns referring to any Person in the Trinity. Recognizing the Messianic nature of many Psalms has made it difficult to follow a consistent policy in such as 20, 21, 22, 45, and 72. In general, where reference can be to a man, even though as a king or a prophet or a priest he may be a type of Christ, capital letters have not been used.

Another policy concerns the capitalization of common nouns metaphorically describing God. Such words have been capitalized when used in direct address (as in 18G the first line of stanza one: "LORD, my Strength"), but not when used in simple metaphor (as in the second and following lines of the same stanza: "The LORD's my fort, my stronghold, etc.").

AUTHORIZATION

The preparation and publication of THE BOOK OF PSALMS FOR SINGING has been a project of the Synod of the Reformed Presbyterian Church of North America to encourage the use of Psalms in the praise of God by all those who would worship Him in Spirit and in truth.

Three of those appointed by the Synod in 1965 to investigate Psalter revision have served continuously since then in the planning and preparation of this edition: Charles McBurney, chairman; Mary E. Coleman, and Robert M. Copeland. Others who by Synod's appointment have contributed toward the completion of the project are Roy Blackwood, Cloyd E. Caskey, Clark Copeland, Mrs. Arvilla Copeland, Mrs. Louise Copeland, William Edgar, Mrs. Eleanor Hutcheson, Gertrude Lee, Mrs. Marian Martin, Robert McFarland, Ronald Nickerson, Edward Robson, John Schaefer, Kenneth G. Smith, Mrs. Elaine Tweed, G.I. Williamson, and Renwick Wright.

CONTENTS

PSALM 1

1A

ARLINGTON. C.M.
1. 1 O great - ly bless - ed is the man Who
2. Nor sit - teth in the scor - ner's chair, 2 But
3. 3 He shall be like a tree that grows Set
4. And all he does shall pros - per well. 4 The
walk - eth not a - stray In coun - sel of un-
plac - eth his de - light Up - on GOD's law, and
by the wa - ter - side, Which in its sea - son
wick - ed are not so, But are like chaff which

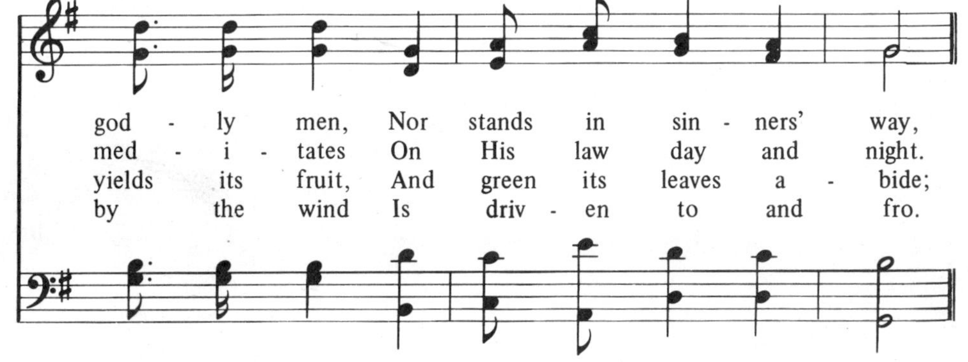
god - ly men, Nor stands in sin - ners' way,
med - i - tates On His law day and night.
yields its fruit, And green its leaves a - bide;
by the wind Is driv - en to and fro.

5. [5] In judgment therefore shall not stand
Such as ungodly are,
Nor in th' assembly of the just
Shall wicked men appear.

6. [6] Because the way of godly men
Is to Jehovah known;
Whereas the way of wicked men
Shall quite be overthrown.

PSALM 1

GIESEN. 88.88.88.

1. [1] How blessed the man who does not walk Where wick-ed men would
2. [3] He shall be like a grow-ing tree Im-plant-ed by the
3. [4] Not so the wick-ed: they are all Like chaff the wind will
guide his feet, Nor stands in paths with sin-ful men, Nor
wa-ter-side Which in its sea-son bears its fruit And
drive a-way. [5] They shall not in the judg-ment stand, Nor
sits up-on the scor-ner's seat. [2] Je-ho-vah's law is
has a leaf that does not fade. In all that may his
sin-ners with the right-eous stay. [6] The LORD the way of
his de-light, His med-i-ta-tion day and night.
hands em-ploy He shall pros-per-i-ty en-joy.
just men knows; The wick-ed to de-struc-tion goes.

PSALM 2

HINTZE. 77.77.D.
1. 1Why do hea-then na - tions rage? Why do peo - ples fol - ly mind?
2. 4But the Lord will scorn them all; He will laugh Who sits on high.
3. 7His de - cree I will make known: Un - to Me the LORD did say,
4. 10Therefore, kings, be wise, give ear; Hear-ken, judg - es of the earth;
2Kings of earth in plots en - gage, Rul - ers are in league com-bined;
5Then His wrath will on them fall; Sore dis - pleased He will re - ply:
"Thou art My be - lov - ed Son; I've be - got - ten Thee this day.
11Serve the LORD with god - ly fear; Min - gle trem - bling with your mirth.
Then a - gainst Je - ho - vah high, And a - gainst Mes - si - ah's sway,
6"Yet ac - cord - ing to My will I have set My King to reign,
8Ask of Me, and Thee I'll make Heir to earth and na - tions all;
12Kiss the Son, His wrath to turn, Lest ye per - ish in the way,
3"Let us break their bands," they cry, "Let us cast their cords a - way."
And on Zi - on's ho - ly hill My A - noint - ed I'll main - tain."
9Them with i - ron Thou shalt break, Dash - ing them in piec - es small."
For His an - ger soon will burn. Blessed are all that on Him stay.

3

PSALM 3

NEW BRITAIN. C.M.
1. [1] O LORD, how are my foes in-creased! A-
2. [3] You are my shield and glo - ry, LORD; You
3. [5] I lay down, slept, and woke a - gain - - The
gainst me man - y rise. [2] How man - y say, "In
lift - ed up my head. [4] I cried out, "LORD!" and
LORD is keep-ing me. [6] I will not fear ten
vain for help He on his God re - lies!"
from His hill To me His an - swer sped.
thou - sand men En - trenched sur - round-ing me.

4. [7] Arise, O LORD! Save me, my God!
You punish all my foes.
You smite the face of wicked men,
Their teeth break with your blows.

5. [8] Deliverance is from the LORD,
Salvation His alone!
O let Your blessing evermore
Be on Your people shown!

PSALM 4

WALLACE. C.M.
1. 1 Give Thou an an - swer when I call, God of my
2. 2 How long will ye, O sons of men, Your emp - ty
3. 3 But know that for Him - self the LORD The god - ly
4. 4 O stand in awe, and see that ye From eve - ry
right - eous - ness; Have mer - cy; hear my prayer; Thou hast
fol - lies prize? How long my glo - ry turn to shame?
man doth choose. The LORD, when I up - on Him call,
sin de - part; And ev - en on your bed com - mune
En - larged me in dis - tress, En - larged me in dis - tress.
How long seek af - ter lies? How long seek af - ter lies?
To hear will not re - fuse, To hear will not re - fuse.
In sil - lence with your heart, In si - lence with your heart.

5. [5] Bring offerings of righteousness,
Your sacrifices just;
Seek ye the LORD with confidence,
And in Him put your trust.

6. [6]"O who will show us any good?"
Is that which many say;
But of Thy countenance the light,
LORD, lift on us for aye.

7. [7] Within my heart bestowed by Thee
More gladness I have found
Than they, ev'n then, when corn and wine
Did most with them abound.

8. [8] I will both lay me down in peace,
And quiet sleep will take
Because Thou only me to dwell
In safety, LORD, dost make.

4B PSALM 4

PENITENCE. 11.11.11.11. (Trochaic).

1. [1]An - swer when I call, O God who jus - ti - fies.
2. [3]Know the LORD His saints has set a - part in grace,
3. [5]May you sac - ri - fice now sac - ri - fic - es just,
4. [7]You have giv - en my heart great - er joy by far
In my stress You freed me; hear in grace my cries.
And the LORD will hear me when I seek His face.
In Je - ho - vah on - ly plac - ing all your trust.
Than when grain and new wine most a - bun - dant are.
[2]Sons of men, how long will you my glo - ry shame?
[4]Trem-ble in your an - ger, yet from sin de - part.
[6]"Who will show us good - ness?" man - y peo - ple say;
[8]So in peace I lie down; I will rest and sleep,
Will you love what's worth - less? Will lies be your aim?
On your bed in si - lence speak with - in your heart.
The light of Your face, LORD, lift on us, we pray.
For, O LORD, You on - ly will me safe - ly keep.

PSALM 5

5A

MORNING LIGHT, 77.77.D.
1. [1]O Je - ho - vah, hear my words; To my thoughts at - ten -tive be.
2. [4]Tru- ly Thou art not a God That in sin doth take de- light;
3. [7]But in Thine a - bun-dant grace To Thy house will I re- pair;
[2]Hear my cry, my King, my God, For I make my prayer to Thee.
E - vil shall not dwell with Thee [5]Nor the proud stand in Thy sight.
Look-ing to Thy ho - ly place, In Thy fear I'll wor - ship there.
[3]With the morn-ing light, O LORD, Thou shalt hear my voice and cry;
E - vil - do - ers Thou dost hate; [6]Li - ars Thou wilt bring to naught.
[8]Since, O LORD, mine en - e - mies For my soul do lie in wait,
In the morn my prayer ar - range And keep con- stant watch will I.
GOD ab - hors the man who loves Deed of blood or ly - ing thought.
Lead me in Thy right - eous -ness; Make Thy way be - fore me straight.

4. [9]For they flatter with their tongue;
In their mouth no truth is found;
Like an open grave their throat;
All their thoughts with sin abound.
[10]Hold them guilty, O my God;
Them for all their sins expel;
Let them fall by their own craft,
For against Thee they rebel.

5. [11]But let all that trust Thy care
Ever glad and joyful be;
Let them joy who love Thy name,
For they guarded are by Thee.
[12]And a blessing rich, O LORD,
To the righteous Thou wilt yield;
Thou wilt compass him about
With Thy favor as a shield.

5B

PSALM 5

ABERYSTWYTH, 77. 77. D.
1. 1 O Je - ho - vah, hear my words; To my thoughts at - ten - tive be.
2. 4 Tru - ly Thou art not a God That in sin doth take de - light;
3. 7 But in Thine a - bun-dant grace To Thy house will I re - pair;
2 Hear my cry, my King, my God, For I make my prayer to Thee.
E - vil shall not dwell with Thee, 5 Nor the proud stand in Thy sight.
Look - ing to Thy ho - ly place, In Thy fear I'll wor - ship there.
3 With the morn - ing light, O LORD, Thou shalt hear my voice and cry;
E - vil - do - ers Thou dost hate; 6 Li - ars Thou wilt bring to naught.
8 Since, O LORD, mine en - e - mies For my soul do lie in wait,
In the morn my prayer ar - range And keep con - stant watch will I.
GOD ab - hors the man who loves Deed of blood or ly - ing thought.
Lead me in Thy right-eous-ness; Make Thy way be - fore me straight.

4. 9 For they flatter with their tongue;
   In their mouth no truth is found;
Like an open grave their throat;
   All their thoughts with sin abound.
10 Hold them guilty, O my God;
   Them for all their sins expel;
Let them fall by their own craft,
   For against Thee they rebel.

5. 11 But let all that trust Thy care
   Ever glad and joyful be;
Let them joy who love Thy name,
   For they guarded are by Thee.
12 And a blessing rich, O LORD,
   To the righteous Thou wilt yield;
Thou wilt compass him about
   With Thy favor as a shield.

PSALM 6

6

OLIVE'S BROW. L.M.
1. [1]In an - ger, LORD, re - buke me not, Nor
2. [3]My soul is great - ly ter - ri - fied. O
3. [5]For none in death re - mem - bers You, Or
4. [6]My groan - ing ev - er wea - ries me, Through
judg - ment in Your wrath de - cide. [2]My weak - ness pit - y,
LORD! - and yet how long You take! [4]Re - turn, O LORD, and
there Your mem - o - ry shall keep. And who can give You
eve - ry night till morn ap - pears. My griev - ing makes my
LORD, and heal, For in my bones I'm ter - ri - fied.
free my soul, And save me for Your mer - cies' sake.
prais - es then, With - in the re - gion of the deep?
bed to swim And wa - ters all my cot with tears.

5. [7]Because of all my enemies
This bitter grief consumes my eyes.
[8]Then let all evil men depart!
The LORD has heard my weeping cries.

6. [9]The LORD my supplication hears;
The LORD has brought my prayers to mind;
[10]My foes shall be ashamed and vexed,
And sudden shame they all will find.

7A PSALM 7: 1-9

LONGWOOD. 10.10.10.10.
1. [1]O LORD my God, in You I ref - uge take.
2. [3]O LORD my God, if wrong is in my hands,
3. [6]A - rise, O LORD! In an - ger lift Your - self
4. In tri - umph o - ver them re - turn on high.
5. [9]O let the e - vil of the wick - ed cease,
O save me from all those who me pur - sue.
[4]If I did e - vil to my friend or foe,
A - gainst the fu - ry of my en - e - mies.
[8]The LORD now sits to judge the peo - ples all.
But eve - ry right - eous one es - tab - lish firm,
[2]Lest he should like a li - on tear my soul
[5]Let my pur - su - er o - ver - take me now
A - wake for me! Your judg - ment You have set.
O vin - di - cate me, LORD, in right - eous - ness,
For You it is Who tries the minds and hearts;
And drag me off, with none to res - cue me.
And tram - ple in the dust my life, my soul.
[7]Let peo - ples in as - sem - bly com - pass You.
Ac - cord - ing to in - teg - ri - ty in me.
O Right - eous God, You are the Judge of men.

PSALM 7:10–17 **7B**

BEULAH CHURCH. 10.10.10.10.
6. 10 My shield and my de - fense is found with God,
7. 12 If one does not re - pent, God whets His sword;
8. 14 See how the wick - ed e - vil thoughts con-ceives,
9. 17 I will give thanks to Him Who is the LORD
For He it is Who saves the right in heart.
He has His bow al - read - y strung and bent.
Is preg - nant with ill - will, and brings forth lies.
Ac - cord - ing to His per - fect right - eous - ness:
11 A right - eous judge, God judg - es right - eous - ly,
13 He has pre - pared His in - stru - ments of death;
15 He digs a pit, but stum - bles in him - self;
And I will sing with psalms for ev - er - more
And God is filled with an - ger eve - ry day.
He makes His ar - rows fi - ery, dead - ly shafts.
16 On his own head his plot - ted mal - ice falls.
The name of Him Who is the LORD Most High.

8A PSALM 8

DUNFERMLINE. C.M.
1. 1O LORD, our Lord, in all the earth How ex - cel - lent Thy name! Thou hast Thy glo - ry spread a - far Up - on the star - ry frame.
2. 2From mouths of suck - lings and of babes Thou hast a strength or - dained, That ad - ver - sar - ies should be stilled And venge - ful foes re - strained.
3. 3When I re - gard the heav'ns a - bove Which Thine own fin - gers framed, And look up - on the moon and stars Which were by Thee or - dained;

4. [4]O what is man, that Thou dost him
Within Thy thought retain?
Or what the son of man, that Thou
To visit him dost deign?

5. [5]For Thou a little lower hast
Him than the angels made;
A crown of glory and renown
Hast placed upon his head.

6. [6]Thou mad'st him lord of all Thy works;
Beneath him all things be:
[7]All flocks and herds, all beasts [8] and birds,
And fishes of the sea,

7. And whatsoever living thing
The paths of ocean claim.
[9]O LORD, our Lord, in all the earth
How excellent Thy name!

PSALM 8

AMSTERDAM. 76.76.77.76.
1. [1] LORD, our Lord, in all the earth How ex - cel - lent Your name!
2. [3] When I view the skies a - bove Which Your own fin - gers made,
3. [5] Next to God You have made man, With light and hon - or crowned.
You a - bove the heav'ns have set The splen - dor of Your fame.
When I see the moon and stars Which You in or - der laid,
[6] You placed him a - bove Your works; Be - neath him all is found:
[2] From the mouths of in - fants young You the power of praise com - pose
[4] What is man so frail and weak That You should re - mem - ber him?
[7] Ox - en, sheep, and all wild beasts, [8] Birds, and fish the o - ceans claim.
In the face of en - e - mies To stop a - veng - ing foes.
What can be the son of man That You should care for him?
[9] LORD, our Lord, in all the earth How ex - cel - lent Your name!

9A PSALM 9:1-10

SANKEY. 11.11.11.11.
1. ¹I now will give whole-heart - ed thanks to the LORD,
2. ³When back - ward my foes were all turned in de - spair,
3. ⁵You chid - ed the na - tions, the wick - ed de - stroyed;
4. ⁷The LORD will e - ter - nal - ly sit on His throne,
5. ⁹The LORD is a strong-hold, a lof - ty strong tower,
And all of Your mar - vel - lous works will re - cord.
They stum - bled and per - ished be - cause You were there.
Their names You e - rased and for - ev - er made void.
Es - tab - lish - ing it for His judg - ment a - lone.
For all the op - pressed in their trou - bles' dark hour.
²In You will be glad and ex - ult - ing - ly cry,
⁴For You have de - fend - ed my judg - ment and cause;
⁶The foe is con-sumed, is com - plete - ly e - rased,
⁸In right - eous - ness He'll judge the world from His seat
¹⁰Those know - ing Your name, LORD, trust You for Your grace;
And praise to Your name will I sing, O Most High.
You sat in just judg - ment up - hold - ing Your laws.
Their cit - ies de - stroyed and their mem - ory ef - faced.
And un - to all peo - ples shall e - qui - ty mete.
You have not for - sak - en those seek - ing Your face.

PSALM 9:11-20

JOANNA, 11.11.11.11.
6. 11 Sing praise to the LORD, Who in Zi - on does dwell;
7. 13 LORD, see what I suf - fer from mal - ice and hate;
8. 15 The na - tions are sunk in the pit they pre - pared;
9. 17 The wick - ed to death's dark a - bode shall be brought,
10. 19 Rise, LORD, that mere man may not make him - self strong;
A - mong all the peo - ples His great do - ings tell.
Have mer - cy! O lift me a - way from death's gate,
Their foot in the net which they hid is en - snared.
And all of the na - tions who God have for - got.
Let na - tions be judged in Your pres - ence for wrong.
12 When blood He a - veng - es, His mem - ory is clear;
14 That I with the daugh - ter of Zi - on may voice
16 The LORD by His judg - ment has made Him - self known,
18 For - got - ten no long - er the cause of the weak,
20 Strike ter - ror with - in them, O LORD; al - ways then
The cry of the poor ne - ver fades from His ear.
Your prais - es, and in Your sal - va - tion re - joice.
He by their own works has the wick - ed o'er - thrown.
Nor per - ished for - ev - er the hope of the meek.
Let na - tions know tru - ly that they are mere men.

10 A PSALM 10:1–11

PENITENTIA. 10.10.10.10.

1. [1] Why do You stand so far a - way, O LORD? Why do You hide Your self in trou - blous times? [2] In ar - ro - gance the wick - ed trap the poor; Let them be caught in schemes they have de - vised.
2. [3] The wick - ed boasts a - bout his heart's de - sires; The cov - et - ous re - nounc -es, spurns the LORD. [4] In pride the wick - ed sees no need to seek; In all his thoughts he says, "There is no God."
3. [5] He's self - as - sured, Your judg-ments far from him. At all his foes he on - ly puffs in scorn. [6] In heart he thinks, "I nev - er shall be moved; Through ag - es all no e - vil shall I meet."
4. [7] His mouth is filled with oaths and lies and threats: Be - neath his tongue are e - vil thoughts and deeds. [8] He sits in am - bush mid the vil - lage homes; The in - no - cent he mur - ders se - cret - ly.

5.
In stealth he watches for some hapless one.
[9] He like a lion crouches in his den.
He hides himself that he may seize the poor;
To seize the poor he traps him in his net.

6.
[10] The hapless one he crushes, tramples down,
When he has made him fall beneath his might.
[11] In heart he thinks, "God has forgotten this;
He hid His face, so He will never see."

SURSUM CORDA, 10.10.10.10.
7. 12 A - rise, O LORD! O God, lift up Your hand!
8. 14 You see! You note dis - or - der and dis - tress.
9. 15 O break the wick - ed, e - vil - do - er's arm!
10. 17 You hear, O LORD, the long - ing of the meek;
For - get not those who have af - flict - ed been.
That You may take it all in - to Your hands.
Seek out his wick - ed - ness till You find none.
Their heart You strength - en; You in - cline Your ear.
13 Why does the wick - ed proud - ly scoff at God
The hap - less may com - mit him - self to You;
16 The LORD is king through all e - ter - ni - ty;
18 Do jus - tice to op - pressed and fa - ther - less
And say in heart, "He'll ne - ver take ac - count"?
You are the help - er of the fa - ther - less.
The hea - then na - tions per - ish from His land.
That man of earth may ter - ri - fy no more.

11 PSALM 11

OLMUTZ, S.M.
1. [1]My trust is in the LORD; How can you say to me, "Now like a bird from per - il haste And to your moun - tain flee!
2. [2]"The wick - ed bend the bow With ar - row fixed for flight, And stealth - i - ly in dark - ness go The true in heart to smite.
3. [3]"Foun - da - tions are de - stroyed! What can the right - eous try?" [4]The LORD is in His ho - ly place; The LORD's throne is on high.
4. His eyes will sure - ly see, His eye - lids try men's sons. [5]The LORD tries just and wick - ed men; His soul hates cru - el ones.

5. [6]Upon all wicked men
He'll rain entangling snares.
Brimstone and fire and burning wind
He for their cup prepares.

6. [7]For righteous is the LORD,
And He loves righteousness;
And every one who upright is
Will see His gracious face.

PSALM 12

BELMONT. C.M.
1. [1]O Thou, Je - ho - vah, grant us help, Be - cause the god - ly cease; And from a - mong the sons of men The faith - ful now de - crease.
2. [2]And to his neigh - bor eve - ry one Doth ut - ter van - i - ty; They with a dou - ble heart do speak And lips of flat - ter - y.
3. [3]The LORD will cut off all false lips, [4]Tongues that speak proud - ly thus: "We'll with our tongue pre- vail; our lips Are ours; who's lord o'er us?"
4. [5]"Be - cause the poor are sore - ly pressed, Be - cause the need - y sighs, To give the safe - ty they de - sire," The LORD says, "I'll a - rise."

5. [6]Jehovah's words are words most pure;
They are like silver tried
In earthen furnace, seven times
That has been purified.

6. [7]LORD, Thou shalt them preserve and keep
For ever from this race.
[8]On every side the wicked walk,
With vile men high in place.

12B PSALM 12

STRENGTH AND STAY. 11.10.11.10.
1. ¹Help, LORD, be - cause the god - ly man now ceas - es;
2. ³O may the LORD cut off all lips that flat - ter,
3. ⁵"Be - cause of deep dis - tress of the af - flict - ed,
4. ⁶Words of the LORD are pure, as smelt - ed sil - ver;
The faith - ful van - ish from the sons of men.
And eve - ry boast - ing tongue that speaks great things;
Be - cause of all the groan - ing of the poor,
⁷You, LORD, will keep them, sev - en times re - fined.
²They emp - ty false - hood speak to one an - oth - er;
⁴Those who have said, "With our tongue we will con - quer;
I will a - rise now," says the LORD Al - might - y;
You'll keep him al - ways from this gen - er - a - tion;
With flat - t'ring lips and dou - ble heart they speak.
Our lips are ours; who is the lord o'er us?"
"I'll set him in the safe - ty which he craves."
⁸The wick - ed prance when vile men are re - vered.

PSALM 13

MEDITATION. C.M.
1. [1]How long wilt Thou for - get me, LORD? Shall it for - ev - er be? O how long shall it be that Thou Wilt hide Thy face from me?
2. [2]How long shall I plan in my soul With grief in heart all day? O how long shall my en - e - my Hold his ex - alt - ed sway?
3. [3]Con - sid - er me, O LORD my God, And an - swer Thou my cry. O to my eyes give light, lest I Should sleep with those who die,

4. [4]And lest my enemy should say,
"I have him overcome,"
Lest adversaries should rejoice
Because I shaken am.

5. [5]But I have trusted in Thy love;
I'll Thy salvation praise.
[6]My heart will sing and bless the LORD
Who dealt with me in grace.

14A PSALM 14

YORKE TUNE. C.M.
1. [1]The fool is say - ing in his heart, "There sure - ly is no God." They are cor - rupt, their deeds are vile, Not one of them does good.
2. [2]The LORD up - on the sons of men From heav - en looks a - broad To see if an - y un - der - stands, If an - y seeks for God.
3. [3]They all have wan - dered far a - stray; They all to vile - ness run. And there is no man do - ing good, No, not a sin - gle one.
4. [4]These work - ers all of wick - ed - ness, Do they not know at all, Who eat my peo - ple as their bread, And on GOD do not call?

5. [5]There are they filled with dread, for God
   Is ever with the just;
[6]You'd shame the counsel of the poor;
   Jehovah is his trust.

6. [7]From out of Zion who will save
   And help to Isr'el bring?
The LORD returns His captive folk;
   For this let Isr'el sing.

PSALM 14 **14B**

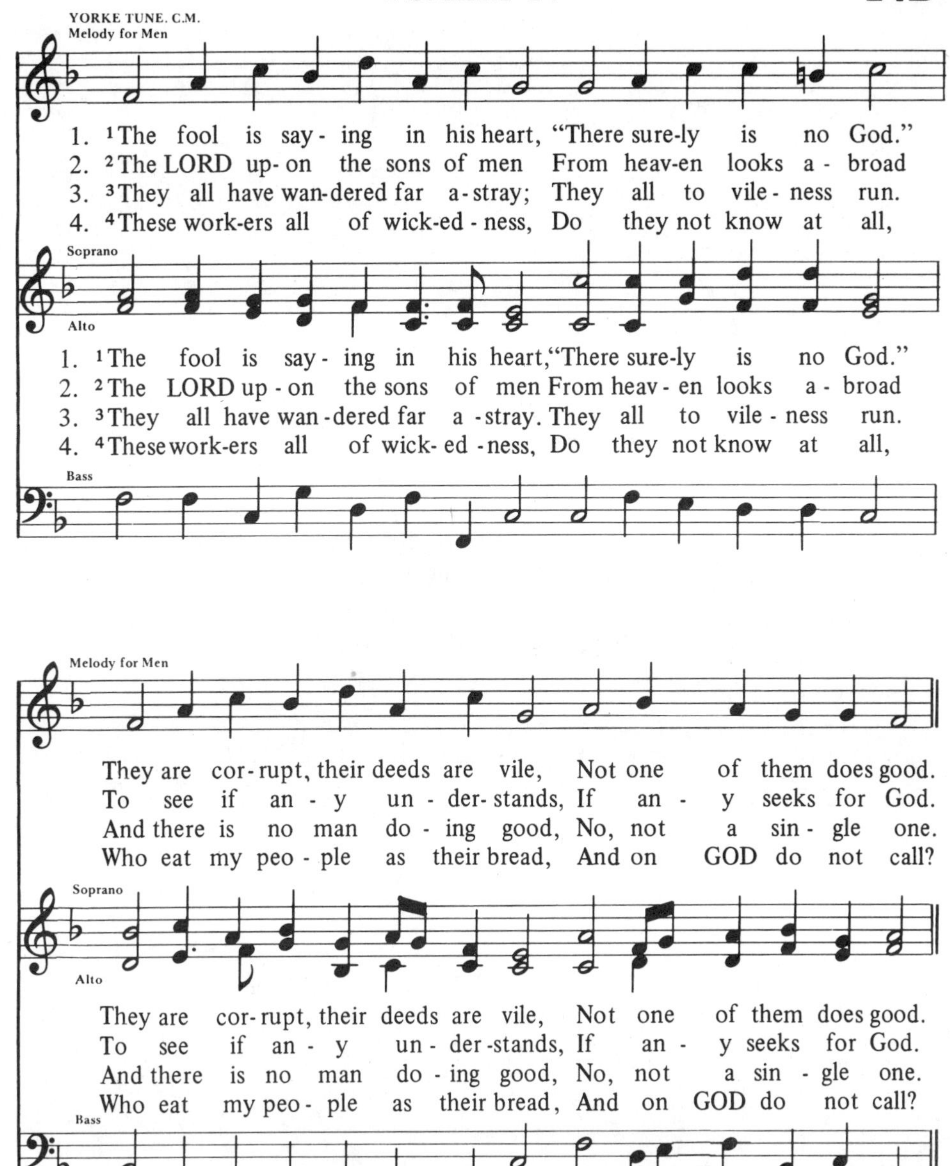

YORKE TUNE. C.M.
Melody for Men
1. [1]The fool is say- ing in his heart, "There sure-ly is no God."
2. [2]The LORD up- on the sons of men From heav-en looks a - broad
3. [3]They all have wan-dered far a - stray; They all to vile - ness run.
4. [4]These work-ers all of wick-ed - ness, Do they not know at all,
Soprano
Alto
1. [1]The fool is say- ing in his heart,"There sure-ly is no God."
2. [2]The LORD up - on the sons of men From heav - en looks a - broad
3. [3]They all have wan -dered far a - stray. They all to vile - ness run.
4. [4]These work-ers all of wick- ed - ness, Do they not know at all,
Bass
Melody for Men
They are cor- rupt, their deeds are vile, Not one of them does good.
To see if an - y un - der- stands, If an - y seeks for God.
And there is no man do - ing good, No, not a sin - gle one.
Who eat my peo - ple as their bread, And on GOD do not call?
Soprano
Alto
They are cor- rupt, their deeds are vile, Not one of them does good.
To see if an - y un - der -stands, If an - y seeks for God.
And there is no man do - ing good, No, not a sin - gle one.
Who eat my peo - ple as their bread, And on GOD do not call?
Bass

5. [5]There are they filled with dread, for God
   Is ever with the just;
   [6]You'd shame the counsel of the poor;
   Jehovah is his trust.

6. [7]From out of Zion who will save
   And help to Isr'el bring?
   The LORD returns His captive folk;
   For this let Isr'el sing.

14C PSALM 14

OLD 128th. 76.76.D.
1. [1]The fool in heart is say - ing, "There sure - ly is no God."
2. [3]All far a - stray have wan-dered; They all to vile - ness run.
3. [5]There shall they be in ter - ror For God is with the just;
Cor - rupt and vile their deeds are; Not one of them does good.
Not one of them is right - eous, No, not a sin - gle one.
[6]You would con - found one strug - gling; Je - ho - vah is his trust.
[2]The LORD looks down from heav - en On sons of men a - broad
[4]Have they of truth no knowl-edge, These e - vil - work - ers all,
[7]Sal - va - tion out of Zi - on Who will to Is - rael bring?
To see which one has wis - dom, If an - y seeks for God.
Who eat like bread my peo - ple And on GOD do not call?
The LORD brings back His cap - tives. Joy, Ja - cob! Is - rael, sing!

PSALM 15

15

LOWRY. 64.64.66.64.

1. [1]LORD, in Thy tent who will A - bide with Thee,
2. [3]Whose tongue doth not de - fame Nor harm his friend,
3. When to his hurt he swears Naught chang - es he;
And on Thy ho - ly hill A dwell - er be?
Who to his neigh - bor's shame No ear doth lend,
[5]His gold no in - crease bears From us - u - ry;
[2]Who walks in up - right - ness, Who work - eth right - eous - ness,
[4]Who has the vile ab - horred But hon - or doth ac - cord
His hands no bribes re - ceive The guilt - less to ag - grieve.
Who doth the truth ex - press Un - feign - ed - ly;
To those who fear the LORD And Him at - tend.
Lo, he who thus doth live Un - moved shall be.

16A PSALM 16

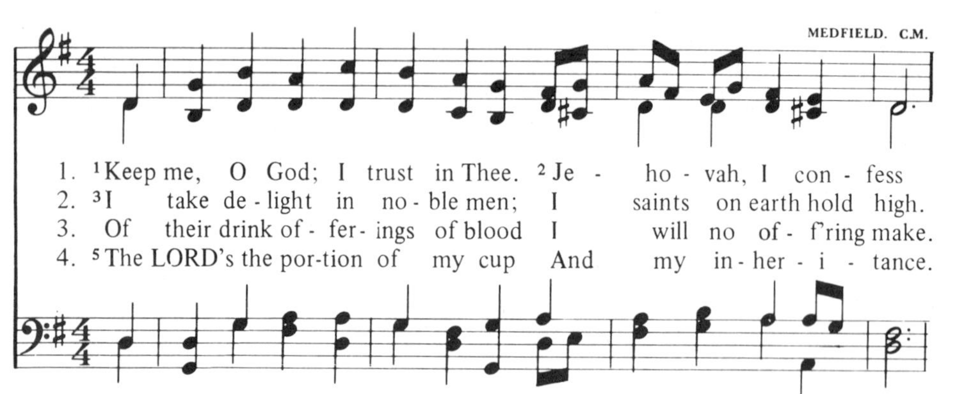
MEDFIELD. C.M.
1. [1]Keep me, O God; I trust in Thee. [2]Je - ho - vah, I con - fess
2. [3]I take de - light in no - ble men; I saints on earth hold high.
3. Of their drink of - fer- ings of blood I will no of - f'ring make.
4. [5]The LORD's the por-tion of my cup And my in - her - i - tance.

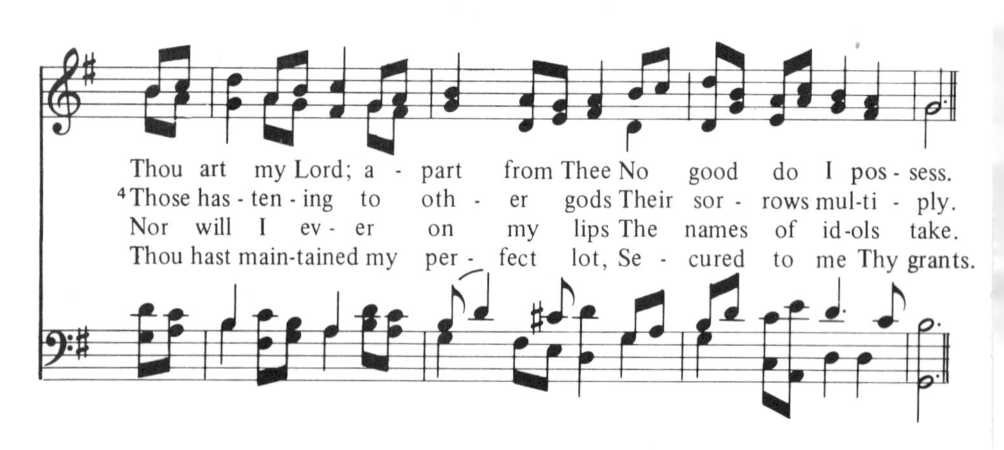
Thou art my Lord; a - part from Thee No good do I pos - sess.
[4]Those has - ten - ing to oth - er gods Their sor - rows mul-ti - ply.
Nor will I ev - er on my lips The names of id-ols take.
Thou hast main-tained my per - fect lot, Se - cured to me Thy grants.

5. [6]The lines that fell to me enclose
A very pleasant site;
The heritage that I received
To me is a delight.

6. [7]I bless the LORD Who gives to me
The counsel that is right;
My heart within me He directs
To teach me in the night.

7. [8]I've set the LORD before my face,
And Him I'll always see.
Because He stands at my right hand
I never moved shall be.

8. [9]Because of this my heart is glad
And joy shall be expressed
By all my glory, and my flesh
In confidence shall rest.

9. [10]Because my soul in nether realms
Shall not be left by Thee;
Corruption Thou wilt not permit
Thy Holy One to see.

10. [11]Thou wilt me show the path of life.
Thy presence holds great store
Of lasting joy; at Thy right hand
Are pleasures evermore.

PSALM 16

FOUNDATION. 11.11.11.11.
1. 1Pre - serve me, O God, for in You do I trust.
2. 4Those wor - ship - ping oth - er gods mul - ti - ply griefs.
3. My lot You main - tain, 6and the lines fell to me
4. 8The LORD ev - er pres - ent be - fore me I keep.
5. Your Ho - ly One You will pre - serve from de - cay.
2My soul to the LORD has said, "You are my Lord.
I will not pour out their li - ba - tions of blood,
In pleas - ant lands; I have a good her - i - tage.
He stands at my right hand; I shall not be moved.
11The path - way of life You will show un - to me;
No good - ness have I be - yond You; and my joy
Nor will I up - on my lips take up their names.
7The LORD Who gives coun - sel to me I will bless.
9My heart's glad. My soul joys. My flesh rests in hope.
In Your glo - rious pres - ence is full - ness of joy.
3I find in the god - ly, the no - ble on earth."
5The LORD's my in - her - it - ed por - tion, my cup.
My in - most self teach - es me all through the night.
10For You will not give up my soul to the grave.
Your right hand holds pleas - ures for me ev - er - more.

17A
PSALM 17:1–5
ST. ANDREW. C.M.
1. [1]Give ear to what is right, O LORD! O lis - ten to my cry!
2. [2]May judg-ment from Your pres-ence come Which will me vin - di - cate,
3. [3]For You have scru - ti - nized my heart; You came to me by night.
4. [4]From acts of men, from vi - o - lence, I'm guard-ed by Your word;
Give heed to this my ear-nest prayer From lips which do not lie.
And al - ways may Your search-ing eyes See what is just and straight.
You've probed and found no ill in - tent; My mouth speaks on - ly right.
[5]My steps held close-ly to Your paths; My foot - steps have not erred.
17B
PSALM 17:6–12
BALERMA. C.M.
5. [6]On You, O God, my soul has called, For
6. [7]In won - drous ways Your mer - cy show, O
7. [8]Keep me the pu - pil of Your eye; Be -
You will an - swer me. O lis - ten to my
You pre - serv - ing those Who seek to find at
neath Your wings me hide [9]From wick - ed men and

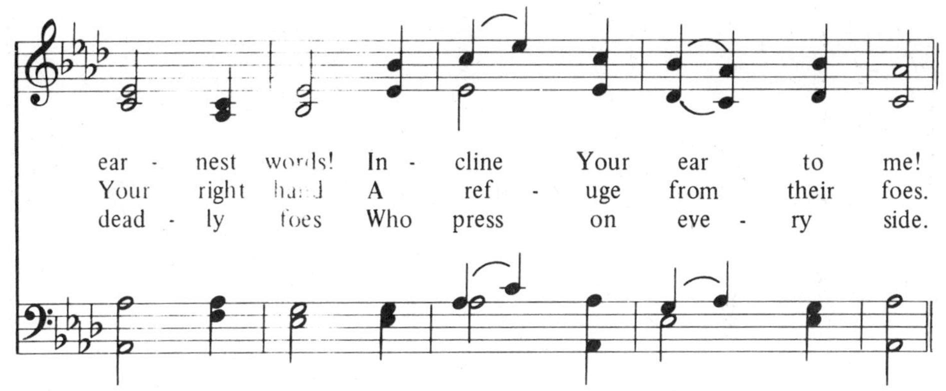
ear - nest words! In - cline Your ear to me!
Your right hand A ref - uge from their foes.
dead - ly foes Who press on eve - ry side.

8. [10]They are enclosed in their own fat;
Their boasting words abound.
[11]They compass us and fix their eyes
To cast us to the ground.

9. [12]My enemy's a lion strong
That craves to tear his prey.
He's like a lion young that lurks
In ambush every day.

PSALM 17:13–15 **17C**

DALEHURST. C.M.

10. [13]A - rise, O LORD.Con-front my foe. O bring him ver - y low!
11. [14]Save me by Your own hand, O LORD, From world - ly men of earth,
12. You filled them with the wealth You stored, Their chil - dren sat - is - fied;
13. [15]But as for me, with right-eous-ness Shall I be- hold Your face.

O save my soul from wick - ed men! Let them feel Your sword's blow.
Who on - ly in this pres - ent life Know an - y - thing of worth.
So they may leave e - nough be - hind Their young ones to pro - vide.
I shall be sat - is - fied to wake And see You face to face.

18A PSALM 18:1–6

UXBRIDGE. L.M.
1. [1]I love You, LORD! You are my strength, [2]The
2. [3]Be - cause He's ev - er to be praised, Un -
3. [4]With cords of death on eve - ry side, I
4. [6]In my dis - tress I called the LORD; My
LORD, my rock, my fort, my power, My God, my hid - ing
to the LORD I lift my cry; For I shall be de-
was as - sailed by floods of sin, [5]En - tan - gled by the
cry to God for help was clear. He from His tem - ple

place, my shield, My horn of safe - ty, and my tower.
liv - ered thus From all the foes who me de - fy.
grave's strong cords, My way with snares of death hemmed in.
heard my voice; My cry be - fore Him reached His ear.

PSALM 18:7–15 18B

FREUEN WIR UNS. L.M.
5. 7The earth then quiv - ered to its depths; The moun - tains
6. 8His nos - trils smoked; His mouth belched fire; And glow - ing
7. 10He swift - ly on a cher - ub flew; On wings of
8. 12Then through the clouds His bril - liance burst With light - nings,
rocked with trem- bling frame; The whole world's firm foun - da - tions
coals flamed forth from Him. 9He bent the sky as He came
wind He rushed in flight. 11He hid Him - self in dark - ness
hail - stones, coals of fire. 13The LORD Most High then thun- dered
shook, Be - cause He in His an - ger came.
down; Thick dark - ness hov - ered un - der Him.
deep, Thick clouds a - bout Him black as night.
forth; He spoke with hail - stones, coals of fire.

9. [14] The deadly arrows He sent forth
Dispersed His foes in wild retreat.
The flaming lightnings He shot out
Made their discomfiture complete.

10. [15] Then channels of the sea were seen,
Laid bare the world's foundations vast;
At Your rebuke, O LORD, they shook,
And at Your nostrils' angry blast.

18C PSALM 18:16–24

CANONBURY. L.M.
11. 16 He reached from heav'n and res - cued me From many - y wa - ters swell - ing high; 17 From those that hate me set me free, From foes that stron - ger were than I.
12. 18 In my dis - tress my foes came on; The LORD was my se - cu - ri - ty; 19 He brought me forth and gave me room, Be - cause He took de - light in me.
13. 20 Ac - cord - ing to my right - eous - ness I am re - ward - ed by the LORD; Ac - cord - ing as my hands were clean, He gives to me a just re - ward.

14. [21] I've kept the pathway of the LORD
And from my God did not depart,
[22] I've kept His judgments in my sight,
His statutes shut not from my heart.

15. [23] Sincere toward Him, I set my guard
To keep myself away from sin.
[24] My righteousness the LORD rewards
As in His sight my hands are clean.

PSALM 18:25–31
18D
GOELDEL. L.M.
16. [25] To gra - cious men You gra - cious are; The per - fect You per - fec - tion show; [26] The pure You show that You are pure; Your cun - ning will the craf - ty know.
17. [27] A hum - ble peo - ple You lift up; But haugh - ty eyes You hum - ble low. [28] You light my lamp and make it shine. The LORD my God makes dark - ness glow.
18. [29] By You I can at - tack a troop, And by my God I leap a wall. [30] Our God! How per - fect is His way! No prom - ise of the LORD can fall.
19. He is a shield a - round all those Who flee to Him from foes a - broad. [31] For who is God, ex- cept the LORD? Who is a rock, ex - cept our God?

18E PSALM 18:32–43

HOLY TRINITY. L.M.
20. [32]My God girds up my loins with strength; My way He per - fects with His hand. [33]He makes my feet swift like the doe's; On heights tri - um - phant makes me stand.
21. [34]My arms can bend a bow of brass; Hands trained by Him for bat - tle wait. [35]Your gift, my shield! Your hand, my help! Your gen - tle - ness has made me great.
22. [36]You for my steps have cleared the way; My feet slide not while I pur - sue; [37]I o - ver - take my flee - ing foes; I turn not till I thrust them through.
23. [38]My foes can rise a - gain no more; They at my feet are fall - en now. [39]For You have made me strong for war; You've made my foes be - neath me bow.

24. [40]You made them turn their backs and flee,
That I my haters might destroy.
[41]They cried for help, but no one came;
They begged the LORD; He sent no joy.

25. [42]I crushed them small as flying dust;
Like trampled mud I let them fall.
[43]You rescued me from peoples' strife,
Made me the head of nations all.

PSALM 18:43–50 **18F**

EISENACH. L.M.
26. 43 A peo - ple I knew not will serve 44 And,
27. 46 Je - ho - vah lives! Blessed be my Rock! The
28. 48 He saves me from my en - e - mies; Yes,
when they hear me, will o - bey. The sons of stran - gers,
God Who saves ex - alt - ed be! 47 The God Who ven - geance
You will now ex - alt me far A - bove the men of
trem - bling come 45 And from their strong-holds fade a - way.
ex - e - cutes, And hum - bles na - tions un - der me.
vi - o - lence Who ris - en up a - gainst me are.

29. [49] I therefore will give thanks to You
Among the nations all, O LORD;
And I will sing the psalms of praise,
To Your great name will praise accord.

30. [50] He to His king salvation gives,
To His anointed shows His grace;
His mercy evermore extends
To David and his promised race.

18G PSALM 18:1–7

MARGARET. 10.10.10.10.
1. [1]How fer - vent - ly I love You, LORD, my Strength!
2. [3]I call the LORD Who wor - thy is of praise,
3. [5]The wait - ing grave be - set me with its cords;
4. My plead - ing voice He from His tem - ple heard;
[2]The LORD's my fort, my strong - hold, sav - ing power.
And so I am de - liv - ered from my foes.
Con - front - ing me, there lay the snares of death.
My cry to Him reached to His list - 'ning ears.
My God's my rock in Whom I safe - ty find,
[4]The bind - ing cords of death en - com - passed me;
[6]In my dis - tress I called up - on the LORD,
[7]The earth then trem - bling quiv - ered; moun - tains reeled;
Sal - va - tion's horn, my shield, and my high tower.
Un - god - li - ness in tor - rents o - ver - whelmed.
And to my God I cried out for His help.
Foun - da - tions shook, for His great an - ger blazed.

PSALM 18:8–16

CRASSELIUS. 10.10.10.10.
5. 8 Smoke is - sued from His nos - trils, from His mouth
6. 10 He rode up - on a cher - ub as He flew,
7. 12 Then from His lof - ty pres - ence through the clouds
8. 14 His ar - rows He sent forth to rout my foes;
9. When You, O LORD, but ut - tered Your re - buke,
De - vour - ing flames that kin - dled coals of fire.
And down He rushed up - on the wings of wind.
His bright - ness burst with hail and coals of fire.
His light - nings He shot out and scat - tered them.
When from Your nos - trils You but breathed on them.
9 He bent the heav - ens low as He came down;
11 He veiled Him - self with dark - ness all a - round;
13 The LORD then thun - dered in the heav - ens high;
15 The chan - nels of the sea were then re - vealed,
16 He reached from heav - en high; He lift - ed me;
Thick dark - ness hov - ered un - der - neath His feet.
He cov - ered His ap - proach with thick black clouds.
The High One spoke with hail and coals of fire.
Un - til the world's foun - da - tions were laid bare,
He drew me out of surg - ing wa - ters deep.

181 PSALM 18:17–28

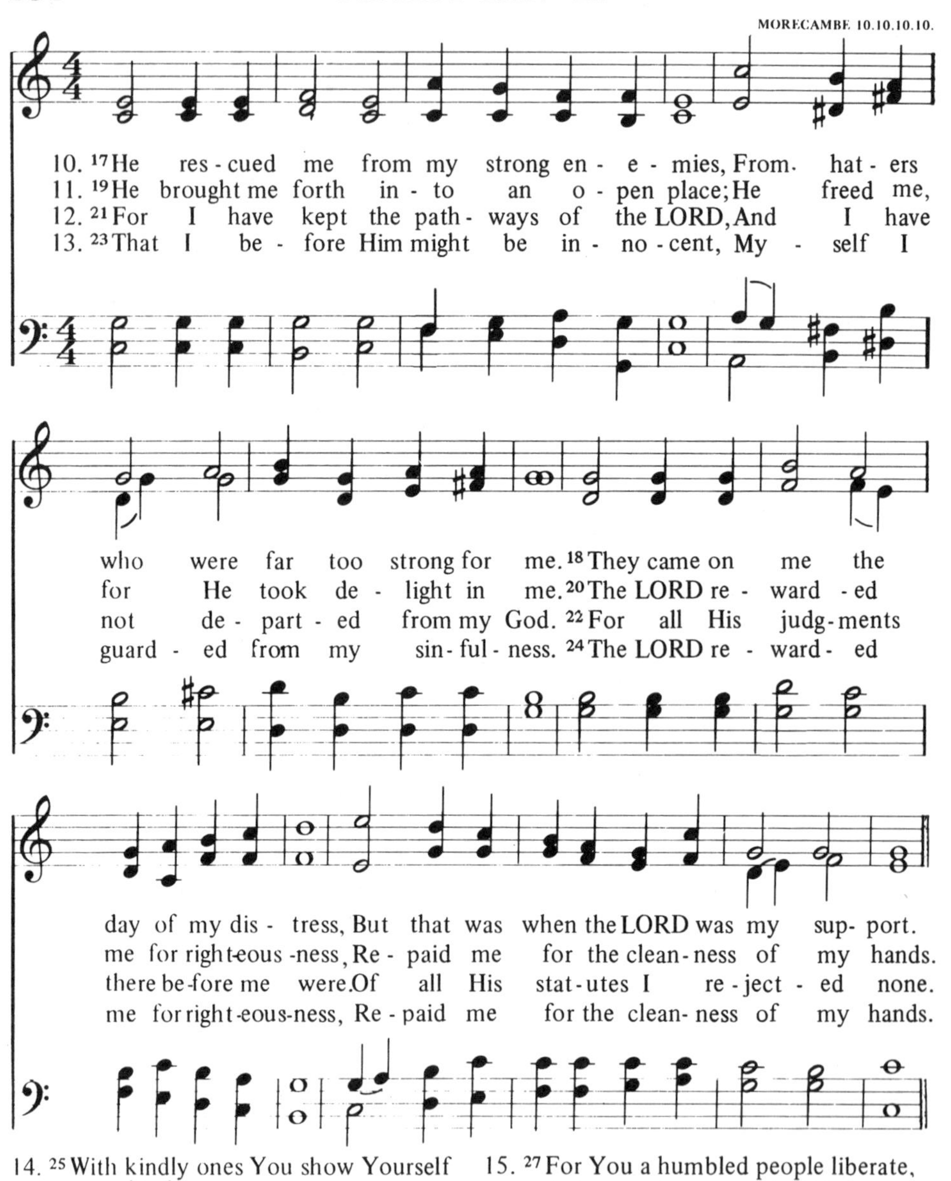
MORECAMBE 10.10.10.10.
10. 17He res - cued me from my strong en - e - mies, From hat - ers
11. 19He brought me forth in - to an o - pen place; He freed me,
12. 21For I have kept the path - ways of the LORD, And I have
13. 23That I be - fore Him might be in - no - cent, My - self I
who were far too strong for me. 18They came on me the
for He took de - light in me. 20The LORD re - ward - ed
not de - part - ed from my God. 22For all His judg - ments
guard - ed from my sin - ful - ness. 24The LORD re - ward - ed
day of my dis - tress, But that was when the LORD was my sup - port.
me for right-eous - ness, Re - paid me for the clean - ness of my hands.
there be - fore me were. Of all His stat - utes I re - ject - ed none.
me for right - eous - ness, Re - paid me for the clean - ness of my hands.

14. 25With kindly ones You show Yourself as kind;
With blameless ones You blameless show Yourself.
26With all the pure You show Yourself as pure;
With crafty ones You cunning show Yourself.

15. 27For You a humbled people liberate,
And eyes that are exalted You bring down.
28For it is You Who makes my lamp to shine;
The LORD my God my darkness fills with light.

PSALM 18:29–36
18J
BIRMINGHAM.10.10.10.10.
16. 29 Be - cause of You I o - ver - come a troop;
17. 31 For who in - deed is God, ex - cept the LORD?
18. 33 Who makes my feet like hind's feet, swift and sure,
19. 35 The shield You gave me was Your sav - ing help;
And with my God I o - ver - leap a wall.
And who is an - y rock, ex - cept our God?
Who makes me stand tri - um - phant on the heights.
Your own right hand has al - ways held me up;
30 God's up - right in His way; His word is tried;
32 He is the God Who girds my loins with strength,
34 He gives my hands the skill and strength for war,
Your care and con - de - scen - sion made me great;
The LORD's a shield to all who trust in Him.
The One who gives per - fec - tion to my way.
So that my arms can bend a bow of brass.
36 You freed my steps; my feet have nev - er slipped.

18K PSALM 18:37–45

PURSUIT. 10.10.10.10.
20. 37 I chased and o - ver - took my en - e - mies;
21. 40 You forced my foes to turn their backs on me,
22. 42 I crushed them small as dust be - fore the wind;
23. A peo - ple serve me whom I nev - er knew.
I turned not back till I de - stroyed them all;
So I de - stroyed all those who hat - ed me.
Like sweep - ings from my door I tossed them out.
44 No soon - er do they hear than they o - bey.
38 They could not rise; they fell be - neath my feet.
41 They cried for help, but there was none to save;
43 You res - cued me from all the peo - ple's strife;
Out - sid - ers pledge their loy - al - ty to me;
39 You made me strong; You crushed them un - der me.
They begged the LORD; He did not an - swer them.
You set me as the head of na - tions all.
45 The for - eign - ers come trem - bling from their forts.

PSALM 18:46–50

PAX DEI. 10.10.10.10.
24. 46 Je - ho - vah lives, and bless - ed be my rock!
25. 48 O Sav - ior from my foes, You raise me up!
26. I will sing prais - es to Your match - less name;
Ex - alt - ed be the God Who me re - deems!
You save me from the men of vi - o - lence.
50 The LORD sal - va - tion gives to His own king.
47 The God Who for me ex - e - cutes re - venge,
49 Be - cause of all You do to make me live,
To His a - noint - ed He His mer - cy shows,
Sub - dues the rag - ing peo - ples un - der me.
I will ex - tol You eve - ry - where, O LORD!
To Da - vid and his sons for ev - er - more.

19A PSALM 19:1–6

CLARKSVILLE. 66.66.88.
1. [1]The spa - cious heav'ns de - clare The glo - ry of our
2. [3]A - loud they do not speak; They ut - ter forth no
3. In heav'n He set a tent, A dwell - ing for the
4. [6]His dai - ly go - ing forth Is from the end of
God; The fir - ma - ment dis - plays His hand - i - work a -
word, Nor in - to lan - guage break; Their voice is nev - er
sun, [5]Which as a might - y man De - lights his course to
heav'n: The fir - ma - ment to him Is for his cir - cuit
broad; [2]Day un - to day doth ut - ter speech,
heard; [4]Yet through the world their line ex - tends,
run. He, bride - groom - like in his ar - ray,
giv'n; And eve - ry - where from end to end,
And night to night doth knowl - edge teach.
Their words to earth's re - mot - est ends.
Comes from his cham - ber, bring - ing day.
His ra - diant heat he doth ex - tend.
And night to night doth knowl - edge teach.

PSALM 19:7–14

MILLENIUM. 66.66.88.
5. 7 Je - ho - vah's per - fect law Re - stores the soul a - gain;
6. The LORD's com-mand is pure, En - light - en - ing the eyes;
7. 10 They're more to be de - sired Than stores of fin - est gold;
HIS tes - ti - mo - ny sure Gives wis - dom un - to men;
9 Je - ho-vah's fear is clean, More last - ing than the skies.
Than hon-ey from the comb More sweet- ness far they hold.
8 The pre - cepts of the LORD are right,
The judg - ments of the LORD ex - press
11 With warn - ings they Thy ser - vant guard;
And fill the heart with great de - light.
His truth and per - fect right - eous - ness.
In keep - ing them is great re - ward.

8. 12 His errors who can know?
Cleanse me from hidden stain.
13 Keep me from wilful sins,
Nor let them o'er me reign.
And then I upright shall appear
And be from great transgression clear.

9. 14 Let all the words I speak
And all the thoughts within
Come up before Thy sight
And Thine approval win.
O Thou Jehovah, unto me
My rock and my Redeemer be.

19C

PSALM 19:1–6

CHANT A.

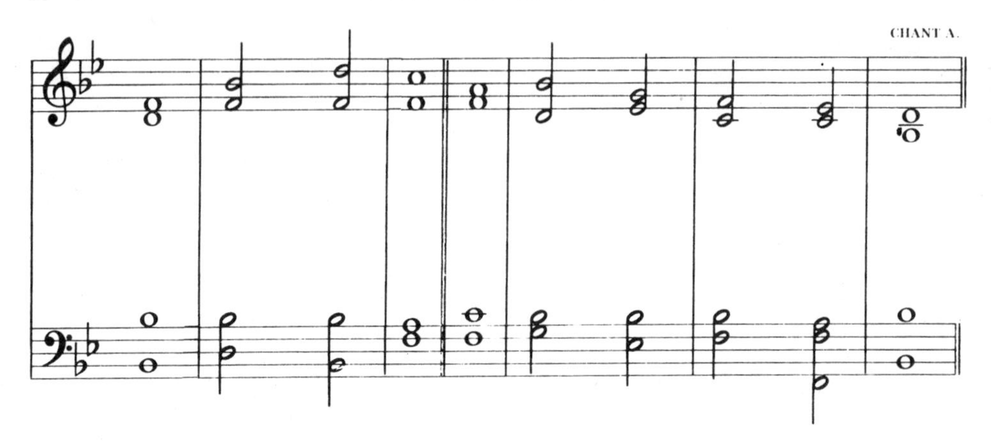

1. [1]The heavens declare the / glory of / God; //
   And the / firma · ment / showeth His / handiwork.

2. [2]Day unto day / utter · eth / speech, //
   And / night unto / night showeth / knowledge.

3. [3]There is no speech nor language where their voice / is not / heard; //
   [4]Their line is gone out through all the earth, and their / words to · the / end of · the / world.

4. In them hath He set a tabernacle / for the / sun, //
   [5]Which is as a bridegroom coming out of his chamber, and rejoiceth as a / strong man to / run a / race.

5. [6]His going forth is from the end of the heavens, and his circuit / unto the / ends of it; //
   And there is nothing / hid from the / heat there / of.

For "AN INTRODUCTION TO CHANTING" please turn to page 440.

PSALM 19:7–11 **19D**

CHANT B.

6. [7]The law of the LORD is perfect, con/verting the / soul:
The testimony of the LORD is sure, / making / wise the / simple.

7. [8]The statutes of the LORD are right, re/joicing the / heart:
The commandment of the LORD is pure, en/lighten/ing the / eyes.

8. [9]The fear of the LORD is clean, en/during for/ever:
The judgments of the LORD are true and / righteous / alto/gether.

9. [10]More to be desired are they than gold, yea, than / much fine / gold:
Sweeter also than honey / and the / honey / comb.

10. [11]Moreover by them is Thy / servant / warned:
And in keeping of / them · there is / great re/ward.

PSALM 19:12–14 **19E**

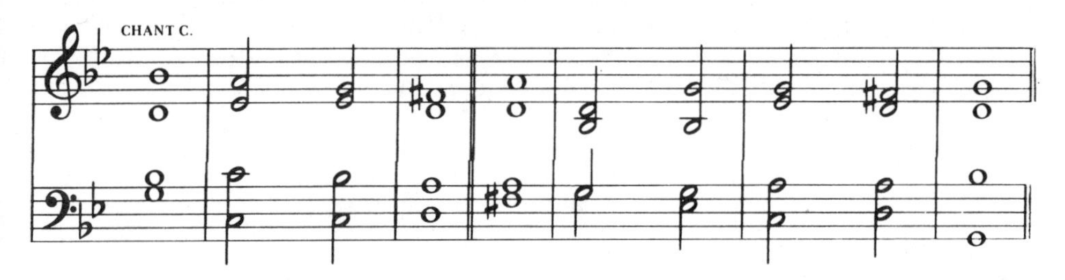
CHANT C.

11. [12]Who can / under·stand his /errors? //
Cleanse Thou / me from / secret / faults.

12. [13]Keep back Thy servant also from pre/sump·tuous / sins; //
Let them / not · have do/minion over / me:

13. Then shall / I be / upright, //
And I shall be / innocent · from the / great trans/gression.

14. [14]Let the words of my mouth, and the meditation / of my / heart, //
Be acceptable in Thy sight, / O LORD, · my / Strength, and · my Re/deemer.

20A PSALM 20

STOCKTON. C.M.D.
1. [1]Je - ho - vah hear thee in the day When trou-ble He doth send;
2. [3]Let Him re - mem - ber all thy gifts, Ac - cept thy sac - ri - fice,
3. [6]Now know I that the LORD doth save His own a - noint - ed king;
And let the name of Ja - cob's God From eve - ry ill de - fend.
[4]Grant thee thine heart's wish, and ful - fill Thy thoughts and coun-sel wise.
He'll hear him from His ho -ly heav'n; His right hand strength shall bring.
[2]O let Him help thee from a - bove, From out His tem- ple court;
[5]In thy sal - va - tion we will joy; In our God's name we will
[7]In char- iots some put con - fi - dence; Some hors-es trust up - on;
4. [8]We rise and up - right stand, when they Are made to bow and fall.
From Zi - on, His own ho - ly hill, O let Him send sup - port.
Set up our ban- ners; and the LORD All thy re - quests ful - fill.
But we re - mem - ber will the name Of our LORD God a - lone.
[9]De - liv - er, LORD, and let the king Give an- swer when we call.

PSALM 20 **20B**

LEIGHTON. L.M.
1. [1]The LORD in your dis - tress at - tend; Let Ja - cob's
2. [3]May He your sac - ri - fice re - gard, And all your
3. [5]In your sal - va - tion we'll re - joice, In our God's
4. [6]I know now that the LORD de - fends And saves His
God ex - alt you still; [2]Help from the ho - ly
of - f'rings bear in mind; May He your heart's de -
name our ban - ners raise. [4]O may Je - ho - vah
own a - noint - ed king. From ho - ly heav'n He
tem - ple send And strength-en you from Zi - on's hill.
sire re - ward, Ful- fill - ing all you have de - signed.
hear your voice, Grant all you ask through all your days.
an - swer sends; His right hand sav - ing power will bring.

5. [7]In chariots some boast confidence,
And on their horses some rely;
But we boast only one defense,
The name of God, the LORD Most High.

6. [8]While we are raised and upright stand,
Our foes are made to bow and fall.
[9]O save the king, LORD, by Your hand,
And answer us the day we call.

21A PSALM 21:1–6

NOEL. C.M.D.
1. [1]The king in Thy great strength, O LORD, Shall ver- y joy - ful be;
2. [3]For Thou wilt meet him with Thy gifts Of bless-ings man - i - fold,
3. [5]In Thy sal-va - tion he is great, And glo - ri - fied is he;
And in Thy sav- ing help he shall Re - joice most fer-vent - ly.
And Thou hast set up - on his head A crown of pur - est gold.
And Thou up- on him hast be-stowed Most glo - rious maj - es - ty.
[2]For Thou up - on him hast be - stowed All that his heart would have;
[4]When he re-quest- ed life of Thee, Thou life to him didst give;
[6]For Thou wilt ev - er set on him The bless-ings of Thy grace,
And Thou from him didst not with-hold What - e'er his lips did crave.
Such length of days Thou gav - est him He ev - er - more should live.
And Thou wilt cause him to be filled With joy be - fore Thy face.

PSALM 21:7–13 **21B**

ELLACOMBE.C.M.D.
4. 7 Be - cause the king trusts in the LORD, Through cov'-nant love that's proved
5. 9 For thou wilt make them blaze as fire In pres-ence of thy power.
6. 12 For thou wilt make them turn their back; Thou wilt thine ar-rows place
Through grace of Him Who is Most High The king shall not be moved.
The LORD shall swal-low them in wrath; The fire shall them de- vour.
Up - on thy strings, in read - i - ness To fly a - gainst their face.
8 Thy hand shall reach to eve - ry man Who is thine en - e - my,
10 Their off-spring thou wilt strike from earth, Their seed from sons of men.
13 In Thine om - nip - o - tence, O LORD, Ex - alt Thy - self on high;
And thy right hand shall find out all Who hate thee need-less - ly.
11 Their e - vil plans, their cun-ning plots A - gainst thee are in vain.
Then we shall sing; with psalms of praise Thy might we glo - ri - fy.

PSALM 21:1–6

LATAKIA.12.9.12.9.
1. [1]Now the king in Your strength shall be joy - ful, O LORD,
2. [3]All the bless - ings of life You did gra - cious - ly give;
3. [5]By the help You have brought is his glo - ry made great;
And shall in Your sal - va - tion re - joice.
On his head placed a crown of fine gold.
You did glo - ry and hon - or im - part.
[2]For each wish of his heart You did free - ly af - ford;
[4]When he asked of You life, You or - dained that he live,
[6]You for - ev - er made him the most bless - ed in state;
You with - held no re - quest of his voice.
That no end to his days would be told.
By Your pres - ence You glad - dened his heart.

PSALM 21:7–13 **21D**

LATAKIA.12.9.12.9.
4. 7For the king in the strength of the LORD ev - er nigh
5. 8You will reach with your hand eve - ry one of your foes,
6. 10From the earth shall their race be con - sumed and de - stroyed,
7. 12You will make them turn 'round, show their backs in swift flight,
Did un - wav - er - ing con - fi - dence place;
Hat - ers find with your right hand of power.
And their off - spring for - ev - er shall fail.
When your ar - rows are aimed at each face.
Through the cov - e - nant love which is in the Most High
9In the day of your an - ger the flames them en - close;
11By the e - vil they planned, by the schemes they em - ployed,
13Be ex - alt - ed, O LORD, in Your strength and Your might!
He shall nev - er be moved from his place.
In His wrath will the LORD them de - vour.
They shall nev - er a - gainst you pre - vail.
We will sing, praise Your power and Your grace.

22A PSALM 22:1–10

NAOMI. C.M.
1. [1]My God, my God, O why have You For - sak - en me? O why Are You so far from giv - ing help And from my groan - ing cry?
2. [2]By day and night, my God, I call; Your an - swer still de - lays. [3]And yet You are the Ho - ly One Who dwells in Is - rael's praise.
3. [4]Our fa - thers put their trust in You; From You their res - cue came. [5]They begged You and You set them free; They were not put to shame.

4. [6]But as for me, I am a worm
And not a man at all.
To men I am despised and base;
Their scornings on me fall.

5. [7]All those who look at me will laugh
And cast reproach at me.
Their mouths they open wide: they wag
Their heads in mockery.

6. [8]"The LORD was his reliance once;
Now see what God will send.
Yes, let God rise and set him free,
This man that was His friend."

7. [9]You took me from my mother's womb
To safety at the breast.
[10]Since birth when I was cast on You
In You, my God, I rest.

PSALM 22:1–10 **22B**

MARTYRS C.M.
1. [1]My God, my God, O why have You For- sak - en me? O why Are You so far from giv - ing help And from my groan - ing cry?
2. [2]By day and night, my God, I call; Your an - swer still de - lays. [3]And yet You are the Ho - ly One Who dwells in Is - rael's praise.
3. [4]Our fa - thers put their trust in You; From You their res - cue came. [5]They begged You and You set them free; They were not put to shame.

4. [6]But as for me, I am a worm
And not a man at all.
To men I am despised and base;
Their scornings on me fall.

5. [7]All those who look at me will laugh
And cast reproach at me.
Their mouths they open wide; they wag
Their heads in mockery:

6. [8]"The LORD was his reliance once;
Now see what God will send.
Yes, let God rise and set him free,
This man that was His friend."

7. [9]You took me from my mother's womb
To safety at the breast.
[10]Since birth when I was cast on You
In You, my God, I rest.

22C PSALM 22:11–20

KINGSFOLD C.M.D.
8. 11 Be not far off, for grief is near, And none to help is found;
9. 15 My strength is on-ly brok-en clay; My mouth and tongue are dry,
10. 17 My bones are plain for me to count; Men see me and they stare.
12 For bulls of Ba-shan in their strength Now cir-cle me a-round.
For in the ver-y dust of death You there make me to lie.
18 My clothes a-mong them they di-vide, And gam-ble for their share.
13 Their li-on-jaws they o-pen wide, And roar to tear their prey.
16 For see how dogs en-cir-cle me! On eve-ry side there stands
19 Now hur-ry, O my Strength, to help! Do not be far, O LORD!
14 My heart is wax, my bones un-knit, My life is poured a-way.
A broth-er-hood of cru-el-ty; They pierce my feet and hands.
20 But snatch my soul from rag-ing dogs, And spare me from the sword.

PSALM 22:21–26

TIVERTON.C.M.
11. 21 From li - on's mouth and ox - en's horns O save me; hear my prayer! 22 And to my breth - ren in the church Your name I will de - clare.
12. 23 Let those that fear the LORD sing praise! Give glo - ry to Him now, All Ja - cob's seed; all Is - rael's seed, In awe be - fore Him bow.
13. 24 For He did not de - spise nor spurn The grief of one op- pressed, Nor did He shun his cry for help, But heard and gave him rest.

14. [25] When I proclaim my praise of You,
Then all the church will hear,
And I will pay my vows in full
Where men hold Him in fear.

15. [26] The wretched poor will eat their fill
And will be made secure.
All those who seek will praise the LORD.
So let your hearts endure.

22E PSALM 22:27–31

NATIVITY C.M.
16. [27]Then men re - mem - ber will the LORD To earth's re - mot - est shore, And all the Gen - tile kin - dreds turn To wor - ship and a - dore.
17. [28]For all do - min - ion in the earth Is on - ly of the LORD. A - mong the na - tions He con - trols The pow - er of the sword.
18. [29]To Him will all the rich bow down Who feast and live at ease. And all whose souls de- scend to dust Will fall up - on their knees.

19. [30]There shall forever be a seed
To serve Him faithfully;
A generation of the Lord
It shall accounted be.

20. [31]And they will come and will make known
To people yet to be
The righteousness that is His own,
For none did this but He.

PSALM 22:1–11

22F

FILLMORE. 88.88.88.
1. [1]My God, my God, O why have You In my dis - tress for-
2. [3]But still You are the Ho - ly One; In Is - rael's praise You
3. [6]Re - proached of men, by all de-spised, A worm and not a
4. [9]You took me safe - ly from the womb; Gave faith when on my
sak - en me? O why so far from giv - ing help, And
dwell - ing have. [4]Our fa - thers put their trust in You; They
man am I; [7]All they that see me laugh in scorn; They
moth - er's breast; [10]From birth de - pen - dent on Your care. You
from my ag - o - niz - ing plea? [2]All day, my God, I
trust - ed, and You res - cue gave. [5]To You they cried; de-
shake their heads and taunt - ing cry, [8]"He trusts the LORD! Let
are my God; In You I rest. [11]Be not far off, for
cry in vain; By night, yet no re - lief I gain.
liv - 'rance came; They trust - ed and were free from shame.
Him de - fend And save him, if He is his friend!"
grief is nigh; There's none on whom I can re - ly.

22G PSALM 22:12–21

WAVERTREE. 88.88.88.
5. 12 As herds of bulls that roam the wild My cru - el
6. 14 My life like wa - ter is poured out, My bones at
7. 16 Like dogs the wick - ed com - pass me, And they have
8. 19 But be not far from me, O LORD! Haste, O my
foes a - bout me throng; They bel - low and they com - pass me
eve - ry joint a - part; 15 Like crack - ing pots my strength is dried;
pierced my hands and feet. 17 I now can num - ber all my bones;
Strength! Give help to me! 20 My soul de - liv - er from the sword.
Like bulls of Ba - shan fierce and strong; 13 Foes o - pen
14 In me like melt - ed wax my heart; 15 My tongue and
With gloat - ing stares all eyes me greet. 18 My clothes a-
My life from dogs and li - ons free. 21 Though by sharp
wide their mouths to slay, Like li - ons roar - ing for their prey.
jaws to - geth - er cling; My soul to dust of death You bring.
mong them they di - vide, And on my robe with dice de - cide.
horns I'm near - ly rent, You have to me Your an - swer sent.

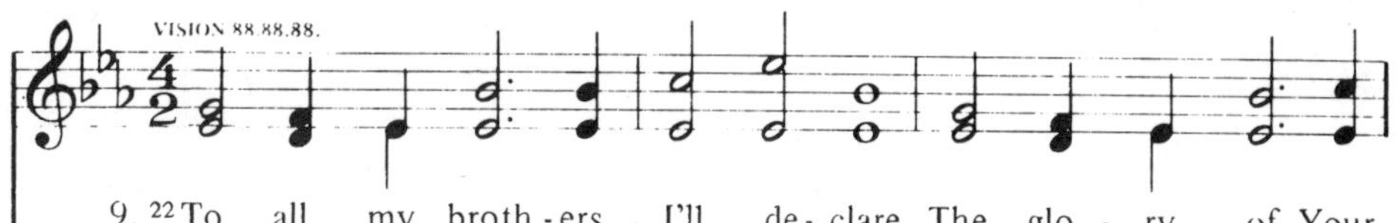
VISION 88.88.88.

9. [22]To all my broth - ers I'll de- clare The glo - ry of Your
10. [24]For He has not de - spised the poor; He has not scorned their
11. [25]With - in the con - gre - ga - tion great I of - fer praise You

ho - ly name. [23]I'll praise You where the peo - ple meet.
wretch-ed state. He has not turned a - way His face
have sup - plied. I'll pay my vows with them who fear;

Who fear the LORD, His praise pro - claim; All sons of Ja - cob,
From an - y - one in trou - ble great. When an - y cried to
[26]The meek with food are sat - is - fied. Who seek the LORD shall

praise His grace, And stand in awe, all Is- rael's race.
Him in grief, He heard his prayer and sent re - lief.
Him a - dore. May your heart live for ev - er - more.

221
PSALM 22:27–31
CREATION 88.88.88.
12. 27 All ends of earth, re - mem - br'ing Him, Shall turn them-
13. 29 The rich and might- y of the earth Shall eat and
14. 30 A seed shall rise to serve His will, And to the
selves un - to the LORD. The kin-dreds of the na-tions then
low be - fore Him bend, And in His pres-ence all shall bow
age it shall be told 31 A - bout our Lord; then they shall come
To Him their hom - age shall ac - cord. 28 Be-cause the
Who help - less to the dust de - scend, The wretch - ed
And shall His right - eous - ness un - fold Un - to a
LORD the king-dom owns And rules a - bove all earth-ly thrones
who, al-though they strive, Yet can - not keep their souls a - live.
peo - ple yet un - known, That this was done by Him a - lone.

PSALM 23

EVAN.C.M.
1. [1]The LORD's my Shep - herd, I'll not want; [2]He
2. [3]My soul He doth re - store a - gain; And
3. [4]Yea, though I walk in death's dark vale, Yet
makes me down to lie In past - ures green; He
me to walk doth make With - in the paths of
will I fear no ill; For Thou art with me,
lead - eth me The qui - et wa - ters by.
right - eous - ness, Ev'n for His own name's sake.
and Thy rod And staff me com - fort still.

4. [5]A table Thou hast furnished me
In presence of my foes;
My head Thou dost with oil anoint,
And my cup overflows.

5. [6]Goodness and mercy all my life
Shall surely follow me;
And in GOD's house for evermore
My dwelling place shall be.

23B PSALM 23

CRIMOND.C.M.
1. [1]The LORD's my Shep - herd, I'll not want; [2]He
2. [3]My soul He doth re - store a - gain; And
3. [4]Yea, though I walk in death's dark vale, Yet
makes me down to lie In past - ures green; He
me to walk doth make With - in the paths of
will I fear no ill; For Thou art with me,
lead - eth me The qui - et wa - ters by.
right - eous - ness, Ev'n for His own name's sake.
and Thy rod And staff me com - fort still.

4. [5]A table Thou hast furnished me
In presence of my foes;
My head Thou dost with oil anoint,
And my cup overflows.

5. [6]Goodness and mercy all my life
Shall surely follow me;
And in GOD's house for evermore
My dwelling place shall be.

PSALM 23

23C

RESIGNATION.11.11.11.11.
1. 1The LORD is my shep - herd; no want shall come nigh.
2. In right ways He leads me for His own name's sake.
3. 5You set me a ta - ble be - fore all my foes.
2With - in the green pas - tures He makes me to lie.
4Al - though through the vale of death's shad - ow I walk,
My head You a - noint, and my cup o - ver - flows.
Be - side the still wa - ters He leads me to rest;
Since You are there with me, no e - vil I fear;
6Your good - ness and mer - cy at - tend my life's ways;
3My soul He re - vives when I'm faint and op - pressed.
Your rod and Your staff give me com - fort and cheer.
I'll dwell in the house of the LORD end - less days.

23D PSALM 23

DOMINUS REGIT ME.11.11.11.11.
1. ¹The LORD is my shep - herd; no want shall come nigh.
2. In right ways He leads me for His own name's sake.
3. ⁵You set me a ta - ble be - fore all my foes.
²With - in the green pas - tures He makes me to lie.
⁴Al - though through the vale of death's shad - ow I walk,
My head You a - noint, and my cup o - ver - flows.
Be - side the still wa - ters He leads me to rest;
Since You are there with me, no e - vil I fear;
⁶Your good - ness and mer - cy at - tend my life's ways;
³My soul He re - vives when I'm faint and op - pressed.
Your rod and Your staff give me com - fort and cheer.
I'll dwell in the house of the LORD end - less days.

PSALM 24

VARINA.C.M.D.
1. [1]The earth be - long-eth to the LORD, And all that it con - tains;
2. [3]Who is the man that shall as - cend In - to the hill of GOD?
3. [5]This is the man who shall re - ceive The bless - ing from the LORD;
The world that is in - hab - it - ed And all that there re - mains.
Or who with - in His ho - ly place Shall have a firm a - bode?
The God of his sal - va - tion shall Him right - eous - ness ac - cord.
[2]For He up - on the wa - ters vast Did its foun - da - tion lay;
[4]Whose hands are clean, whose heart is pure, And un - to van - i - ty
[6]Lo, this the gen - er - a - tion is That af - ter Him in - quire,
He firm - ly has es - tab - lished it Up - on the floods to stay.
Who has not lift - ed up his soul, Nor sworn de - ceit - ful - ly.
O Ja - cob, who do seek Thy face With all their heart's de - sire.

4. [7]Ye gates, lift up your heads on high;
Ye doors that last for aye,
Be lifted up, that so the King
Of glory enter may.
[8]But who of glory is the King?
The mighty LORD is this;
Ev'n that same LORD that great in might
And strong in battle is.

5. [9]Ye gates, lift up your heads on high;
Ye doors that last for aye,
Be lifted up, that so the King
Of glory enter may.
[10]But who is He that is the King
Of glory? Who is this?
The LORD of Hosts and He alone
The king of glory is.

24B PSALM 24

MEAR.C.M.
1. [1]The earth be - long-eth to the LORD, And all that it con - tains;
2. [2]For He up - on the wa - ters vast Did its foun - da - tion lay;
3. [3]Who is the man that shall as - cend In - to the hill of GOD?
4. [4]Whose hands are clean, whose heart is pure, And un - to van - i - ty
The world that is in - hab - it - ed And all that there re - mains.
He firm - ly has es - tab - lished it Up - on the floods to stay.
Or who with - in His ho - ly place Shall have a firm a - bode?
Who has not lift - ed up his soul, Nor sworn de - ceit - ful - ly.

5. [5]This is the man who shall receive
The blessing from the LORD;
The God of his salvation shall
Him righteousness accord.

6. [6]Lo, this the generation is
That after Him inquire,
O Jacob, who do seek Thy face
With all their heart's desire.

7. [7]Ye gates, lift up your heads on high;
Ye doors that last for aye,
Be lifted up, that so the King
Of glory enter may.

8. [8]But who of glory is the King?
The mighty LORD is this;
Ev'n that same LORD that great in might
And strong in battle is.

9. [9]Ye gates, lift up your heads on high,
Ye doors that last for aye,
Be lifted up, that so the King
Of glory enter may.

10. [10]But who is He that is the King
Of glory? Who is this?
The LORD of Hosts and He alone
The King of glory is.

PSALM 24
24C
GREYFRIARS.11.11.11.11.
1. 1The earth and the rich - es with which it is stored,
2. 3O who shall the mount of Je - ho - vah as - cend?
3. 5He shall from Je - ho - vah a bless - ing re - ceive;
4. 7O gates, lift your heads! Age - less doors, lift them high!
5. 9O gates, lift your heads! Age - less doors, lift them high!
The world and its dwell - ers, be - long to the LORD.
Or who in the place of His ho - li - ness stand?
The God of sal - va - tion shall right - eous - ness give.
The great King of glo - ry to en - ter draws nigh!
The great King of glo - ry to en - ter draws nigh!
2For He on the seas its foun - da - tion has laid,
4The man of pure heart and of hands with - out stain,
6Thus look - ing to Him is a whole bless - ed race,
8O who is the King that in glo - ry draws near?
10This great King of glo - ry, O Who can He be?
And firm on the wa - ters its pil - lars has stayed.
Who has not sworn false - ly nor loved what is vain.
All those who, like Ja - cob, are seek - ing Your face.
The LORD, might - y LORD of the bat - tle is here!
Je - ho - vah of hosts, King of glo - ry is He!

25A PSALM 25:1–7

LEOMINSTER.S.M.D.
1. 1To Thee I lift my soul, O LORD; 2I trust in Thee,
2. 4Show me Thy ways, O LORD; Thy paths, O teach Thou me;
3. 6Thy ten - der mer - cies,LORD, To mind do Thou re - call,
My God; let me not be a-shamed Nor foes ex - ult o'er me.
5And do Thou lead me in Thy truth; There-in my teach - er be.
And lov - ing - kind -ness - es, for they Have been through ag- es all.
3Yea, none that wait on Thee Shall be a - shamed at all;
For Thou art God that dost To me sal - va - tion send,
7My sins of youth, my faults Do Thou, O LORD, for - get;
But those that wan - ton - ly trans- gress, Up - on them shame shall fall.
And I up - on Thee all the day Ex - pect - ing do at- tend.
In lov - ing - kind -ness think on me And for Thy good - ness great.

PSALM 25:1–7

DETROIT.S.M.
1. [1]To Thee I lift my soul, O LORD; [2]I
2. [3]Yea, none that wait on Thee Shall be a-
3. [4]Show me Thy ways, O LORD; Thy paths, O
4. For Thou art God that dost To me sal-
trust in Thee, My God; let me not
shamed at all; But those that wan - ton -
teach Thou me; [5]And do Thou lead me
va - tion send, And I up - on Thee
be a - shamed Nor foes ex - ult o'er me.
ly trans - gress, Up - on them shame shall fall.
in Thy truth; There - in my teach - er be.
all the day Ex - pect - ing do at - tend.

5. [6]Thy tender mercies, LORD,
To mind do Thou recall,
And lovingkindnesses, for they
Have been through ages all.

6. [7]My sins of youth, my faults
Do Thou, O LORD, forget;
In lovingkindness think on me
And for Thy goodness great.

25C
PSALM 25:8–15
WELCOME VOICE.S.M.D.
7. 8 The LORD is good and just; The way He'll sin - ners show;
8. 11 Now for Thine own name's sake, O LORD, I Thee en - treat
9. 14 The se - cret of the LORD Shall all who fear Him know;
9 The meek in judg-ment He will guide And make His path to know.
To par - don my in - i - qui - ty, For it is ver - y great.
The knowl-edge of His cov - e - nant He un - to them will show.
10 All path - ways of the LORD Are truth and mer - cy sure,
12 Who fears the LORD is taught The way to un - der - stand;
15 My eyes up - on the LORD Con - tin - ual - ly are set;
To such as keep His cov - e - nant And tes - ti - mo-nies pure.
13 His soul shall ev - er dwell at ease, His seed pos - sess the land.
For He it is that shall bring forth My feet out of the net.

PSALM 25:16–22 25D

TRENTHAM. S.M.
10. 16O turn to me Thy face; To me Thy mercy show; For I am very desolate, And brought exceeding low.
11. 17My griefs of heart abound; My sore distress relieve. 18See my affliction and my pain, And all my sins forgive.
12. 19Consider Thou my foes Because they many are; And it a cruel hatred is Which they against me bear.

13. [20]O do Thou keep my soul;
Do Thou deliver me;
And let me not be put to shame
Because I trust in Thee.

14. [21]Because I wait for Thee
Let truth and right defend;
[22]Redemption, Lord, to Israel
From all his troubles send.

26A
PSALM 26:1–7
SPOHR. C.M.
1. [1]Judge me, O LORD, for I have walked In my integrity, And ever with unwav'ring heart Have trusted, LORD, in Thee.
2. [2]Examine me, and prove me, LORD; Try heart and mind, I pray. [3]Thy mercy is before my eyes; Thy truth has led my way.
3. [4]I will not with dissemblers go, With false men will not wait. [5]I will not sit with wicked men; Their company I hate.
4. [6]I'll wash my hands in innocence, Approach Thine altar, LORD, [7]That with a thankful voice I may Thy wonders all record.

PSALM 26:8–12

SERENITY. C.M.
5. 8The hab - i - ta - tion of Thy house, O
6. 9With sin - ners gath - er not my soul; Spare
7. 11But as for me, I'll hum - bly walk In
8. 12Be - cause my foot is stand - ing now Up -
LORD, is my de - light; The place in which Thy
me . from blood they spill. 10In their hand is a
my in - teg - ri - ty. Re-deem Thou me, and
on a lev - el place; With-in the con - gre -
glo - ry dwells Is love - ly in my sight.
wick - ed scheme; Their right hand bribes do fill.
in Thy grace Be mer - ci - ful to me.
ga - tion great Je - ho - vah I will bless.

27A PSALM 27:1–4

BOSTON. C.M.
1. [1]The LORD's my light and sav - ing strength; Who shall make me dis - mayed? My life's strength is the LORD; of whom Then shall I be a - fraid?
2. [2]For when my en - e - mies and foes, Most wick - ed per - sons all, A - gainst me rose to eat my flesh They stum - bled and did fall.
3. [3]A - gainst me though a host en - camp, My heart yet fear - less is; Though war a - gainst me rise, I will Be con - fi - dent in this.

4. [4]One thing I of the LORD desired
And will seek to obtain:
That all days of my life I may
Within GOD's house remain;

5. That I the beauty of the LORD
Behold may and admire,
And that I in His holy place
May rev'rently inquire.

PSALM 27:5–9 27B

LYNTON. C.M.
6. [5]He'll hide me, cov - ered, in His tent;
7. [6]And e - ven at this pres - ent time
8. I sac - ri - fic - es to His house
9. [7]O Thou, Je - ho - vah, hear my voice
Hide on the e - vil day With - in His house; He'll
My head shall lift - ed be A - bove all those that
With joy - ful - ness will bring; I will Je - ho - vah
When - e'er I cry to Thee; Up - on me al - so
lift me up Up - on a rock to stay.
are my foes And round en - com - pass me.
praise; yea, I To Him will prais - es sing.
mer - cy have, And do Thou an - swer me.

10. [8]When Thou didst say, "Seek ye My face,"
Then unto Thee reply
Thus did my heart: "Thy gracious face,
Jehovah, seek will I."

11. [9]Far from me hide not Thou Thy face;
Put not away from Thee
Thy servant in Thy wrath; Thou hast
A helper been to me.

27C PSALM 27:9–14

LOUISE. C.M.
12. 9b Leave me not nor for - sake, O God; Thou Sav - iour art to me; 10 Though both my par - ents cast me off I'm tak - en up by THEE.
13. 11 O LORD, in - struct me in Thy way; Do Thou my lead - er be; Make plain my path be- cause of those That ha - tred bear to me.
14. 12 Nor give me to my foes' de - sire; For wit - ness - es that lie A - gainst me ris - en are, and such As breathe out cru - el - ty.

15. 13 I should have fainted had I not
Believed that I would see
Jehovah's goodness in the land
Of them that living be.

16. 14 O do thou wait upon the LORD;
Yea, let thy strength be great,
And let thy heart encouraged be;
Upon Jehovah wait.

PSALM 27:1–4

27D

BEVAN. 66.66.88.
1. [1]The LORD's my shin - ing light And my sal - va - tion
2. [2]When ad - ver - sar - ies came To eat my flesh a -
3. [4]My one de - sire has been, Still to the LORD I'll
sure; Who can fill me with fright Or
way, Those wick - ed tripped in shame, And
pray, That all my days with - in The
move my heart se - cure? The LORD's my strong-hold
fell to their dis - may.[3]Though hosts sur - round, I
LORD's house I may stay, The LORD's own beau - ty
ev - er near; Of Whom then shall I stand in fear?
will not quail; And still I trust, though war as - sail.
to ad - mire, And in His tem - ple to in - quire.

27E PSALM 27:5–9

SAMUEL. 66.66.88.
4. [5]When trou - bles fill my day, When fears and dan - gers
5. [6]My head shall lift - ed be A - bove my en - e -
6. [7]LORD, hear me when I cry! O an - swer me in
7. [9]Hide not Your face from me, Your ser - vant now, I
throng, Se - cure - ly hid I'll stay In His pa -
mies. With - in His tent with glee I'll of - fer
grace! [8]Each time I hear You say, "En - quire and
pray; The day You an - gry be O turn me
vil - ion strong. He'll hide me in His tent al - ways;
sac - ri - fice. With shouts of joy my song I'll bring;
seek My face," My heart in glad re - sponse will speak,
not a - way! You've been my help. For - sake me not!
And high up - on a rock me raise.
There prais - es to the LORD I'll sing.
"Your face, O LORD, I'll al - ways seek."
God, my Sal - va - tion, leave me not!

PSALM 27:10–14 27F

ST. JOHN. 66.66.88.
8. 10 Though par - ents may be - tray, The LORD will care for
9. 12 O to my foes' de - sire Hand me not o - ver
10. 13 O had I not be - lieved That I would sure - ly
me. 11 Teach me, O LORD, Your way; On
now! They cun - ning - ly con - spire Their
see The good - ness of the LORD With
lev - el path lead me. For me my foes in
charg - es false to vow. Their eve - ry breath is
those that liv - ing be! 14 Wait for the LORD! With
am - bush wait; My way is lined with those who hate.
cru - el - ty; How hope - less seems my cause to be!
strength re - stored, Be brave in heart. Wait for the LORD.

28A PSALM 28

DUNDEE. C.M.
1. [1]I cry to You, O LORD, my Rock; Do not be deaf to me, For if You heed me not, I'll be Like those in grave that lie.
2. [2]O hear my sup - pli - cat - ing voice When un - to You I cry, When to Your ho - ly sanc - tu - 'ry I lift my hands on high.
3. [3]O drag me not a - way with men Who work in - i - qui - ty, Who to their neigh - bors speak of peace While plot - ting treach - er - y.
4. [4]Re - pay them just - ly for their deeds And e - vil of their way, And for the work done by their hands A due re - ward re - pay;

5. [5]Since they do not regard the works
And actions of His hand,
The LORD will pull them down, no more
Will build them up to stand.

6. [6]Now let Jehovah blessed be
Who heard me when I cried.
[7]Jehovah is my strength and shield;
On Him my heart relied.

7. I have been helped; my heart is glad;
My joyous praise I'll sing.
[8]Jehovah is our refuge strong;
The Savior is our King.

8. [9]O save Your people; give them help
And bless Your heritage.
Be their own shepherd, carry them
Secure through every age.

PSALM 28

28B

BARNABAS. 76.76.77.76.
1. [1]LORD, my Rock, to You I cry! O be not deaf to me!
2. [3]Drag me not a - way from You With men en-gaged in sin,
3. [5]Since the do-ings of the LORD, His works, they yet ig - nore,
4. Glad in heart, I'll raise my song.[8] The LORD pro-tects His own.
If You speak not, I must lie With those en-tombed that be.
Who with peace their neigh-bors woo While mur-der lurks with - in.
He'll make ru - in their re-ward Nor build them an - y more.
His A - noint-ed He makes strong; He saves and guards His throne.
[2]Hear when I be-fore You stand, There to voice my ear - nest plea,
[4]Give to them their cup of woe, All the e - vils they have wrought.
[6]Bless the LORD! My cry He heard![7] My de-fense, my shield, the LORD!
[9]Save Your peo - ple; pros-per them; Bless them for Your her - i - tage.
When I lift im-plor - ing hands To-ward Your sanc-tu - 'ry.
Let them by Your judg - ment know The woes which they have brought.
My heart trust-ed in His word; With help I am re - stored.
Be their shep-herd. Car - ry them Se - cure through eve-ry age.

29A PSALM 29

KREMSER. 12.11.12.11.

1. [1]O give to Je - ho - vah, you sons of the Might - y,
2. [3]The voice of Je - ho - vah re - sounds on the wa - ters;
3. [5]The voice of Je - ho - vah is break - ing the ce - dars!
4. [7]The voice of Je - ho - vah di - vides flames of light - ning
Both glo - ry and strength to Je - ho - vah ac - cord!
The glo - ri - ous God thun - ders forth from the height.
Je - ho - vah rips Leb - a - non's ce - dars a - part!
And caus - es the fi - er - y flash - es to break!
[2]O give to the LORD His name's great - ness of glo - ry!
The LORD is up - on the great sweep of the wa - ters—
[6]The slopes of Mount Her - mon — like calves they are leap - ing!
[8]The voice of the LORD makes the wil - der - ness trem - ble;
In splen - dor of ho - li - ness wor - ship the LORD!
[4]The LORD's voice in splen - dor! The LORD's voice in might!
And Leb - a - non's hills like young an - te - lope start!
The LORD makes the des - ert of Ka - desh to shake!

5. [9]The voice of the LORD makes the deer twist in labor!
The high-standing forest of trees it strips bare!
And all of the length and the breadth of His temple
And all things within it His glory declare!

6. [10]The LORD on His throne sat above the great deluge!
The LORD on His throne sits as King without cease!
[11]The LORD is the One Who gives strength to His people!
The LORD is the One Who will bless them with peace!

PSALM 29

29B

GIVE YE TO JEHOVAH. 12.11.12.11.
1. [1]O give to Je - ho - vah, you sons of the Might - y,
Both glo - ry and strength to Je - ho - vah ac - cord!
[2]O give to the LORD His name's great - ness of glo - ry!
In splen - dor of ho - li - ness wor - ship the LORD!

PSALM 30

ANGEL'S STORY. 76.76.D.
1. 1O LORD, I will ex - alt You, For You have lift - ed me;
2. 4His saints, O praise Je - ho - vah And thank His ho - ly name.
3. 6In pros - perous days I boast - ed, "Un - moved I shall re - main."
My foes You have al - lowed not To glo - ry o - ver me.
5His an - ger lasts a mo - ment, His grace a whole life time.
7O LORD, You by Your fa - vor My mount in strength main - tain;
2O LORD my God, I plead - ed That You might heal and save;
For sor - row, like a pil - grim, May tar - ry all the night,
For when Your face was hid - den, I soon was trou - bled sore.
3LORD, You from death have ran - somed And kept me from the grave.
But then a shout of joy comes When dawns the morn - ing light.
8I'll cry to You, Je - ho - vah; The LORD I will im - plore.

4. 9Is there in my blood profit
When in the grave I dwell?
Will dust proclaim Your praises,
Your truth and glory tell?
10O hear me now, Jehovah!
Be gracious unto me!
To You I cry, Jehovah!
O now my helper be!

5. 11You now have turned my sorrow
To dancing full of joy;
You loosened all my sack-cloth
And girded me with joy.
12To You sing psalms, my glory,
And never silent be!
O LORD my God, I'll thank You
Through all eternity.

PSALM 30

FARMER. 76.76.D.
1. 1O LORD, I will ex - alt You, For You have lift - ed me;
2. 4His saints, O praise Je - ho - vah And thank His ho - ly name.
3. 6In pros - perous days I boast - ed, "Un - moved I shall re - main."
My foes You have al - lowed not To glo - ry o - ver me.
5His an - ger lasts a mo - ment, His grace a whole life time.
7O LORD, You by Your fa - vor My mount in strength main-tain;
2O LORD my God, I plead - ed That You might heal and save;
For sor - row, like a pil - grim, May tar - ry all the night,
For when Your face was hid - den, I soon was trou - bled sore.
3LORD, You from death have ran - somed And kept me from the grave.
But then a shout of joy comes When dawns the morn - ing light.
8I'll cry to You, Je - ho - vah; The LORD I will im - plore.

4. 9Is there in my blood profit
When in the grave I dwell?
Will dust proclaim Your praises,
Your truth and glory tell?
10O hear me now, Jehovah!
Be gracious unto me!
To You I cry, Jehovah!
O now my helper be!

5. 11You now have turned my sorrow
To dancing full of joy;
You loosened all my sack-cloth
And girded me with joy.
12To You sing psalms, my glory,
And never silent be!
O LORD my God, I'll thank You
Through all eternity.

31A PSALM 31:1–6

GABRIEL. C.M.
1. [1]In Thee, O LORD, I put my trust; A - shamed let me not be; Ac - cord - ing to Thy right - eous - ness Do Thou de - liv - er me.
2. [2]Bow down Thine ear to my re - quest And swift de - liv - 'rance send; To save me be a rock of strength, A for - tress to de - fend.
3. [3]Since Thou my rock and for - tress art, For Thy name's sake now guide [4]And res - cue me from se - cret nets; Thou dost my strength a - bide.

4. [5]I to Thy hand with confidence
My spirit do commend;
For unto me, LORD God of truth,
Redemption Thou dost send.

5. [6]Who lying vanities observe
I greatly have abhorred;
But as for me, my confidence
Is fixed upon the LORD.

PSALM 31:7–14

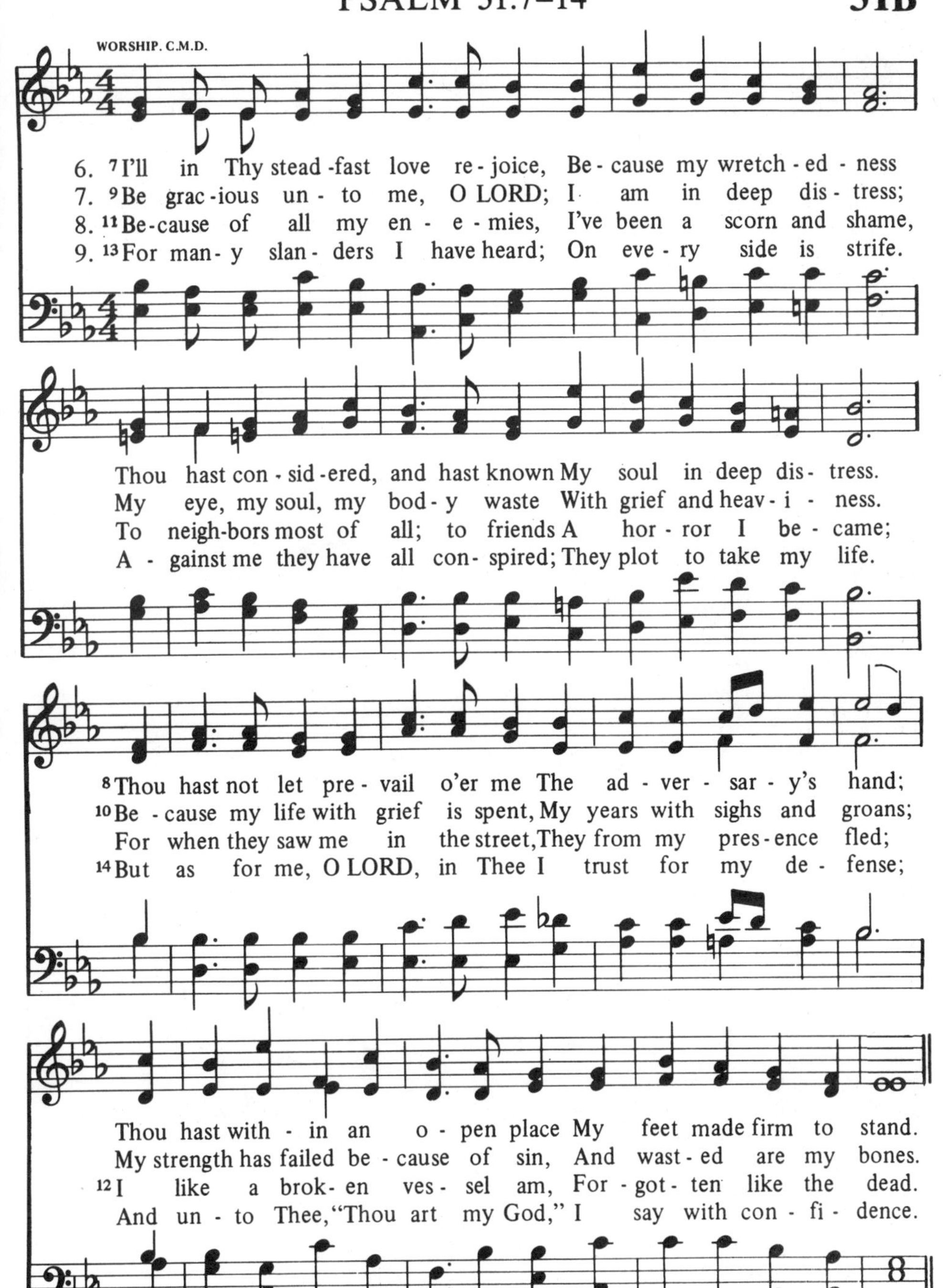
WORSHIP. C.M.D.
6. 7 I'll in Thy stead-fast love re-joice, Be-cause my wretch-ed-ness
7. 9 Be grac-ious un-to me, O LORD; I am in deep dis-tress;
8. 11 Be-cause of all my en-e-mies, I've been a scorn and shame,
9. 13 For man-y slan-ders I have heard; On eve-ry side is strife.
Thou hast con-sid-ered, and hast known My soul in deep dis-tress.
My eye, my soul, my bod-y waste With grief and heav-i-ness.
To neigh-bors most of all; to friends A hor-ror I be-came;
A-gainst me they have all con-spired; They plot to take my life.
8 Thou hast not let pre-vail o'er me The ad-ver-sar-y's hand;
10 Be-cause my life with grief is spent, My years with sighs and groans;
For when they saw me in the street, They from my pres-ence fled;
14 But as for me, O LORD, in Thee I trust for my de-fense;
Thou hast with-in an o-pen place My feet made firm to stand.
My strength has failed be-cause of sin, And wast-ed are my bones.
12 I like a brok-en ves-sel am, For-got-ten like the dead.
And un-to Thee, "Thou art my God," I say with con-fi-dence.

31C

PSALM 31:15–18

HARVEY'S CHANT. C.M.

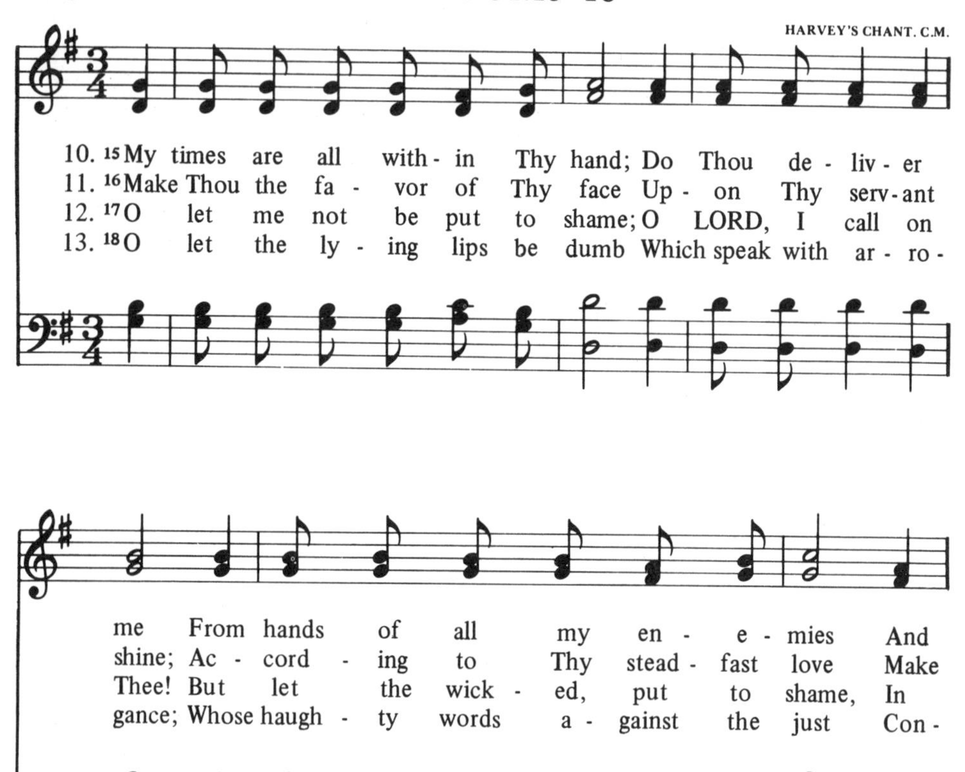

10. 15 My times are all with - in Thy hand; Do Thou de - liv - er
11. 16 Make Thou the fa - vor of Thy face Up - on Thy serv - ant
12. 17 O let me not be put to shame; O LORD, I call on
13. 18 O let the ly - ing lips be dumb Which speak with ar - ro -
me From hands of all my en - e - mies And
shine; Ac - cord - ing to Thy stead - fast love Make
Thee! But let the wick - ed, put to shame, In
gance; Whose haugh - ty words a - gainst the just Con -

those pur - su - ing me, And those pur - su - ing me.
Thy sal - va - tion mine, Make Thy sal - va - tion mine.
She - ol si - lent be, In She - ol si - lent be.
tempt and pride ad - vance, Con - tempt and pride ad - vance.

PSALM 31:19–24

ANCYRA. C.M.D.

14. [19] How great the good Thou hast re- served For all those fear - ing Thee!
15. [21] O let Je- ho - vah bless - ed be! For He has mag - ni - fied
16. [23] O love the LORD, ye god - ly ones! The LORD the faith - ful guards;

Be - stowed on those who trust Thee still That sons of men may see.
His stead - fast love to me with - in A cit - y for - ti - fied.
And He the proud and haugh - ty ones A - bun - dant - ly re - wards.

[20] Thou hast a hid - ing place for them, Safe from the snares of man;
[22] Al - though I said in my a - larm, "I'm cut off from Thine eyes!"
[24] O then be strong! Take to your heart The cour-age He will send,

Thy shel - ter from the strife of tongues For them Thou dost main - tain.
Yet Thou, when I pe - ti - tioned Thee, Hast heard my plead - ing cries.
All ye whose hope and con - fi - dence Up - on the LORD de - pend.

31E PSALM 31:1–8

LANCASHIRE. 76.76.D.
1. [1]In You, LORD, I take ref - uge; A - shamed let me not be.
2. [3]You are my rock and for - tress; For Your sake lead and guide.
3. [6]I hate those serv - ing i - dols; My trust is in the LORD.
Your right - eous - ness e - ter - nal Ex - press by sav - ing me;
[4]Free me from nets they've hid - den; My strong-hold You a - bide.
[7]I'll tri - umph in Your mer - cy; For an - guish You re - gard.
[2]In - cline Your ear to hear me; With speed de - liv - er me.
[5]I now com-mit my spir - it In - to Your out-stretched hand.
You've known my soul's af - flic-tions, [8]Kept me from hos - tile hand.
To me O be a strong rock, A fort to res - cue me.
I know You have re - deemed me, LORD God of truths that stand.
My feet You have es - tab - lished Where they have room to stand.

PSALM 31:9–16

31F

LLANGLOFFAN. 76.76.D.
4. 9 O LORD, have mer- cy on me, For an - guish fills my life;
5. 11 To all my foes a by - word, A dread to those near me,
6. When foes con - spire a - gainst me, My mur- der med - i - tate,
My eye, my soul, my bod - y Are all con-sumed with grief.
A scorn to all my neigh - bors, At sight of me they flee.
14 In You, O LORD, I'm trust - ing; "You are my God," I state.
10 My life is drained by sor- row, My years with sigh- ing spent;
12 Like dead men I'm for - got - ten, A brok - en jar thrown out.
15 My times are all in Your hand; Free me from foes who chase.
I've lost my strength by sin - ning; My bones are weak and bent.
13 I've slan - ders heard of man - y, And fear is all a - bout.
16 Your face shine on Your ser - vant; O save me in Your grace.

31G PSALM 31:17–24

SAINTS' PRAISE. 76.76.D.
7. 17 Let me not be a-shamed, LORD, Be-cause on You I call.
8. 19 How great the good You've treas-ured For them who wor-ship You,
9. 21 The LORD be ev-er bless-ed, For He has made me know
10. 23 O love the LORD, you god-ly! The LORD the faith-ful keeps.
A-shamed shall be the wick-ed, As dead men si-lenced all.
Pre-pared for those who trust You Where sons of men may view.
The mer-cy and pro-tec-tion His ci-ty walls be-stow.
But He re-pays the haugh-ty That what he sows he reaps.
18 All false lips shall be si-lenced, Whose speech is in-so-lent,
20 You by Your pres-ence hide them From all men plot-ting wrongs;
22 I said when filled with pan-ic, "I'm cut off from Your eyes!"
24 Be strong! He'll keep re-fresh-ing Your heart with cour-age great;
Who bold-ly blame the right-eous And proud-ly show con-tempt.
You keep them in Your shel-ter Safe from the strife of tongues.
Yet when to You I called out, You heard my plead-ing cries.
O do with hope and pa-tience Up-on Je-ho-vah wait.

PSALM 32:1–6

32A

TABLER. C.M.
1. [1]O bless - ed is the man to whom
2. [2]Blessed is the man to whom the LORD
3. [3]When I from speak - ing had re - frained,
4. [4]Be - cause up - on me day and night
Has free - ly par - doned been All the trans - gres - sion
Im - put - eth not his sin, And in whose spir - it
And si - lent was my tongue, My bones were wax - ing
Thy hand did heav - y lie; So that my mois - ture
he has done, And cov - ered is his sin.
is no guile, Nor fraud is found there - in.
old be - cause I cried out all day long.
has been turned To sum - mer's drought there - by.

5. [5]I thereupon have unto Thee
   Acknowledged all my sin,
   And likewise my iniquity
   I have not hid within.

6. "I to Jehovah will confess
   My trespasses," said I;
   And of my sin Thou didst forgive
   All the iniquity.

7. [6]Because of this shall every saint
   His prayer direct to Thee;
   In such a time he shall Thee seek
   As found Thou mayest be.

8. Yea, when the floods of waters great
   Are swelling to the brim,
   They shall not overwhelm his soul
   Nor once come near to him.

32B PSALM 32:7–11

MAIN. C.M.
9. 7 Thou art my hid - ing place; Thou shalt From trou - ble keep me free; With songs of my de- liv - er - ance Shalt Thou en - com - pass me.
10. 8 I will in - struct thee and thee teach The way that thou shalt go; And with Mine eye up- on thee set I will di - rec - tion show.
11. 9 Then be not like the horse or mule Which do not un - der - stand; Whose mouth, that they may come to thee, A bri - dle must com - mand.

12. [10] The sorrows of the wicked man
Exceedingly abound;
But him that trusteth in the LORD
Shall mercy compass round.

13. [11] Ye righteous, in the LORD be glad;
In Him do ye rejoice;
All ye that upright are in heart,
For joy lift up your voice.

PSALM 32:1–7

32C

VOX DILECTI. C.M.D.
1. 1What bless - ed - ness for him whose guilt Has all for - giv - en been!
2. 3When I kept si - lent, my bones aged; My groan - ing filled each day.
3. Then You did all my sin for - give And take my guilt a - way.
When his trans-gres - sions par-doned are, And cov-ered is his sin.
4Your hand op-pressed me day and night;My mois-ture dried a - way.
6For this when You are near at hand Let all the god - ly pray.
2O blessed the man 'gainst whom the LORD Counts no in - i - qui - ty,
5Then I to You ad - mit - ted sin, Hid not my guilt - i - ness;
The ris - ing floods will harm him not. 7You are my hid - ing place.
And in whose spir - it there is not De - ceit or treach - er - y.
I said, "I will be - fore the LORD Trans - gres-sions now con - fess."
And You will com - fort me with songs Of vic - to - ry and grace.

32D PSALM 32:8–11

CAMPBELL. C.M.D.
4. [8] In - struc-tion I will give to you And · teach you as you go.
5. [10] The wick-ed man - y pangs en - dure, But stead-fast cov - 'nant love
My watch-ful eye will guide your steps; My coun- sel you will know.
En - cir- cles eve - ry man whose trust Is in the LORD a - bove.
[9] Be not like sense-less horse or mule Which if you would sub - due
[11] Be glad and shout, you right-eous ones, And in the LORD re - joice!
You must with bit and bri - dle hold To bring him close to you.
And all whose hearts are just and true Sing out with joy - ful voice.

PSALM 33:1–9
33A
RAVENDALE. 886.886.
1. [1]You right - eous, praise the LORD with joy; It's good that just men praise em - ploy.[2]With thanks the LORD O praise! The harp and ten - stringed vi - ol bring, [3]With skill re - sound - ing prais - es sing; A new song to Him raise.
2. [4]For up - right is Je - ho - vah's word, He does in all His work re - cord His faith - ful - ness and worth. [5]In jus - tice and in do - ing right Je - ho - vah al - ways takes de - light. His mer - cy fills the earth.
3. [6]Je - ho - vah's word the heav - ens made, And all the host of them ar - rayed His breath has caused to be. [7]He rolls the wa - ters heap on heap; He gath - ers all the might - y deep In cav - erns of the sea.
4. [8]Let all the earth Je - ho - vah fear; Let all that dwell both far and near In awe be - fore Him stand. [9]When He had spok - en it was done, And fin - ished was each work be - gun When once He gave com - mand.

33B PSALM 33:10–15

JEHOVAH NISSI. 886.886.
5. [10]He made the na - tions' coun - sel vain; The
6. [12]O tru - ly is the na - tion blessed Whose
7. [13]The LORD looks forth from hea - ven high; On
plots the hea - then would main-tain Je - ho - vah caused to fail.
God, be - fore the world con-fessed, Je - ho - vah is a - lone;
sons of men He turns His eye.[14] There seat - ed on His throne
[11]Je - ho - vah's coun - sel shall en - dure; His
And blessed the peo - ple is whom He Has
He looks to earth on all man - kind. [15]As
pur - pos - es of heart most sure Through a - ges all pre - vail.
made His her - it - age to be And chos - en for His own.
one He fash - ions eve - ry mind; To Him their deeds are known.

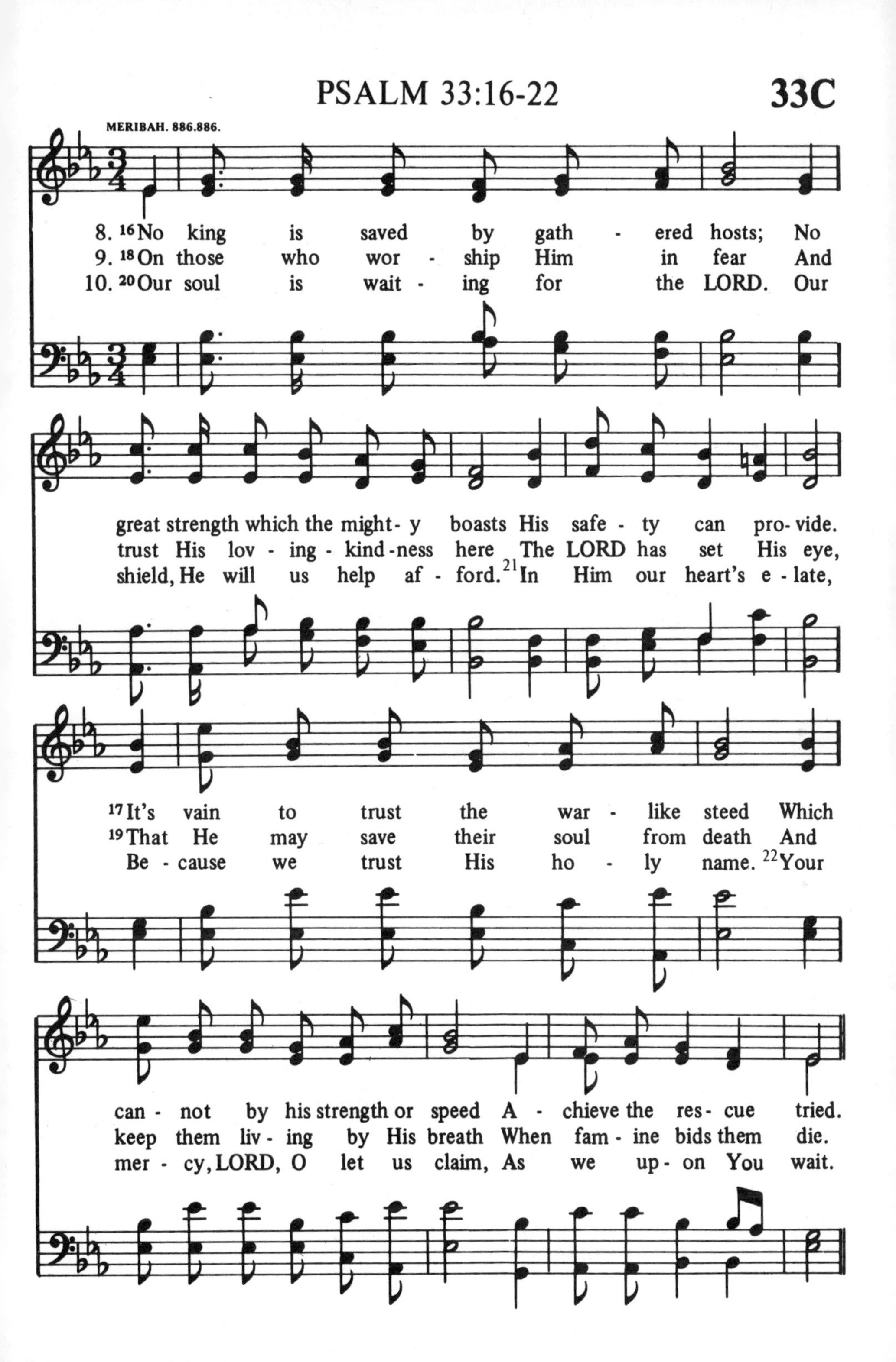
PSALM 33:16-22
33C
MERIBAH. 886.886.
8. 16 No king is saved by gath - ered hosts; No
9. 18 On those who wor - ship Him in fear And
10. 20 Our soul is wait - ing for the LORD. Our
great strength which the might - y boasts His safe - ty can pro- vide.
trust His lov - ing - kind -ness here The LORD has set His eye,
shield, He will us help af - ford. 21 In Him our heart's e - late,
17 It's vain to trust the war - like steed Which
19 That He may save their soul from death And
Be - cause we trust His ho - ly name. 22 Your
can - not by his strength or speed A - chieve the res- cue tried.
keep them liv - ing by His breath When fam - ine bids them die.
mer - cy, LORD, O let us claim, As we up - on You wait.

34A PSALM 34:1–10

CHAMPS ELYSEES. C.M.D.
1. [1]At all times I will bless the LORD, In praise my mouth em-ploy;
2. [5]They looked to Him and ra- diant were; A - shamed they shall not be.
3. [8]O taste and see the LORD is good; Who trust in Him are blessed.
[2]My soul shall in Je - ho-vah boast; The meek shall hear with joy.
[6]This poor man cried; Je - ho-vah heard, From trou - ble set him free.
[9]Fear GOD, His saints; none that Him fear Shall be with want op-pressed.
[3]O mag - ni - fy the LORD with me; Let us ex - alt His name.
[7]The an - gel of the LORD en -camps, And round en- com- pass- eth
[10]The li - ons young may hun - gry be, And they may lack their food;
[4]In all my fears I sought the LORD; From Him de - liv-'rance came.
All those a - bout that do Him fear, And them de - liv - er - eth.
But they that tru - ly seek the LORD Shall not lack an - y good.

PSALM 34:11–22

34B

STOCKTON. C.M.D.
4. 11O come, my sons, give heed to me; I'll teach Je - ho - vah's fear.
5. 15Up - on the race of right - eous men The LORD has set His eye;
6. 17The race of right - eous men cry out; The LORD to them gives ear;
7. 19The right-eous man - y tri - als has; From all the LORD sets free;
12Who longs for life and loves full days That he may see good here?
His ears are o - pen un - to them That He may hear their cry.
De - liv - ers them each one to free From all their trou - bles here.
20He keeps in safe - ty all his bones; Not one can bro - ken be.
13Re - strain your lips from speak - ing lies; Keep back your tongue from ill;
16The face of GOD is set a - gainst All who do wick - ed - ly,
18The LORD is al - ways near to them Who have a bro - ken heart,
21Ill shall the wick - ed slay; con - demned Are all who hate the just.
14De - part from e - vil, and do good; Seek peace; pur - sue it still.
That He may ful - ly from the earth Cut off their mem - o - ry.
And He to those in spir - it crushed Sal - va - tion will im - part.
22The LORD re - deems His ser - vants' soul; Con - demns none who Him trust.

34C PSALM 34:1–10

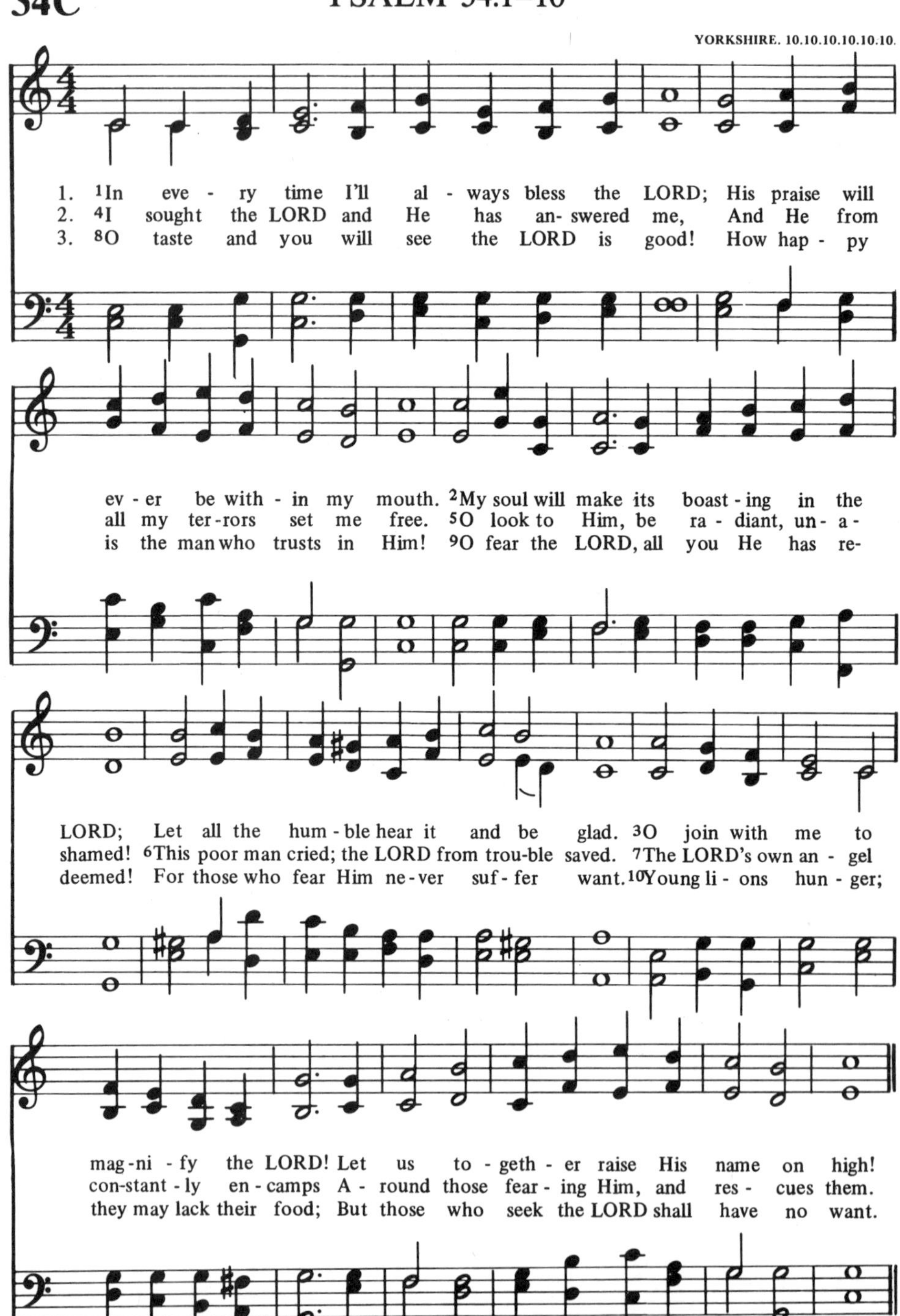

YORKSHIRE. 10.10.10.10.10.10.
1. 1In eve - ry time I'll al - ways bless the LORD; His praise will
2. 4I sought the LORD and He has an- swered me, And He from
3. 8O taste and you will see the LORD is good! How hap - py
ev - er be with - in my mouth. 2My soul will make its boast - ing in the
all my ter - rors set me free. 5O look to Him, be ra - diant, un - a -
is the man who trusts in Him! 9O fear the LORD, all you He has re-
LORD; Let all the hum - ble hear it and be glad. 3O join with me to
shamed! 6This poor man cried; the LORD from trou-ble saved. 7The LORD's own an - gel
deemed! For those who fear Him ne - ver suf - fer want. 10Young li - ons hun - ger;
mag - ni - fy the LORD! Let us to - geth - er raise His name on high!
con-stant - ly en - camps A - round those fear - ing Him, and res - cues them.
they may lack their food; But those who seek the LORD shall have no want.

PSALM 34:11-22

34D

INVOCATION. 10.10.10.10.10.10.
4. 11O come, you chil - dren, lis - ten un - to me; And I will
5. 15Je - ho - vah's eyes are toward the right - eous ones; His ears are
6. 18The LORD is near to eve - ry bro - ken heart, And those who
7. 21But e - vil sure - ly shall the wick - ed slay, And those who
teach you how to fear the LORD. 12Who longs for life and loves to see good
o - pen to their eve - ry cry. 16The LORD's face is a - gainst all e - vil
are in spir - it crushed He saves. 19Though man-y are the tri - als of the
hate the just will be con-demned. 22The LORD pro-vides re - demp - tion for the
days? 13From e - vil keep your tongue, your lips from lies. 14De-part from e - vil,
men To cut off mem - o - ry of them from earth. 17The right-eous cry; Je -
just, The LORD de - liv - ers him from eve - ry one. 20For He is safe - ly
soul Of eve - ry - one who tru - ly serves His will, And none will be con -
and be do - ing good; Seek peace and strive for it with all your heart.
ho - vah hears and saves; From all their trou - bles He de - liv - ers them.
keep - ing all his bones; Not one of them can ev - er bro - ken be.
demned a - mong all those Who for their on - ly ref - uge fly to Him.

34E PSALM 34:11–22

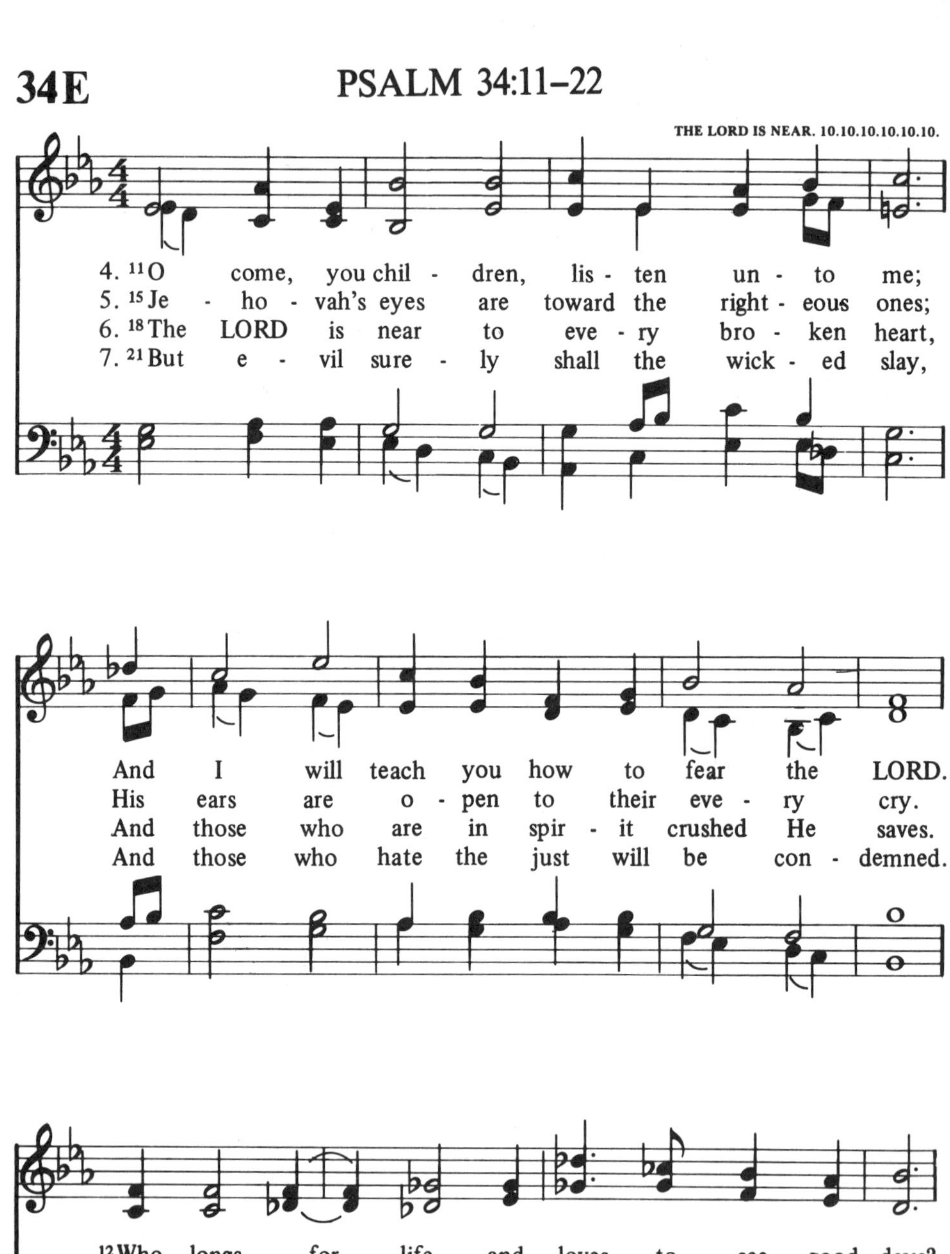
THE LORD IS NEAR. 10.10.10.10.10.10.
4. 11 O come, you chil - dren, lis - ten un - to me;
5. 15 Je - ho - vah's eyes are toward the right - eous ones;
6. 18 The LORD is near to eve - ry bro - ken heart,
7. 21 But e - vil sure - ly shall the wick - ed slay,
And I will teach you how to fear the LORD.
His ears are o - pen to their eve - ry cry.
And those who are in spir - it crushed He saves.
And those who hate the just will be con - demned.

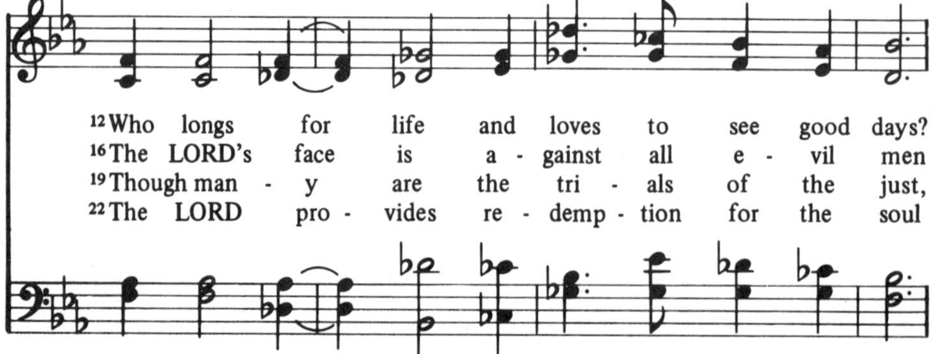
12 Who longs for life and loves to see good days?
16 The LORD's face is a - gainst all e - vil men
19 Though man - y are the tri - als of the just,
22 The LORD pro - vides re - demp - tion for the soul

13 From e - vil keep your tongue, your lips from lies.
To cut off mem - o - ry of them from earth.
The LORD de - liv - ers him from eve - ry one.
Of eve - ry - one who tru - ly serves His will,
14 De - part from e - vil, and be do - ing good;
17 The right - eous cry; Je - ho - vah hears and saves;
20 For He is safe - ly keep - ing all his bones;
And none will be con - demned a - mong all those
Seek peace and strive for it with all your heart.
From all their trou - bles He de - liv - ers them.
Not one of them can ev - er bro - ken be.
Who for their on - ly ref - uge fly to Him.

35A PSALM 35:1–6

HAMBURG. L.M.
1. [1]Plead, LORD, a - gainst con - tend - ing foes, And fight with
2. [3]Draw out the spear and stop the way A - gainst the
3. [4]Let those who seek to take my soul Them - selves be
4. [5]Let them be chaff be - fore the wind, Je - ho - vah's

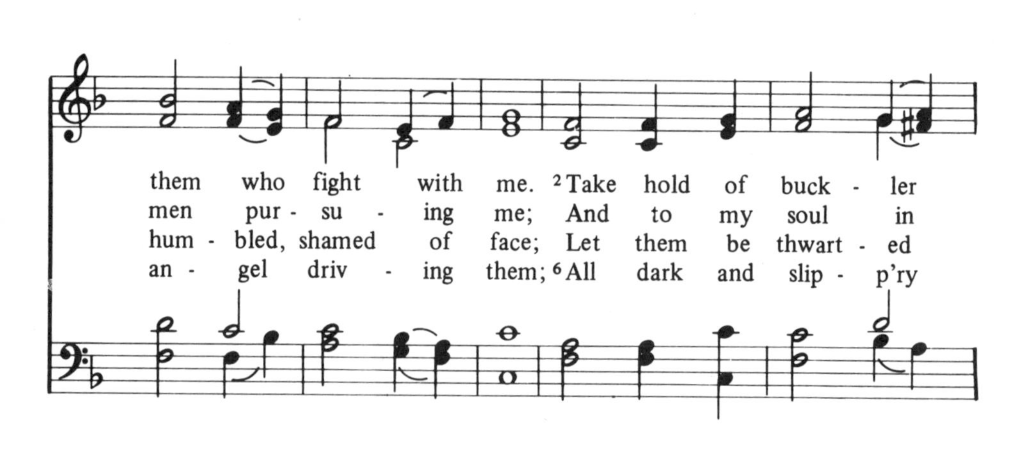
them who fight with me. [2]Take hold of buck - ler
men pur - su - ing me; And to my soul in
hum - bled, shamed of face; Let them be thwart - ed
an - gel driv - ing them; [6]All dark and slip - p'ry

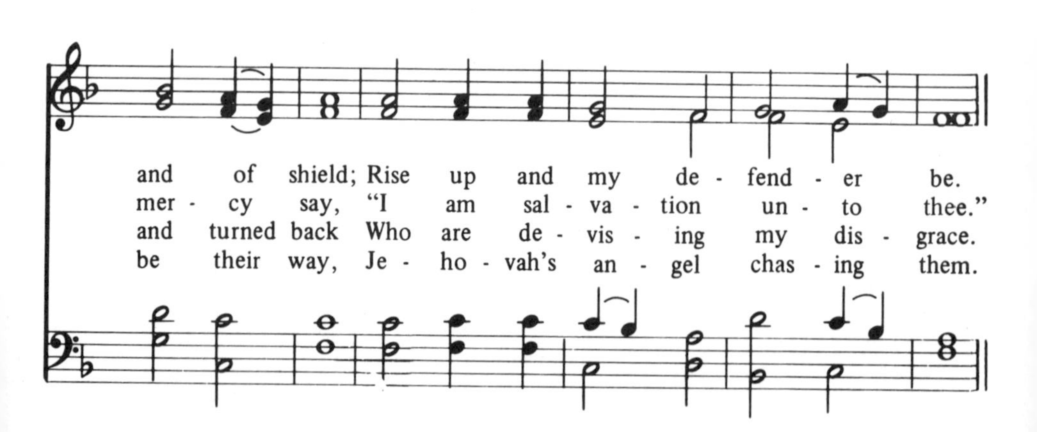
and of shield; Rise up and my de - fend - er be.
mer - cy say, "I am sal - va - tion un - to thee."
and turned back Who are de - vis - ing my dis - grace.
be their way, Je - ho - vah's an - gel chas - ing them.

PSALM 35:7–10
35B
WAREHAM. L.M.
5. [7]With - out a cause their net they hid To take me
6. [8]Let him the un - ex - pect - ed meet; Let him be
7. [9]My soul shall in the LORD re - joice, In His sal-
8. "For Thou the poor de - liv - er - est From one who
in the pit pre - pared. With - out a cause they
caught with - in the snare Which he has spread for
va - tion boast - ful be; [10]Ex - ult - ing, all my
is for him too strong; The poor and need - y
dug the pit In which my soul might be en - snared.
oth - er feet, And fall to des - o - la - tion there.
bones will say, "Je - ho - vah, who is like to Thee?
Thou dost spare From one who'd rob or do him wrong."

35C PSALM 35:11–18

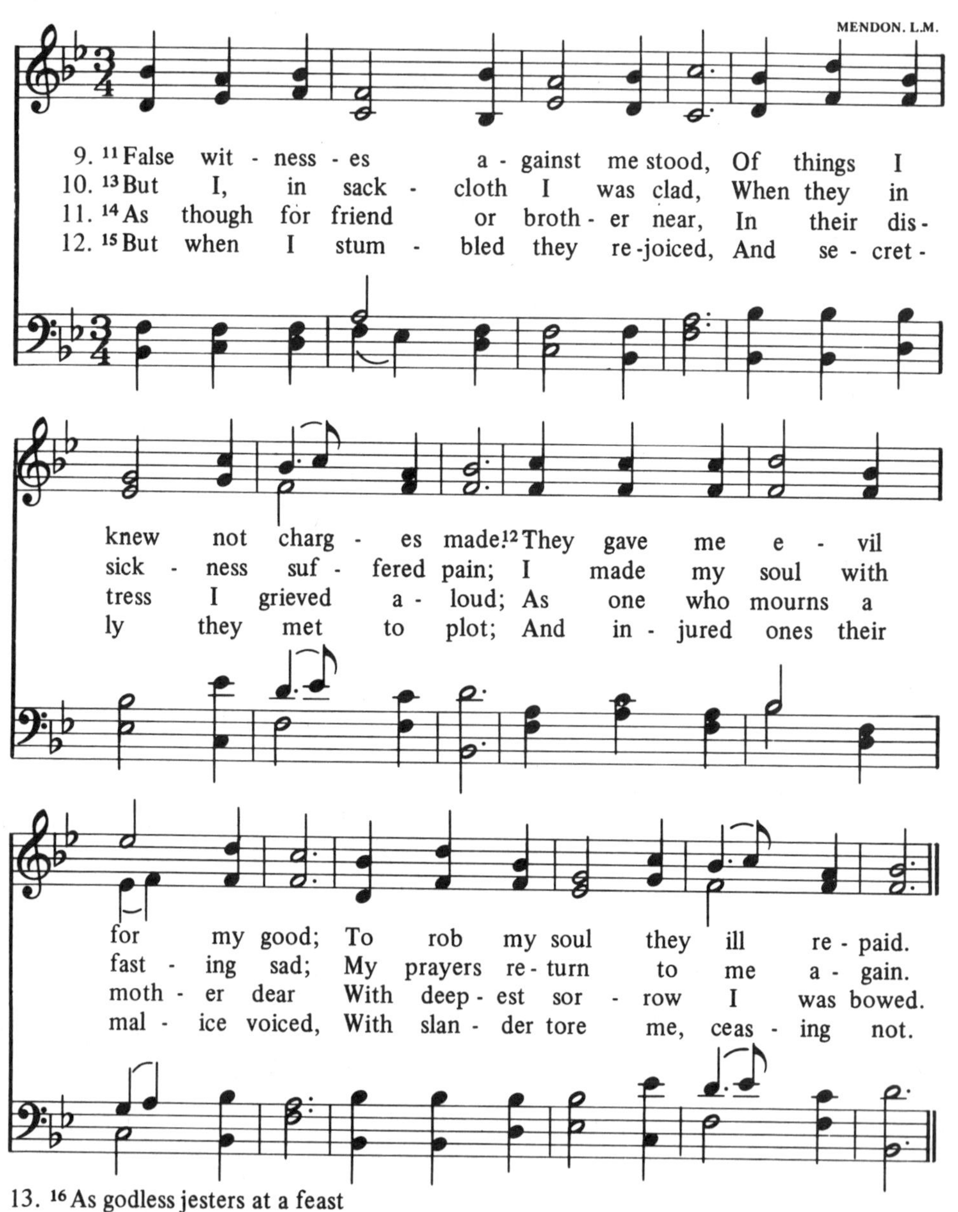

MENDON. L.M.
9. 11 False wit - ness - es a - gainst me stood, Of things I
10. 13 But I, in sack - cloth I was clad, When they in
11. 14 As though for friend or broth - er near, In their dis -
12. 15 But when I stum - bled they re-joiced, And se - cret -
knew not charg - es made! 12 They gave me e - vil
sick - ness suf - fered pain; I made my soul with
tress I grieved a - loud; As one who mourns a
ly they met to plot; And in - jured ones their
for my good; To rob my soul they ill re - paid.
fast - ing sad; My prayers re - turn to me a - gain.
moth - er dear With deep - est sor - row I was bowed.
mal - ice voiced, With slan - der tore me, ceas - ing not.

13. [16] As godless jesters at a feast
They with their teeth have gnashed at me.
[17] How long, O Lord, wilt Thou look on?
Wilt Thou unheeding all this see?

14. From their destructions pluck my soul,
And snatch my life from lions strong.
[18] Then with the saints I'll give Thee thanks.
And praise Thee in the mighty throng.

PSALM 35:19–23 **35D**

ZEPHYR. L.M.
15. 19 Let not my wrong - ful en - e - mies Raise o - ver
16. 20 They speak not peace; de - ceit they plot A - gainst the
17. 22 LORD, Thou hast seen; then be not still! O Lord, be
me their joy - ful cries, Nor those whose hate I
men of peace - ful mien; 21 They o - pen wide their
not far from my sight! 23 Stir up Thy - self! To
mer - it not With se - cret scorn - ing wink their eyes.
mouth at me And say, “A - ha! our eyes have seen!”
jus - tice wake! My God, my Lord, up - hold my right!

35E PSALM 35:24–28

WARRINGTON. L.M.
18. 24 Judge me in jus - tice, LORD my God, And let them
19. 26 Let them be shamed and hum - bled all Who joy at
20. 27 But let them shout and loud re - joice Who long to
21. "Be - cause He loves His serv - ant's peace!" 28 And thus my
not re - joice at me, 25 Nor say in heart, "He is de-
my ca - lam - i - ty; Let them be clothed with shame, dis-
see me jus - ti - fied; And let them say with cease - less
tongue will med - i - tate Up - on Thy per - fect right - eous -
voured! Be - hold, our soul's de - sire we see!"
grace, Who mag - ni - fy them - selves o'er me.
voice, "The LORD be ev - er mag - ni - fied!
ness, And all the day Thy praise re - late.

PSALM 36:1–4 36A

MANOAH. C.M.
1. [1]Trans-gres - sion to the wick - ed speaks; Deep
2. [2]Be - cause him - self he flat - ters so In
3. [3]The words he ut - ters with his mouth Are
4. [4]His thoughts and plans up - on his bed In -
in the heart it lies. There sure - ly is no
his own blind - ed eyes, That he in his in-
wick - ed - ness and lies; He has re - frained from
i - qui - ty in - vent; He sets him - self in
fear of God At all be - fore his eyes,
i - qui - ty Sees no - thing to de - spise.
do - ing good And ceas - es to be wise.
ways not good, From e - vil won't re - lent.

36B PSALM 36:5–12

PEACE. C.M.D.
5. [5]Thy mer- cy, LORD, ex -tends to heav'n; Thy faith- ful - ness, the sky.
6. [8]They with the boun - ty of Thy house Shall be well sat - is - fied;
7. [10]To them that know Thee, ev - er - more Thy lov - ing- kind- ness show,
[6]Thy jus - tice is like mounts of God; Thy judg- ments depths de-fy.
From riv- ers full of Thy de- lights Thou dost their drink pro-vide.
And still on men of up -right heart Thy right- eous - ness be - stow.
LORD, Thou pre - serv - est man and beast.[7]How pre-cious, God, Thy grace!
[9]Be - cause the foun - tain filled with life Is on - ly found with Thee;
[11]Let not the foot of pride crush me, Nor wick - ed hand de - tain.
Be - neath the shad- ow of Thy wings Men's sons their trust shall place.
And in that pur- est light of Thine We clear - ly light shall see.
[12]There e - vil - do - ers fall; thrust down, They can - not rise a - gain.

PSALM 37:1–6 37A

ST. ANNE. C.M.
1. 1Have no dis - turb - ing thoughts a - bout Those do - ing wick - ed - ly, And be not en - vi - ous of those Who work in - i - qui - ty.
2. 2For e - ven like the grow - ing grass Soon be cut down shall they; And like the green and ten - der plant They all shall fade a - way.
3. 3Set thou thy trust up - on the LORD; Con - tin - ue do - ing good. Dwell thou se - cure - ly in the land; Make faith - ful - ness thy food.

4. [4]Joy in the LORD; He'll grant each gift
For which thy heart may call.
[5]Commit thy way unto the LORD;
Trust Him; He'll do it all.

5. [6]And like the morning light He shall
Thy righteousness display;
And He thy judgment shall bring forth
Like noontide of the day.

37B PSALM 37:7–15

HEAVENLY FOLD. C.M.D.
6. 7 Rest in the LORD; wait pa-tient- ly; Fret not for an - y - one
7. 9 For e - vil - do - ers soon shall be Cut off, no more to stand;
8. 11 The meek and hum-ble of the land In - her - i - tors shall be;
9. 14 The wick - ed men have drawn their swords And bent their bows to slay,
Who pros - pers in his wick - ed way, Com-plet - ing schemes be- gun.
But those who wait up - on the LORD In - her - it shall the land.
And they shall then de- light them-selves In full pros - per - i - ty.
To cast the need - y down and kill The men of up-right way.
8 Cease be- ing thou by an-ger stirred; Make thou of wrath an end.
10 For yet a lit - tle while, and then The wick-ed shall not be;
12 The wick -ed plots a - gainst the just And grinds his teeth in wrath;
15 But yet the sword which they have drawn Shall en - ter their own heart;
Fret not thy-self, for fret - ting will To e - vil - do- ing tend.
His place thou shalt con - sid - er well, But him thou shalt not see.
13 Be - cause He sees his day will come The Lord at him shall laugh.
Their bows which they are bend - ing shall In bro - ken piec- es part.

PSALM 37:16–22

ST. MICHEL'S. C.M.D.
10. 16 The lit - tle that the right-eous has Is more and bet - ter far
11. 19 They shall not be a - shamed when they The time of e - vil see;
12. 21 The wick - ed bor - rows, but his debt He nev - er does re - pay;
Than great a - bun - dance man - y have Who whol - ly wick - ed are.
And when the days of fam - ine come They sat - is - fied shall be.
Where-as the right - eous gra - cious is And free - ly gives a - way.
17 For wick - ed arms shall bro - ken be; The LORD the just sus - tains.
20 But wick - ed men, Je - ho - vah's foes, Like mead - ow flowers are they;
22 For those who have been blessed by Him In - her - it shall the land;
18 The LORD knows days of per - fect men; Their her - it - age re - mains.
And they shall van - ish; as does smoke They all shall fade a - way.
And those who have been cursed by Him, Cut off, shall no more stand.

37D
PSALM 37:23–28
WARWICK. C.M.
13. 23The ver - y steps of man have been Es -
14. 24Though he may stum - ble, he shall not Fall
15. 25I have been young, now man - y years Have
tab - lished by the LORD; He takes great pleas -ure
so he can - not stand, Be - cause Je - ho - vah
o'er my life been spread; I've nev - er seen the
in man's way, His prog - ress to re - cord.
is the One Who holds him by his hand.
right - eous left, His chil - dren beg - ging bread.
16. 26All day he's gracious and he lends;
His sons a blessing are.
27Depart from evil, and do good,
And dwell for evermore.
17. 28Because Jehovah justice loves
And never leaves His own,
They are preserved for evermore,
But sinners overthrown.
37E
PSALM 37:29–34
DODD. C.M.
18. 29The right- eous shall in - her - it earth, And ev - er in it dwell.
19. 31The law of God is in his heart; No stum-bling steps he'll make.
20. 33The LORD will nev - er leave the just With- in the wick- ed's hands,
21. 34Wait on the LORD and keep His way; Ex - alt you then shall He

30 The just man's mouth will wis - dom speak; His tongue will jus - tice tell.
32 The wick - ed spies up - on the just And seeks his life to take.
Nor let the right - eous be con-demned When he in judg - ment stands.
That you in - her - it shall the land, The wick - ed's ru - in see.
PSALM 37:35–40
37F
ST. PETER. C.M.
22. 35 I saw the wick - ed, ruth - less man, A tree whose leaves a - bound; 36 I passed one day and he was gone; Though sought, could not be found.
23. 37 Con - sid - er well the per - fect man; The up - right watch and see; For cer - tain - ly the man of peace Shall have pos - ter - i - ty.
24. 38 But those who are trans - gres - sors will Be wiped out one and all. Pos - ter - i - ty of wick - ed men Will be cut off and fall.
25. 39 Salvation of the righteous ones
Is from the LORD alone.
He will a perfect refuge be
In times distress is known.
26. 40 Jehovah helps and rescues them;
He will deliver them
From wicked men; He will them save
Because they trust in Him.

38A PSALM 38

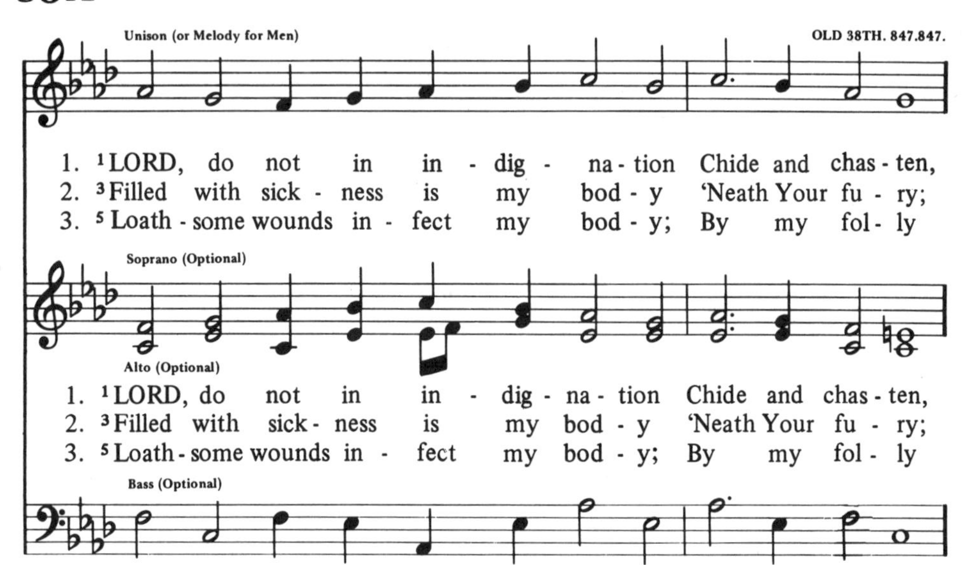

Unison (or Melody for Men)
OLD 38TH. 847.847.
1. [1]LORD, do not in in - dig - na - tion Chide and chas - ten,
2. [3]Filled with sick - ness is my bod - y 'Neath Your fu - ry;
3. [5]Loath - some wounds in - fect my bod - y; By my fol - ly
Soprano (Optional)
Alto (Optional)
1. [1]LORD, do not in in - dig - na - tion Chide and chas - ten,
2. [3]Filled with sick - ness is my bod - y 'Neath Your fu - ry;
3. [5]Loath - some wounds in - fect my bod - y; By my fol - ly
Bass (Optional)

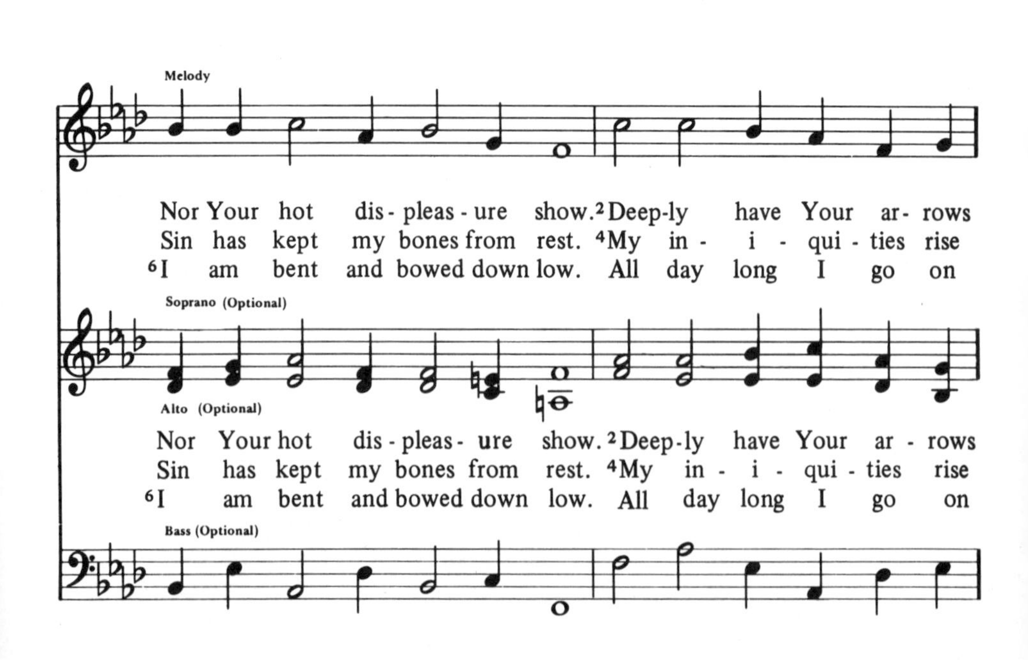

Melody
Nor Your hot dis - pleas - ure show. [2]Deep-ly have Your ar - rows
Sin has kept my bones from rest. [4]My in - i - qui - ties rise
[6]I am bent and bowed down low. All day long I go on
Soprano (Optional)
Alto (Optional)
Nor Your hot dis - pleas - ure show. [2]Deep-ly have Your ar - rows
Sin has kept my bones from rest. [4]My in - i - qui - ties rise
[6]I am bent and bowed down low. All day long I go on
Bass (Optional)

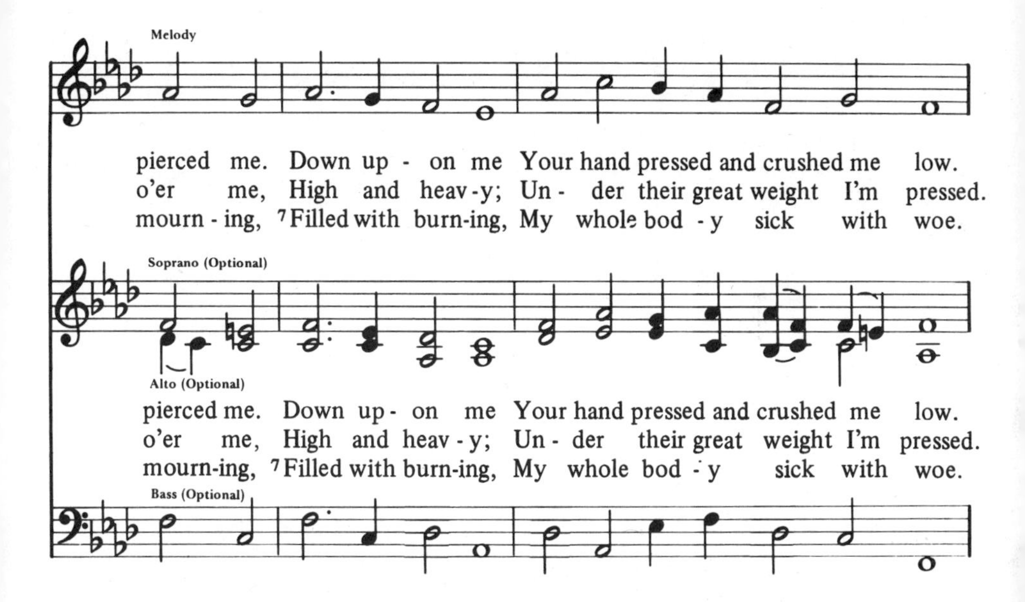
Melody
pierced me. Down up - on me Your hand pressed and crushed me low.
o'er me, High and heav-y; Un - der their great weight I'm pressed.
mourn - ing, 7 Filled with burn-ing, My whole bod - y sick with woe.
Soprano (Optional)
Alto (Optional)
pierced me. Down up- on me Your hand pressed and crushed me low.
o'er me, High and heav - y; Un - der their great weight I'm pressed.
mourn-ing, 7 Filled with burn-ing, My whole bod - y sick with woe.
Bass (Optional)

4. [8] I am bruised, benumbed, and dying,
Weak from sighing
At the murm'ring of my heart.
[9] O Lord, You know all my longing,
All my sighing;
No groan kept from You apart.

5. [10] Fearful now my heart throbs wildly;
My strength leaves me;
All the light of my eyes fails.
[11] Friends and loved ones act offended;
All my kindred
Stand off while my plague prevails.

6. [12] Foes are seeking to ensnare me;
They would kill me.
They plot treachery all day.
[13] As though deaf, I do not listen.
I say nothing,
[14] Never argue, silent stay.

7. [15] LORD, You are the One I wait for.
You will answer!
Lord, my God, my hope abide.
[16] Keep them from rejoicing o'er me
Arrogantly;
Let none gloat when my feet slide.

8. [17] Always I'm about to stumble,
Grieving, humble.
[18] I confess iniquity;
I distressed am for my error.
[19] Foes have vigor;
Many hate me wrongfully.

9. [20] For my good they evil pay me,
Hostile toward me.
[21] O forsake me not, O LORD!
O my God, be not far from me;
[22] Haste to help me!
Be my sure salvation, Lord.

38B

PSALM 38:1–8

ST. SYLVESTER. 87.87.

1. [1]LORD, do not in hot dis - pleas - ure Speak in stern re-proof to me;
2. [2]For Thy hand most sore-ly press - es; Fast Thine ar-rows stick with-in;
3. [4]For my man-i - fold trans - gress - sions Have gone up a-bove my head;

Let Thy chast-'ning be in meas-ure And Thy stroke from an-ger free.
[3]Wrath my wear-y flesh dis - tress - es, Gives my bones no rest for sin.
Like a bur - den their op - pres -sions Weigh me down with con-stant dread.

4. [5]Loathsome are my wounds neglected;
My own folly makes it so;
[6]Bowed with pain, with grief dejected,
All day long I mourning go.

5. [7]For my loins are filled with burning,
All my flesh with sore distress;
[8]Faint and bruised, I'm ever mourning
In my heart's disquietness.

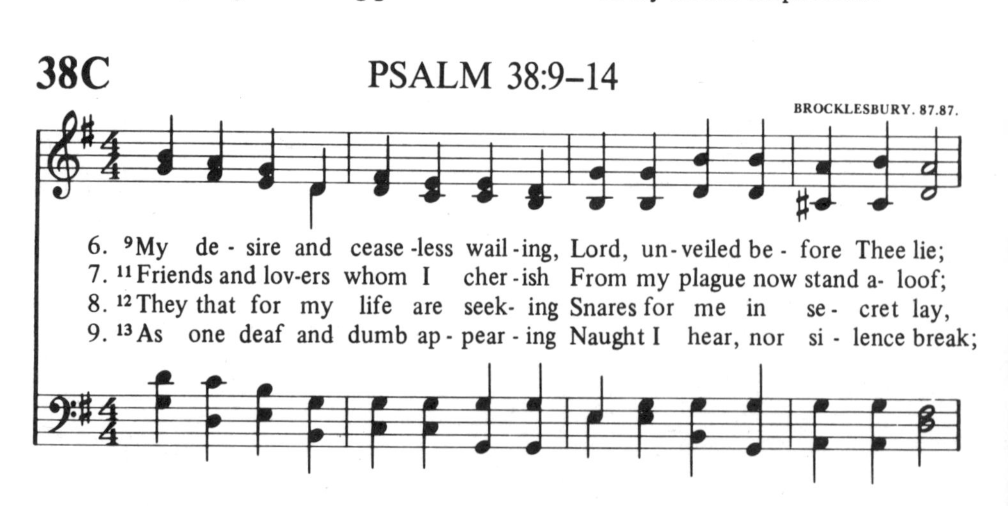
38C
PSALM 38:9–14
BROCKLESBURY. 87.87.
6. 9My de - sire and cease -less wail-ing, Lord, un-veiled be - fore Thee lie;
7. 11Friends and lov-ers whom I cher-ish From my plague now stand a- loof;
8. 12They that for my life are seek- ing Snares for me in se - cret lay,
9. 13As one deaf and dumb ap - pear - ing Naught I hear, nor si - lence break;

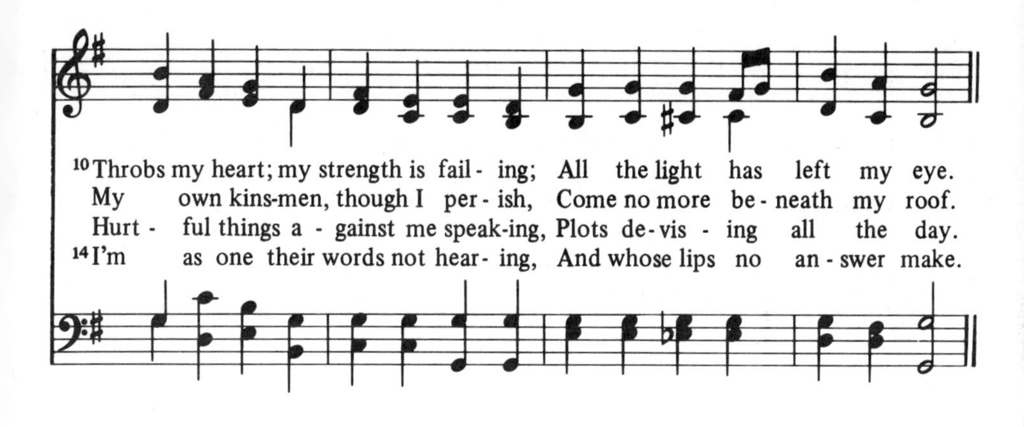
10 Throbs my heart; my strength is fail - ing; All the light has left my eye.
My own kins-men, though I per - ish, Come no more be - neath my roof.
Hurt - ful things a - gainst me speak-ing, Plots de - vis - ing all the day.
14 I'm as one their words not hear - ing, And whose lips no an - swer make.

PSALM 38:15–22

38D

MT. VERNON. 87.87.
10. 15 LORD my God, in Thee I'm trust-ing; Thou, O Lord, wilt an - swer me;
11. 17 Since I read - y am to stum-ble, Ev - er with me grief has been;
12. 19 Full of life and great in num - ber, Strong the foes who me with-stood;
13. 21 O my God, do not for -sake me; O Je - ho - vah, be Thou near;

16 Lest they joy, a - gainst me boast-ing, When my slip - ping feet they see.
18 Guilt I'll own with spir - it hum-ble, And be sor - ry for my sin.
20 E - vil they for kind - ness ren-der, Hat - ing me for do - ing good.
22 To my help - er I be - take me; As my Sav - ior, Lord, ap - pear.

39A PSALM 39:1–6

LANGRAN. 10.10.10.10.
1. [1]"I will take heed and guard my ways," I said,
2. [2]In si - lence dumb I ceased from speak - ing good;
3. [4]"My end, O LORD, and meas - ure of my days
4. "Each man at best is al - to - geth - er vain.
"So that my tongue no sin - ful word shall stain;
My heart with - in was hot, my sor - row stirred;
Make me to know, and thus my frail - ty see.
[6]Each man doth sure - ly walk in emp - ty show;
As with a bri - dle I will keep my mouth,
[3]And while I mused the fire be - gan to burn;
[5]Lo, Thou hast made my days an hand - breadth long;
They heap up wealth and vex them - selves for naught,
While in my pres - ence wick - ed men re - main."
Then spake I with my tongue this ear - nest word:
My life - time is as noth - ing un - to Thee.
Nor know to whom their gar - nered rich - es go.

PSALM 39:7–13

EVENTIDE. 10.10.10.10.
5. 7 "And now, O Lord, what wait I long - er for?
6. 9 "Yes, I was dumb; I o - pened not my mouth
7. 11 "Thou with re - bukes dost chas - ten man for sin;
8. 12 "LORD, hear my prayers; heed Thou my cry and tears;
My ex - pec - ta - tion ev - er is in Thee;
Be - cause this work was done at Thy com - mand.
His beau - ty fades be - neath the touch of death;
A stran - ger here I pass as all be - fore.
8 De - liv - er me from all my sin - ful - ness;
10 But now re - move Thy stroke a - way from me;
It is con - sumed as by the fret - ting moth.
13 O spare me that I may re - cov - er strength
The scorn of fool - ish men O make not me.
I am con - sumed be - neath Thy smit - ing hand.
Oh, sure - ly eve - ry man is but a breath.
Be - fore I go a - way and be no more."

40A

PSALM 40:1–4

ARLINGTON. C.M.

1. [1]I wait - ed long up - on the LORD, Yea,
2. [2]He took me from a fear - ful pit, From
3. [3]He put a new song in my mouth, Our
4. [4]O great - ly bless - ed is the man Who

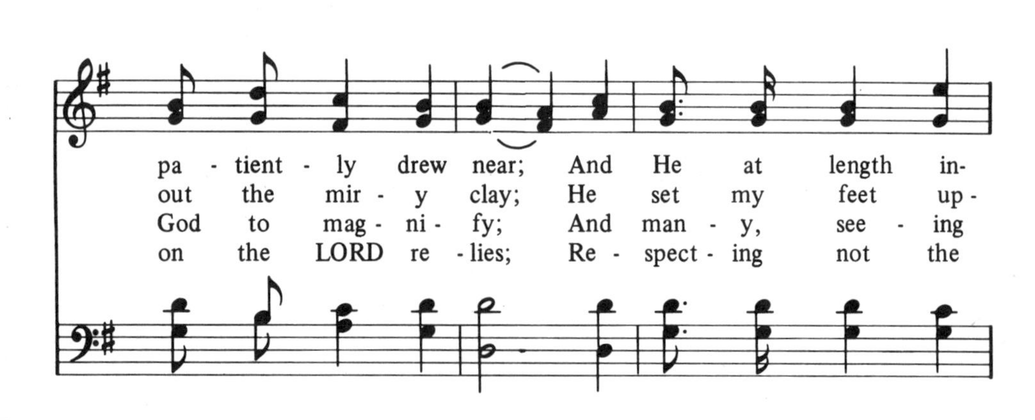
pa - tient - ly drew near; And He at length in-
out the mir - y clay; He set my feet up -
God to mag - ni - fy; And man - y, see - ing
on the LORD re - lies; Re - spect - ing not the

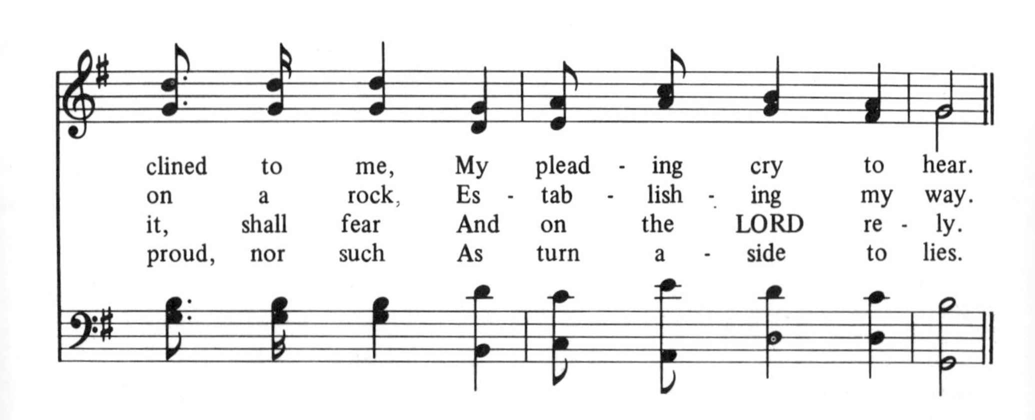
clined to me, My plead - ing cry to hear.
on a rock, Es - tab - lish - ing my way.
it, shall fear And on the LORD re - ly.
proud, nor such As turn a - side to lies.

PSALM 40:1–4

COVENANTERS. C.M.
1. [1]I wait - ed long up - on the LORD, Yea,
2. [2]He took me from a fear - ful pit, From
3. [3]He put a new song in my mouth, Our
4. [4]O great - ly bless - ed is the man Who

pa - tient - ly drew near; And He at length in -
out the mir - y clay; He set my feet up -
God to mag - ni - fy; And man - y, see - ing
on the LORD re - lies; Re - spect - ing not the

clined to me, My plead - ing cry to hear.
on a rock, Es - tab - lish - ing my way.
it, shall fear And on the LORD re - ly.
proud, nor such As turn a - side to lies.

40C
PSALM 40:5-10
FOREST GREEN. C.M.D.
5. 5O LORD my God, how man - y are The won- ders Thou hast done!
6. 6No sac-ri - fice of blood or meal Is what Thou hast de - sired;
7. 8"To do Thy will I take de- light, O Thou my God that art;
8. 10I nev - er have with - in my heart Con-cealed Thy right- eous - ness;
How man-y are the gra - cious thoughts Which thou toward us hast shown!
My ears Thou hast pre-pared to hear, No off-'ring hast re - quired.
Be - cause that ho - ly law of Thine Is deep with - in my heart."
I Thy sal - va - tion have de-clared And shown Thy faith-ful - ness.
No one can sort and set them out; None can com-pare to Thee!
7Then in re-sponse these were my words, "I come! Be-hold and see!
9With - in the con - gre - ga - tion great I right-eous-ness did preach;
Thy mer -cy great, Thy stead-fast love, I ev - er have re - vealed,
If I would tell and speak of them, They could not num-bered be.
With - in the vol- ume of the book It writ- ten is of me:
Be - hold, Je-ho -vah, Thou dost know, I'll not re - strain my speech.
And from the con-gre - ga- tion great Thy truth have not con - cealed.

PSALM 40:11–17

40D

GREEN HILL. C.M.
9. 11 O LORD, Thou wilt not now with - hold Thy ten - der - ness from me; Thy stead - fast love and faith - ful - ness Pre - serve me con - stant - ly.
10. 12 So man - y ills be - set me round They count - less seem to be; In - i - qui - ties have closed me in Un - til I can - not see;
11. They're more than hairs up - on my head; My heart is fail - ing me. 13 Be pleased, O LORD, to res - cue me; Make haste; O LORD, help me!

12. [14] Let them be humbled and ashamed
Who would my soul destroy;
Turned back, dishonored let them be
Who see my hurt with joy.

13. [15] Let them be overcome with shame;
Let them frustrated be,
Who in their scorn and malice say,
"Aha! Aha!" to me.

14. [16] Let all those seeking Thee rejoice;
Let them in Thee be glad;
Those loving Thy salvation say,
"The LORD be magnified!"

15. [17] Although I poor and needy am,
The Lord takes thought of me.
My Help and my Deliverer,
My God, do not delay!

40E
PSALM 40:1–9
FINGAL. 66.66.D.
1. [1]I waited for the LORD; He stooped and heard my cry.
2. Man-y will see with awe, And so will trust the LORD.
3. [6]You want no of-fer-ing, Nor ask a sac-ri-fice,
4. [8]“To do Your will, O God, To me is my de-light.
[2]He brought me from the pit, Out of the dun-geon mire,
[4]Blessed he who trusts in GOD, And turns not to false men.
But You have giv-en me A read-y ear to hear.
Your law is part of me, Deep in my heart, O God.”
My feet set on a rock, My foots-teps made se-cure.
[5]You have worked won-ders, LORD; No-one com-pares to You!
You ask no of-f’rings burnt Nor sac-ri-fice for sin.
[9]In con-gre-ga-tion great I told Your right-eous-ness.
[3]My lips He gave a song, A song to praise our God.
Should I de-clare each one, Their num-ber is too great.
[7]So I say, “Here I come, As in the scroll in-scribed.
You know, LORD, I spoke out; I did not close my lips.

PSALM 40:10-17

LAUSANNE. 66.66.D.
5. 10 I hid not in my heart Your truth and sav - ing help;
6. 12 Mis - for - tunes be - yond count Have tak - en hold of me.
7. 13 Come to my res - cue, LORD; O LORD, make haste to help.
8. 16 Let all men who seek You Be glad and in You joy;
Your faith - ful - ness I preached In the as - sem - bly great.
My sins close in on me So that I can - not see.
Let all who seek my life Be shamed and be con - fused.
Who Your sal - va - tion love Say, "Glo - ry to the LORD!"
11 You'll not with - hold from me Your ten - der mer - cies, LORD,
In great - er sum are they Than hairs up - on my head.
14 Let them fall back in shame Who want to see my hurt;
17 Though I'm in want and poor, The Lord takes thought of me.
And Your un- fail - ing love Will ev - er keep me safe.
So my heart fails in me; My cour - age fades a - way.
15 Let them be dumb who jeer, "A - ha, A - ha" to me.
My Help, my Sav - ior, come! O God, do not de - lay!

41A PSALM 41:1-9

ISHPEMING. C.M.D.
1. [1]How blessed the man who guides the poor By coun - sel strong and clear;
2. [3]The LORD sus - tains him on his bed Of sick - ness and of pain.
3. [5]My foes speak e - vil things of me And to each oth - er say,
4. [7]All those who hate me whis - per ill, A-gainst me harm de - vise.
The LORD will sure - ly res - cue him When e - vil days draw near.
And from his bed You make him rise; He will his health re - gain.
"When will he die; when will his name Com-plete - ly pass a - way?"
[8]"Some e - vil holds him fast," they say, "Brought down he will not rise."
[2]The LORD will guard him in the land; His life is blessed in - deed;
[4]Now as for me, I said, "O LORD, Have mer - cy on my soul.
[6]And when he comes to see me here His words are all de - ceit.
[9]And e - ven my fa - mil - iar friend In whom my trust was real,
Nor will You let him fall be - fore His ad - ver - sar - ies' greed.
Be - cause a - gainst You I have sinned, Re - store and make me whole."
He gath - ers e - vil in his heart And tells it in the street.
The one who ate my bread, has turned And lift - ed up his heel.

PSALM 41:10-13

41B

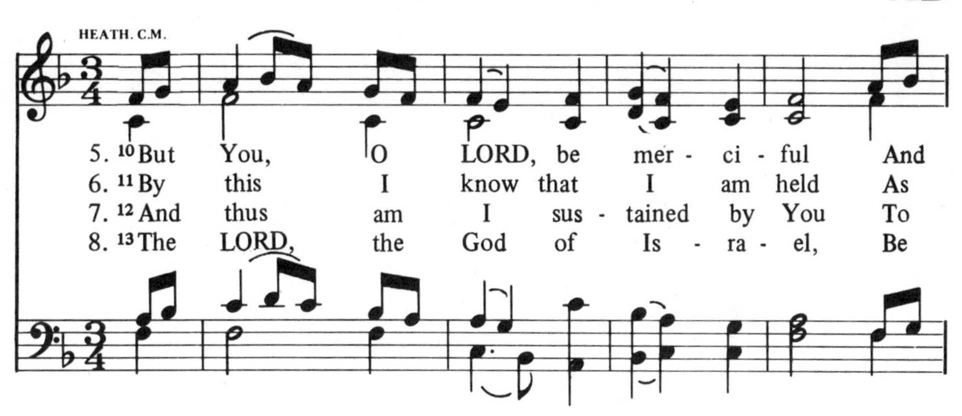
HEATH. C.M.
5. 10 But You, O LORD, be mer - ci - ful And
6. 11 By this I know that I am held As
7. 12 And thus am I sus - tained by You To
8. 13 The LORD, the God of Is - ra - el, Be

raise me in Your grace; And then a rec - om -
pre - cious in Your eyes: My foes do not raise
be com - plete and well, And in Your pres - ence
blessed and blessed a - gain From age to ev - er -

pense com - plete Up - on them I will place.
o - ver me Their glad ex - ult - ing cries.
ev - er - more You make me safe - ly dwell.
last - ing age. A - men, and still A - men.

41C

PSALM 41:13

ALPHA. Irregular.
13 Bless - ed be the LORD, the God of Is - ra -

el, from ev - er - last - ing to ev - er -

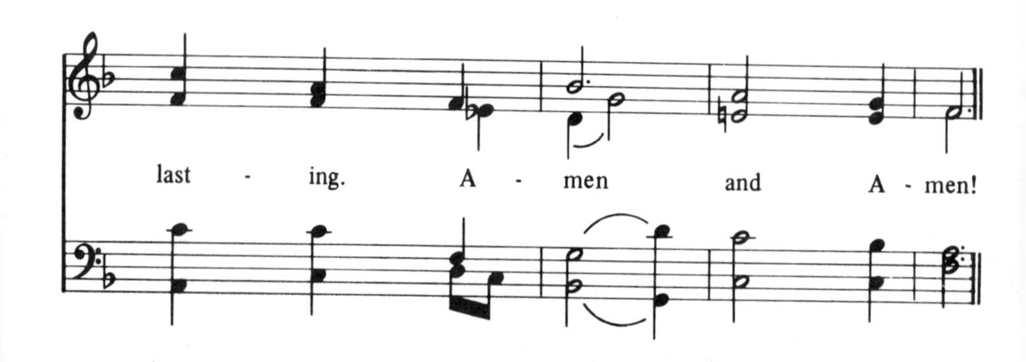
last - ing. A - men and A - men!

PSALM 42:1–5

42A

ST. AGNES. C.M.
1. ¹As in its thirst the pant - ing hart
2. ²My soul for God, the liv - ing God,
3. ³My tears have un - to me been food
4. ⁴Poured out with - in me is my soul
To wa - ter brooks doth flee, So pants my long - ing
Doth thirst; when shall I near Be - fore the face of
Both in the night and day, While un - to me con -
When this I think up - on: How of - ten with the
soul, O God, That I may come to Thee.
God ap - proach And in His sight ap - pear?
tin - ual - ly, "Where is thy God?" they say.
ea - ger throng I rev' - rent - ly had gone,

5. How to the house of God I went
With voice of joy and praise,
Yea, with the multitude that kept
The solemn holy days.

6. ⁵O why, my soul, art thou bowed down?
Why so discouraged be?
Hope now in God! I'll praise Him still!
My help, my God is He!

42B PSALM 42:6-11

WETHERBY. C.M.
7. [6]O God, my soul's cast down in me; I
8. [7]With thun - der of Thy wa - ter - falls Deep
9. [8]And yet Je - ho - vah will com - mand His
10. [9]To God Who is my rock I'll say, "O
Thee re - mem - ber will From Jor - dan land, from
un - to deep doth call; Thy bil - lows all roll
mer - cy in the day; By night His song shall
why for - get me so? Be - neath op - pres - sion
Her - mon's height, And ev'n from Mi - zar hill.
o - ver me; On me Thy break - ers fall.
be with me; To God, my Life, I'll pray.
of my foes Why do I mourn - ing go?"

11. [10]As with a sword within my bones
My enemies upbraid,
While unto me, "Where is thy God?"
Continu'lly is said.

12. [11]O why, my soul, art thou bowed down?
Why so discouraged be?
Hope now in God! I'll praise Him still!
My Help, my God is He!

PSALM 42

NASHVILLE. 888.888.
1. ¹Like hart that longs for flow - ing streams, So longs my soul, O God, for You. ²I thirst for God, the liv - ing God. When can I see the face of God? ³My tears are food both day and night. Men say to me, "Where is your God?"
2. ⁴My soul poured out, I see a - gain The throng I led to reach God's house: The shouts, the songs, the crowds, the feast. ⁵My soul, why so bowed down, dis-turbed? Hope now in God! I'll praise Him still! He is my Help! He is my God!
3. ⁶With soul down - cast I You re - call — This love - ly land where Jor - dan flows, Mount Her-mon towers, Mount Mi - zar stands — ⁷Then wave calls wave. The thun - der roars Like wa - ter-spouts! Your break - ing waves, Your bil - lows all roll o - ver me!

4. [8] The LORD commands by day His love,
By night His song, to be with me.
A prayer to God, God of my life!
[9] I pleading say to God, my Rock:
"Why me forget? Why let me mourn
Because my foe oppresses me?"

5. [10] As if to shatter all my bones,
My adversaries taunt again;
All day they scoff, "Where is your God?"
[11] My soul, why so bowed down, disturbed?
Hope now in God! I'll praise Him still!
He is my Help! He is my God!

43
PSALM 43

AZMON. C.M.
1. 1De - fend me, God, and plead my case A -
2. 2O God in Whom I ref - uge take, Why
3. 3O send Your light forth and Your truth; O

gainst a god - less clan; De - liv - er me from
have You cast me off? Why must I griev - ing
let them lead me well And bring me to Your

fraud - u - lent, Un - just and wick - ed man.
walk a - bout While foes op - press and scoff?
ho - ly hill, The place You choose to dwell.

4. [4]Then I will to God's altar go,
To God, my boundless joy.
To render thanks to God, my God,
The harp I will employ.

5. [5]O why, my soul, are you bowed down?
Why so discouraged be?
Hope now in God! I'll praise Him still!
My Help, my God is He!

PSALM 44:1–8 44A

PINNEO. C.M.D.
1. [1]O God, we with our ears have heard, Our fa - thers have us told,
2. [3]They by their sword gained not the land, Nor did their arm them save,
3. We through Thy name will tram- ple those Who ad - ver - sar- ies be.
The work that Thou didst in their days, Those hon-ored days of old.
But Thy right hand, Thine arm, Thy face, To them Thy fa-vor gave.
[6]For in my bow I will not trust, Nor will my sword save me.
[2]Thou didst the hea - then dis-pos - sess, Then plant them by Thy hand;
[4]Thou art my King! For Ja - cob, God, Sal - va-tion now com-mand.
[7]But Thou hast saved us from our foes, Our ha-ters put to shame.
Thou didst af - flict the peo-ples all, Then spread them through the land.
[5]Through Thee we shall push back the foes That now a - gainst us stand.
[8]In God we boast - ed all the day; We'll ev - er thank Thy name.

44B PSALM 44:9–16

ST. FLAVIAN. C.M.
4. 9 But now Thou hast re - ject - ed us, Hast brought us un - to shame, And when our hosts go forth to war, Thou dost not go with them.
5. 10 And Thou dost cause us to turn back Be - fore our en - e - my. And for them - selves our hat - ers take What - ev - er spoil they see.
6. 11 Thou gav - est us like sheep for food, 'Mong hea - then scat - tered us. 12 Thou cheap - ly dost Thy peo - ple sell, No prof - it make by us.

7. [13] Thou makest us a great reproach
To neighbors near and far,
A scorn and laughing stock to those
That all around us are.

8. [14] A byword Thou hast made us be
Among the nations all,
The cause of taunts and shaking heads
Among the peoples all.

9. [15] Before me all the livelong day
I see my sad disgrace;
And I am covered with the shame
That clouds my troubled face,

10. [16] Because of him who speaks reproach
And voices blasphemy,
Because of the avenging foe
And cruel enemy.

PSALM 44:17-26 44C

RESOLUTION. C.M.D.
11. 17 All this has come on us, yet we Have not for - got - ten Thee,
12. 20 If we've for - got - ten our God's name, To strange gods stretched our hands,
13. 24 Why dost Thou hide Thy face? O why For - get how we're dis - tressed?
Nor ev - er in Thy cov - e - nant Have dealt un - faith - ful - ly.
21 Will God not find this out? For He Heart se - crets un - der - stands.
See our op - pres - sion, 25 for our soul In - to the dust is pressed;
18 Our heart has not turned back; our steps Have not from Thy way strayed,
22 But for Thy sake we're killed all day, As sheep to slaugh - ter brought.
Our bod - y cleaves un - to the earth. 26 A - rise, our Help a - bove!
19 Though crushed by Thee where jack - als roam And cov-ered with death's shade.
23 A - rise, O Lord! Why dost Thou sleep? A - wake! Re - ject us not!
O now re - deem us for the sake Of all Thy stead-fast love.

44D
PSALM 44:1-8
ROBINSON. 11.11.11.11.
1. 1O God, we have heard and our fa - thers have told
2. 3They gained not the land by the edge of their sword;
3. 4O God, You a - lone are for - ev - er my King;
4. 6No trust will I place in my sword or my bow,
What won - ders You did in the great days of old.
Their own arm to them could no safe - ty af - ford,
Com - mand, and for Ja - cob de - liv - er - ance bring.
7For You are our Sav - ior from hat - er and foe.
2Where na - tions were crushed and cast out by Your hand;
But Your right hand, Your arm, the light of Your face.
5Through You we will sure - ly put down all our foes,
8In God we will boast Who has put them to shame,
You plant - ed our fa - thers to dwell in the land.
You showed them Your fa - vor, Your won - der - ful grace.
Through Your name will tram - ple on them that op - pose.
All day and for - ev - er give thanks to Your name.

PSALM 44:9–19 **44E**

MARA. 11.11.11.11.
5. 9But You have for - sak - en, to shame brought our boasts;
6. 11You give us like sheep to be slaugh - tered for food,
7. 13You make all our neigh - bors re - proach us in pride,
8. 15And all the day long I be - hold my dis - grace,
9. 17We suf - fered this, yet we did not for - get You;
No more in - to bat - tle You go with our hosts.
A - mong all the na - tions dis - persed and pur - sued.
And cause those a - round us to scoff and de - ride.
And cov - ered am I with the shame of my face,
We al - ways have been to Your cov - e - nant true.
10You make us turn back from the foe in dis - may,
12You sell off Your peo - ple to stran - gers for naught;
14Our name a - mong na - tions a by - word You've made;
16Be - cause the blas - phem - er and scof - fer I hear,
18Our heart is not turned and our steps have not strayed,
And spoil - ers who hate us have made us their prey.
Their price to Your treas - 'ry no in - crease has brought.
The peo - ple all laugh at us, shak - ing the head.
While foe and a - veng - er a - gainst me ap - pear.
19Though crushed a - mid ru - ins and un - der death's shade.

44F PSALM 44:20-26

MOBILE. 11.11.11.11.
10. 20 If we have for - got - ten the name of our God,
11. 22 But all the day long for Your sake we're con- sumed;
12. 24 O why are You hid - ing the light of Your face,
Or un - to an i - dol our hands spread a - broad,
Like sheep for the slaugh - ter to death we are doomed.
For - get - ting the bur - den and grief of our race?
21 Shall God not search out and un - cov - er this sin,
23 A - rouse Your - self! Why are You sleep - ing, O LORD?
25 Our soul is bowed down; we lie crushed in the dust.
Who knows eve - ry heart and the se - crets with - in?
A - wake! Do not leave us for - ev - er ig - nored.
26 Rise! Help and re - deem us! Your mer - cy we trust.

PSALM 45:1-5

LOUISVILLE. S.M.
1. [1]My heart doth o - ver - flow; A no - ble theme I sing. My tongue's a skil - ful writ - er's pen To speak a - bout the King, To speak a - bout the King.
2. [2]More fair than sons of men Thy lips with grace o'er - flow, Be - cause His bless - ing ev - er - more Did God on Thee be - stow, Did God on Thee be - stow.
3. [3]Thy sword gird on Thy thigh, O Thou su - preme in might, And gird Thy - self with maj - es - ty And with Thy splen - dor bright, And with Thy splen - dor bright.

4. [4]To victory ride forth
   For meekness, truth, and right;
   And may Thy right hand teach to Thee
   The deeds of dreadful might.

5. [5]Thine arrows sharpened are,
   Men under Thee to bring,
   To pierce the heart of enemies
   Who fight against the King.

PSALM 45:6-9

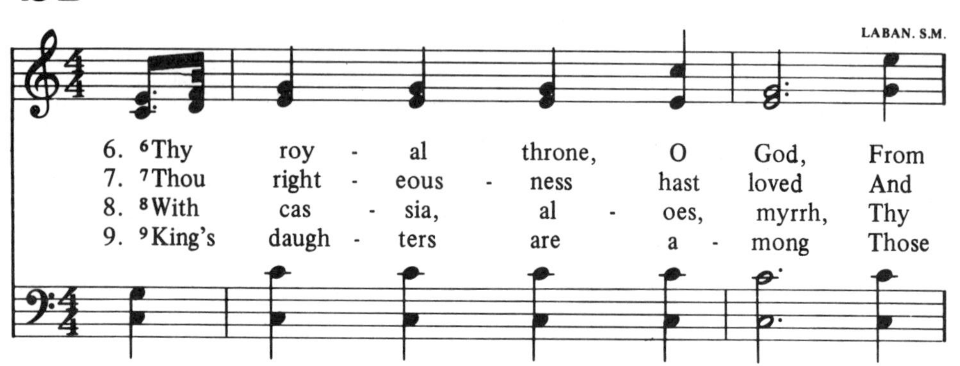
LABAN. S.M.
6. [6]Thy roy - al throne, O God, From
7. [7]Thou right - eous - ness hast loved And
8. [8]With cas - sia, al - oes, myrrh, Thy
9. [9]King's daugh - ters are a - mong Those

ev - er - last - ing is; A right - eous scep - ter
wick - ed - ness ab - horred; On Thee, 'bove all, has
robes sweet fra - grance had; From pal - ac - es of
who in hon - or stand. Thy bride ar - rayed in

ev - er - more Thy king - dom's scep - ter is.
God, Thy God, The oil of glad - ness poured.
i - vo - ry The sweet harps made Thee glad.
O - phir gold There stands at Thy right hand.

PSALM 45:10-17 45C

DIADEMATA. S.M.D.
10. 10 O daugh - ter, hear and heed; In - cline to me thine ear:
11. 12 The daugh - ter then of Tyre There with a gift shall be,
12. 14 She to the King is led In fine em - broi - der - y;
13. 16 Then in Thy fa - thers' stead Thy chil - dren Thou shalt take
"For-get thou now thy peo - ple all, Thy fa-ther's house-hold dear.
And all the weal-thy of the land Will make re - quests of Thee.
The brides-maids in her train, her friends, Are brought to hon - or Thee.
And eve - ry-where in all the earth Them no- ble princ-es make.
11 Thy beau - ty to the King Shall then de - light - ful be;
13 The daugh - ter of the King All glo - rious waits with - in;
15 At - tend - ants fol - low - ing Their joy and glad - ness bring,
17 Through eve-ry com- ing age I'll make Thy name to live;
Be- cause He is thy Lord, do thou To Him bow rev-'rent - ly."
Her love - ly gown with threads of gold Has in - ter - wo - ven been.
Un - til they all have en - tered there The pal - ace of the King.
The peo - ples there-fore ev - er - more Their praise to Thee shall give.

46A

PSALM 46

MATERNA. C.M.D.
1. [1]God is our ref - uge and our strength, In straits a pres- ent aid;
2. [4]A riv - er is whose streams make glad The cit - y of our God,
3. [6]The na - tions raged; the king-doms moved; And when the earth had heard
[2]And, there-fore, tho' the earth re - move We will not be a - fraid;
The ho - ly place where - in the Lord Most High has His a - bode.
The might - y voice He sent a - broad It melt - ed at His word.
Tho' hills a-midst the seas be cast, [3]Tho' trou-bled wa- ters roar,
[5]Yea, God is in the midst of her; Un - moved she stands for aye;
[7]The LORD of hosts is on our side Our safe - ty to se - cure;
Yea, tho' the swell - ing bil - lows shake The moun-tains on the shore.
And God will sure - ly grant her help Be - fore the break of day.
The God of Ja - cob is for us A ref - uge strong and sure.

4. [8]O come, behold what wondrous works
Have by the LORD been wrought;
Come, see what desolations great
He on the earth has brought.
[9]To utmost ends of all the earth
Wars into peace He turns;
The bow He breaks, the spear He cuts,
In fire the chariot burns.

5. [10]Be still and know that I am God;
Among the nations I
Will be exalted; I on earth
Will be exalted high.
[11]The LORD of hosts is on our side
Our safety to secure;
The God of Jacob is for us
A refuge strong and sure.

PSALM 46

46B

HETHERTON. C.M.D.
1. 1God is our ref - uge and our strength, In straits a pres- ent aid;
2. 4A riv - er is whose streams make glad The cit - y of our God,
3. 6The na - tions raged; the king- doms moved; And when the earth had heard
2And, there - fore, though the earth re - move We will not be a - fraid;
The ho - ly place where - in the Lord Most High has His a - bode.
The might - y voice He sent a - broad, It melt - ed at His word.
Though hills a - midst the seas be cast, 3Though trou- bled wa - ters roar,
5Yea, God is in the midst of her; Un - moved she stands for aye;
7The LORD of hosts is on our side Our safe - ty to se - cure;
Yea, though the swell - ing bil- lows shake The moun-tains on the shore.
And God will sure - ly grant her help Be - fore the break of day.
The God of Ja - cob is for us A ref - uge strong and sure.

4. 8O come, behold what wondrous works
Have by the LORD been wrought;
Come, see what desolations great
He on the earth has brought.
9To utmost ends of all the earth
Wars into peace He turns;
The bow He breaks, the spear He cuts,
In fire the chariot burns.

5. 10Be still and know that I am God;
Among the nations I
Will be exalted; I on earth
Will be exalted high.
11The LORD of hosts is on our side
Our safety to secure;
The God of Jacob is for us
A refuge strong and sure.

46C
PSALM 46
EIN' FESTE BURG. 88.88.66.668.
1. [1]God is our ref - uge and our strength,
2. [4]A riv - er brings re - fresh - ing streams
3. [8]O come, see what the LORD has done:
A pres - ent help in our dis - tress.
To cheer the cit - y of our God,
He des - o - la - tions brought on earth;
[2]We will not there - fore be a - fraid
The Most High's ho - ly dwell - ing place.
[9]On earth He puts an end to wars,
Tho' all the earth should be re - moved,
[5]God is in her; she won't be moved;
Breaks bow and spear, and char - iots burns.

Tho' moun - tains great be hurled In -
At dawn will God help her. 6 The
10 Be still! Know I am God. Ex-
to the o - cean's depths, 3 Tho' seas may
hea - then rage; realms quake; He lifts His
alt - ed o'er all men, Ex - alt - ed
roar and foam And bil - lows shake the shore,
voice; earth melts. 7 The LORD of hosts with us!
o'er all earth. 11 The LORD of hosts with us!
Tho' moun - tains trem - ble at their power.
Our for - tress strong is Ja - cob's God.
Our for - tress strong is Ja - cob's God.

47A PSALM 47

PETERSHAM. C.M.D.
1. 1 All peo-ples, clap your hands for joy; To God in tri- umph shout;
2. 4 The land of our in - her - i - tance He choos - es out for us,
3. 7 For God is King of all the earth; Sing praise with skill- ful - ness.
2 For awe-some is the LORD Most High, Great King the earth through-out.
And He to us the glo - ry gives Of Ja - cob whom He loves.
8 God rules the na -tions; God sits on His throne of ho - li - ness.
3 He brings the peo-ples un - der us In mas- ter - y com - plete;
5 God is as - cend -ed with a shout, The LORD with trum-pet - ing.
9 As - sem - ble, men of A- brah'm's God! Come, peo -ple, princ -es, nigh!
And He it is Who na - tions all Sub - dues be-neath our feet.
6 Sing prais - es un - to God! Sing praise! Sing prais - es to our King!
The shields of earth be - long to God; He is ex - alt - ed high.

PSALM 47

CHANT D.

1. [1]Clap your hands, / all ye / people; //
Shout unto / God · with the / voice of / triumph. //

[2]For the LORD most / high is / terrible; //
He is a great / King over / all the / earth.

2. [3]He shall subdue the / people / under us, //
And the / nations / under our / feet. //

[4]He shall choose our in/heri·tance / for us, //
The excellency of / Jacob / whom He / loved.

3. [5]God is gone / up · with a / shout, //
The / LORD · with the / sound · of a / trumpet. //

[6]Sing praises to / God, sing / praises: //
Sing praises / unto our / King, sing / praises.

4. [7]For God is the / King of · all the / earth; //
Sing ye / praises with / under/standing. //

[8]God reigneth / over the / heathen: //
God sitteth up/on the / throne · of His / holiness.

5. [9]The princes of the people are / gathered to/gether, /
Even the / people · of the / God of / Abraham; //

For the shields of the earth be/long unto / God: //
He is / great/ly ex/alted.

For "AN INTRODUCTION TO CHANTING" please turn to page 440.

48A PSALM 48:1-7

TALLIS ORDINAL. C.M.
1. ¹Great is Je - ho - vah, and His praise Should be pro - claimed a - broad, With - in His hill of ho - li - ness, The cit - y of our God.
2. ²Mount Zi - on stands most beau - ti - ful, The joy of eve - ry land. The cit - y of the might - y King On her north side doth stand.
3. ³God's known a - mong her pal - ac - es To be her for - tress high. ⁴For, lo, the kings as - sem - bled there; To - geth - er they passed by.

4. ⁵At what they saw they were amazed
And filled with great dismay.
So troubled were they at the sight
They turned and ran away.

5. ⁶With panic they were seized; they writhed
Like her whom birth pangs take.
⁷For Thou with wind out of the east
Dost ships of Tarshish break.

PSALM 48:8-14 **48B**

ZERAH. C.M.
6. [8]In our God's cit - y we have seen What we be - fore were told,
7. [9]With- in Thy courts, O God, we thought Up - on Thy gra- cious ways;
8. Thy hand is full of right-eous-ness; [11]Let Zi - on's joy be great;
That God Who is the LORD of hosts Will ev - er it up - hold,
[10]O God, ac - cord-ing to Thy name Through all the earth's Thy praise,
Let Ju - dah's daugh-ters joy - ful - ly Thy judg-ments cel - e - brate,
That God Who is the LORD of hosts Will ev - er it up - hold.
O God, ac - cord - ing to Thy name Through all the earth's Thy praise.
Let Jud - ah's daugh - ters joy - ful - ly Thy judg-ments cel - e - brate.

9. [12]Encompass Zion, count her towers,
[13]And mark her bulwarks well;
Consider ye her palaces;
To sons her story tell.

10. [14]Because this God will be our God
To all eternity;
Yes, even on through death itself
Our constant guide is He.

49A
PSALM 49:1-5
SEYMOUR. 77.77.
1. [1]Hear this, all ye peo - ples, hear; Earth's in-hab - i - tants, give ear;
2. [3]For my mouth shall wis - dom speak: Knowl-edge with my heart I'll seek,
3. [5]Why should I to fear give way, When I see the e - vil day,
[2]All of high and low de - gree, Rich and poor, give ear to me.
[4]Lend to par - a - bles my ear, With the harp make dark things clear.
When with wick-ed - ness my foes Shall sur - round me and op - pose?
49B
PSALM 49:6–15
MERCY. 77.77.
4. [6]They that trust in treas - ured gold, Though they
5. [8]Life's re - demp - tion– high its price! Noth - ing
6. [10]For a - like be - fore their eyes Die the
boast of wealth un - told, [7]None can bid his broth - er
can for it suf - fice, [9]That from death one should be
fool - ish and the wise; Then their rich - es' hoard - ed

live, None to God a ran - som give;
free And cor - rup - tion nev - er see.
heap, Oth - er hands in turn shall keep.

7. [11] Yet within their heart they say
That their houses are for aye,
That their dwelling places grand
Shall for generations stand.

8. To their lands they give their name,
In the hope of lasting fame;
[12] But man's honor quickly flies.
He, like beasts that perish, dies.

9. [13] Though this folly marks their ways,
Though the world their sayings praise,
[14] In the grave like sheep they're laid;
Death their shepherd there is made.

10. O'er them soon shall rule the just,
All their beauty turn to dust;
[15] But from death God will retrieve,
To Himself my soul receive.

PSALM 49:16–20 49C

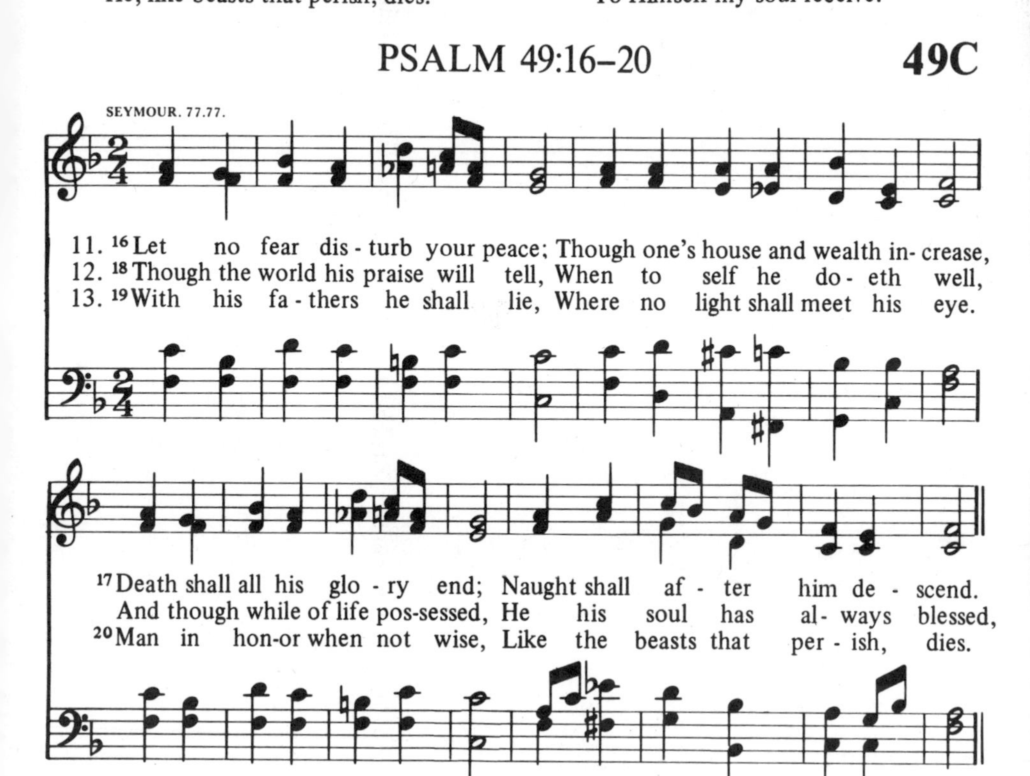
SEYMOUR. 77.77.
11. 16 Let no fear dis - turb your peace; Though one's house and wealth in - crease,
12. 18 Though the world his praise will tell, When to self he do - eth well,
13. 19 With his fa - thers he shall lie, Where no light shall meet his eye.
17 Death shall all his glo - ry end; Naught shall af - ter him de - scend.
And though while of life pos-sessed, He his soul has al - ways blessed,
20 Man in hon-or when not wise, Like the beasts that per - ish, dies.

50A PSALM 50:1-6

SILVER STREET. S.M.
1. [1]The mighty God the LORD Has spoken
2. [2]From Zion's holy hill, Perfection's
3. [3]Our God shall surely come; Keep silence
4. [4]And to the heav'ns above He sendeth

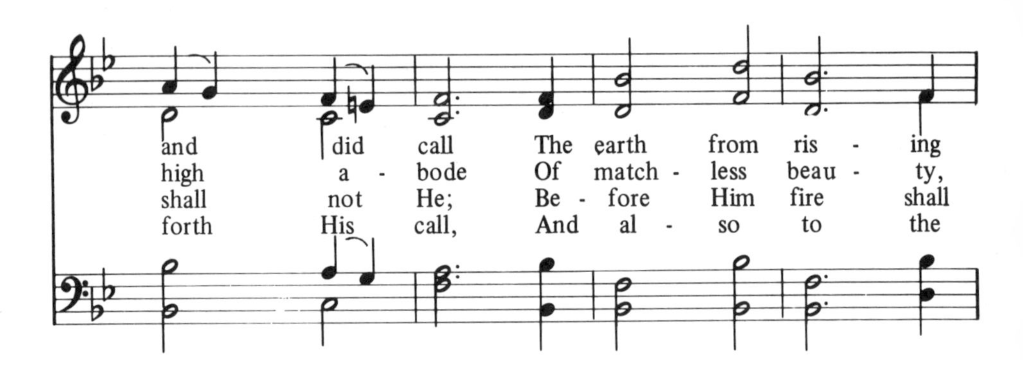
and did call The earth from rising
high abode Of matchless beauty,
shall not He; Before Him fire shall
forth His call, And also to the

of the sun To where it has its fall.
even thence In glory shineth God.
waste; great storms Shall round about Him be.
earth, that He May judge His people all.

5. [5]"Together let My saints
   Before Me gathered be;
   Those that by sacrifice have made
   A covenant with Me."

6. [6]Then shall the heav'ns declare
   His righteousness abroad,
   Because He only is the judge;
   Yea, none is judge but God.

PSALM 50:7-15 **50B**

ST. THOMAS. S.M.
7. 7"O ye, My peo - ple, hear; I'll speak and tes - ti - fy A - gainst thee, O thou Is - ra - el, For God, thy God, am I.
8. 8"For sac - ri - fic - es I No blame will on thee lay, Nor for burnt of - fer - ings of thine Be - fore Me eve - ry day.
9. 9"I'll take no calf nor goat From house or fold of thine; 10For cat - tle on a thou - sand hills And all wild beasts are Mine.

10. [11]"The birds of mountains great
Are all to Me well known;
The beasts that roam the field untamed,
They, too, are all My own.

11. [12]"Then if I hungry were
I would not tell it thee,
Because the world with all its wealth
Belongeth unto Me.

12. [13]"Will I eat flesh of bulls?
Or goats' blood drink will I?
[14]Thanksgiving offer thou, and pay
Thy vows to God Most High.

13. [15]"And do thou call on Me
When troublous days draw nigh;
To thee I'll give deliverance;
Thou shalt Me glorify."

50C PSALM 50:16–23

MONTGOMERY. S.M.D.
14. 16 But to the wick - ed man Saith God, "How dost thou dare
15. 18 "Thou gav - est thy con - sent When thou a thief hast seen;
16. 21 "Be -cause I si - lence kept While thou these things hast wroug
17. 22 "Now ye that God for - get, Con - sid - er this with care
To take My cov -'nant in thy mouth, My stat - utes to de - clare,
And with the vile a - dul - ter - er Thou hast par - tak - er been.
That I was whol - ly like thy - self Has been thy ver - y though
Lest I when there is none to save Should you in piec - es tear.
17 Since thou dost e - ven hate The warn - ings thou hast heard,
19 Thy mouth to ill is giv'n; Thy tongue de - ceit doth frame;
Yet I will thee re - prove And set be - fore thine eyes,
23 He hon - ors Me who brings The sac - ri - fice of praise;
And thou hast thrown be - hind thy back The teach-ings of My word?
20 Thou dost a - gainst thy broth - er speak, Thy moth - er's son de - fame.
Ar - rayed in or - der, thy mis -deeds And thine in - i - qui - ties.
I'll God's sal - va - tion show to him Who or - ders right his ways."

PSALM 51:1-8

51A

HELENA. C.M.
1. [1]O God, ac - cord - ing to Thy grace Be
2. [2]O wash me whol - ly from my guilt And
3. [4]A - gainst Thee on - ly have I sinned, Done
4. [5]Be - hold, in e - vil I was formed, Con -
mer - ci - ful to me; In Thine a - bound - ing
make me clean with - in; [3]For my trans - gres - sions
e - vil in Thy sight; So in Thy judg - ment
ceived and born in sin; [6]But Thou wilt make me
love blot out All my in - i - qui - ty.
I con - fess; I ev - er see my sin.
Thou art just, And in Thy sen - tence right.
wise in heart; Thou seek - est truth with - in.

5. [7]Do Thou with hyssop sprinkle me;
I shall be clean, and, lo,
When Thou hast washed me, then I shall
Be whiter than the snow.

6. [8]Of gladness and of joyfulness
Make me to hear the voice,
That so these very bones which Thou
Hast broken may rejoice.

51B PSALM 51:9–15

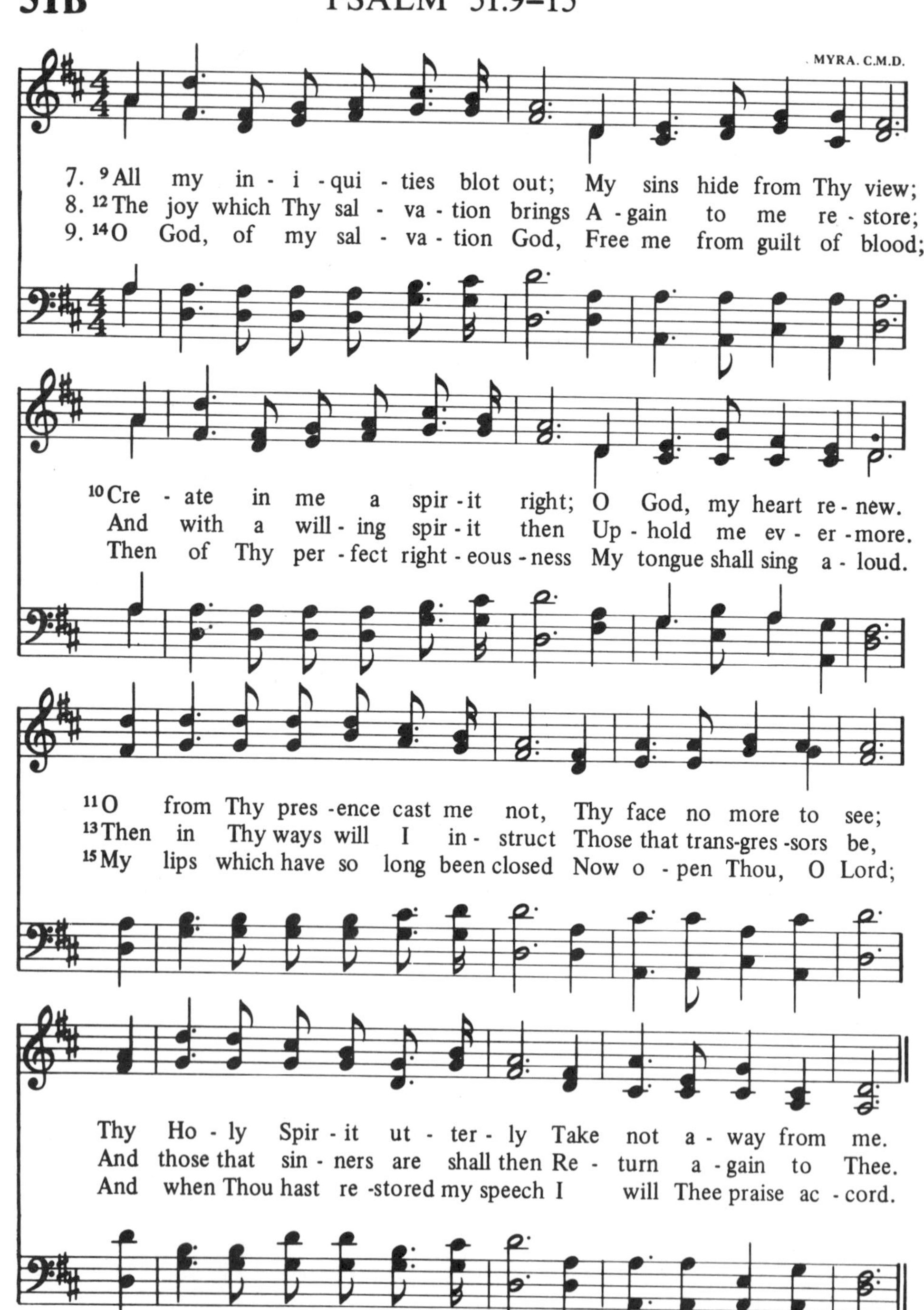

MYRA. C.M.D.
7. [9]All my in - i - qui - ties blot out; My sins hide from Thy view;
8. [12]The joy which Thy sal - va - tion brings A - gain to me re - store;
9. [14]O God, of my sal - va - tion God, Free me from guilt of blood;
[10]Cre - ate in me a spir - it right; O God, my heart re - new.
And with a will - ing spir - it then Up - hold me ev - er - more.
Then of Thy per - fect right - eous - ness My tongue shall sing a - loud.
[11]O from Thy pres - ence cast me not, Thy face no more to see;
[13]Then in Thy ways will I in - struct Those that trans-gres - sors be,
[15]My lips which have so long been closed Now o - pen Thou, O Lord;
Thy Ho - ly Spir - it ut - ter - ly Take not a - way from me.
And those that sin - ners are shall then Re - turn a - gain to Thee.
And when Thou hast re - stored my speech I will Thee praise ac - cord.

PSALM 51:16-19

51C

PRAYER. C.M.
10. 16 No sac - ri - fice dost Thou de - sire, Else
11. 17 A brok - en spir - it is to God A
12. 18 In Thy good pleas - ure fa - vor show To
13. 19 Then right - eous of - f'rings shall Thee please, And

would I give it Thee; Nor wilt Thou with burnt-
pleas - ing sac - ri - fice; A brok - en and a
Zi - on, Thine own hill; The walls of Thy Je -
of - f'rings burnt, which they, With whole burnt - of - f'rings
of - fer - ing At all de - light - ed be.
con - trite heart Thou, God, wilt not de - spise.
ru - sa - lem Build up of Thy good will.
and with calves, Shall on Thine al - tar lay.

51D PSALM 51:1–8

TOPLADY. 77.77.77.

1. [1]God, be mer - ci - ful to me; On Thy grace I rest my plea;
2. [3]For my sins be - fore me rise, Ev - er pres - ent to my eyes.
3. [5]Lo, brought forth was I in sin; When con-ceived I was un- clean.
4. [7]Then with hys - sop sprin - kle me, And from sin I clean shall be.

In Thy vast, a - bound - ing grace, My trans - gres - sions all e - rase.
[4]I have sinned 'gainst Thee a - lone, In Thy sight this e - vil done;
[6]Lo, Thou dost de - sire to find Truth sin - cere with - in the mind:
Wash me from its stain, and, lo, I shall whit - er be than snow.

[2]Wash me whol - ly from my sin; Cleanse from eve - ry ill with - in.
That Thy judg-ment may be clear, And Thy sen - tence just ap - pear.
And Thou wilt with - in my heart Wis - dom un - to me im - part.
[8]Make me hear joy's cheer- ing voice; Make my brok - en bones re - joice.

PSALM 51:9-15

51E

AJALON. 77.77.77.

5. [9]From my sins hide Thou Thy face; My in - i - qui - ties e - rase.
6. [12]Give sal-va - tion's joy a - gain, And a will - ing mind sus- tain.
7. [14]Free me from the guilt of blood, God, of my sal - va - tion God;

[10]O my God, re - new my heart, And a spir - it right im - part.
[13]Then Thy per - fect ways I'll show That trans-gres - sors may them know;
Then with joy my tongue shall raise Songs Thy right-eous-ness to praise.

[11] Cast me not a - way from Thee, Nor Thy Spir - it take from me.
They con - vert - ed then shall be; Sin - ners shall be turned to Thee.
[15]O - pen Thou my lips, O Lord; Then my mouth shall praise ac - cord.

51F PSALM 51:16–19

GUIDE. 77.77.77.
8. 16 Sac - ri - fice Thou wilt not take, Else would I the of - f'ring make. Of - f'rings burnt bring no de - light,
9. 18 Pros - per Zi - on in Thy grace; Sa - lem's brok - en walls re - place. 19 Then shall sac - ri - fic - es right,
17 But a brok - en heart, con - trite, God's ac - cept - ed sac - ri - fice, Thou, O God, wilt not de - spise.
Whole burnt - of - f'rings Thee de - light; So will men, their vows to pay, Bull - ocks on Thine al - tar lay.

PSALM 52

MASONS' CHANT. C.M.
1. [1]Why boast your - self, O might - y man, Of
2. [2]You with your sub - tle tongue have planned De -
3. [3]You cher - ish e - vil more than good And
4. [5]For - ev - er God will pull you down, Will
e - vil and of wrong? The lov - ing kind - ness of our
struc-tion to com - plete. Your tongue a sharp - ened ra - zor
false-hood more than right. [4]You cher - ish all de - vour - ing
seize you with His hand, Will tear you from your dwell - ing
God Is pres - ent all day long.
is, A work - er of de - ceit.
words, O tongue which lies de - light.
place, Up - root you from the land.

5. [6]The righteous will behold and fear,
Will laugh at him and say,
[7]"Behold the man who would not make
Our God his strength and stay."

6. "This is the man who placed his trust
In wealth's abundant store,
And in the evil he desired
Confirmed himself the more."

7. [8]But I within the house of God
Am like an olive tree,
And in the steadfast love of God
My trust shall ever be.

8. [9]Forever I will give Thee thanks,
What Thou hast done proclaim;
In presence of Thy godly ones
I'll wait on Thy good name.

52B PSALM 52

OLD 77TH. 88.77.D.
1. [1]Might-y man, why boast in e - vil? All the day is God's great mer-cy.
2. [5]God will break you down for-ev - er. He will pluck you from your dwell-ing;
3. [8]But in God's house I am grow - ing Like a green tree bear - ing ol - ives.
[2]You plot mis-chief with your tongue, Ra - zor-sharp to work de - ceit.
He will lift you by your roots From the land of liv - ing men.
In the stead-fast love of God I am trust-ing ev - er - more.
[3]You love e-vil more than good-ness, Ly-ing more than truth-ful speak-ing.
[6]Just men see with awe, ex-claim - ing, [7]"This man made not God his ref- uge,
[9]I will give You thanks for ev - er, For I know that You have done this.
[4]You love all de-vour-ing words, O you sharp, de- ceit- ful tongue.
Trust-ed his a- bun-dant wealth, Strong in what de - struc-tion brought."
And I'll hope in Your good name, Wait - ing with Your god - ly ones.

BOYLSTON. S.M.
1. [1]"There is no God," has said The fool - ish in his heart; Cor - rupt are they; their works are vile; They all from good de - part.
2. [2]Up - on the sons of men God looked from heav'n a - broad, To see if an - y un - der - stood, If an - y sought for God.
3. [3]To - geth - er all are vile; They all are back - ward gone; And there is none that do - eth good, No, not so much as one.

4. [4]Have men that evil work
No knowledge gained at all,
Who eat my people as their bread,
And on God do not call?

5. [5]Great terror on them came,
And they were much dismayed,
Although there was no cause why they
Should be at all afraid.

6. His bones who thee besieged
God hath dispersed abroad;
Thou hast them put to shame, because
They were despised of God.

7. [6]Let Isr'el's help arise
From Zion! God will bring
His captives! Jacob shall rejoice,
And Israel shall sing.

54A PSALM 54

54A
PSALM 54
BINGHAM. C.M.
1. 1Save me, O God, by Thy great name; By
2. 3For they that stran - gers are to me A -
3. 4Be - hold, the Lord sus - tains my soul. God
Thy power vin - di - cate. 2Hear Thou my prayer, O
gainst me now a - rise, And vio - lent men seek
is my help - er still. 5De - stroy my foes, and
God; give heed To eve - ry word I state.
for my life, On God set not their eyes.
in Thy truth Re - turn to them their ill.

4. [6]I with a free-will offering
Will sacrifice to Thee.
And I will thank Thy name, O LORD;
It's good eternally.

5. [7]Because from all of my distress
He has delivered me;
My eye was satisfied to look
Upon my enemy.

PSALM 54

54B

EBENEZER. 87.87.D.

1. [1]By Your name, O God, now save me; Grant me jus-tice by Your strength
2. [4]See how God has been my help - er, How my Lord sus- tains my soul:

[2]To these words of mine give an - swer; O my God, now hear my prayer.
[5]To my foes He pays back e - vil– In Your truth de - stroy them all!

[3]Stran-gers have come up a - gainst me, E - ven men of vi - o - lence.
[6]I will sac- ri - fice with glad- ness; I will praise Your name, O LORD.

And they seek my life's de - struc-tion; God is not with- in their thoughts.
[7]He has saved me from all trou- ble; I have looked on all my foes.

55A PSALM 55:1-8

SARAH. C.M.
1. [1]Give ear to this my prayer, O God, Nor
2. [3]Be - cause I hear the voice of foes, Be -
3. [4]Deep an - guish is with - in my heart; Death's
hide Thee from my cry. [2]Give an - swer, for I
cause the wick - ed press; For they in an - ger
ter - rors o'er me roll. [5]Great trem - bling, fear - ful -
can - not rest But must com - plain and sigh,
bear a grudge And on me bring dis - tress.
ness, and dread Have o - ver - whelmed my soul.

4. [6]I cried, "O that I, like a dove,
Had wings to fly away.
Then would I flee and try to find
A restful place to stay.

5. [7]"Lo, I would wander far and lodge
In some lone desert waste;
[8]From stormy wind and tempest high
I would escape in haste."

PSALM 55:9–15 **55B**

ST. MATTHEW. C.M.D.
6. [9]O swal - low up their tongues, O Lord; Con -fuse them and di - vide;
7. [11]A realm of vast de - struc - tion thrives With - in her ver - y heart,
8. [13]But it was thou, a man, a friend, My col-league all a - long;
For in the ci - ty I've seen strife And vi - o - lence a - bide.
And from her streets op - pres - sion, fraud, And graft do not de - part.
[14]We shared sweet fel - low - ship and walked To God's house in the throng.
[10]For day and night up - on her walls The cit - y they sur - round,
[12]It was no foe re - proach-ing me, For that I could en - dure;
[15]Let death o'er-take them; to the pit A - live let them de - part;
While mis-chief and in - i - qui - ty In - side of her is found.
It was no hat - er ris - ing up, Or I could hide se - cure;
For wick - ed - ness is in their house And lives with - in their heart.

55C PSALM 55:16–23

SAXONY. C.M.
9. 16 I'll call on God; the LORD will save; 17 I
10. 18 He will re - deem my soul in love That
11. 19 Yes, God will hear and an - swer them; He
will com - plain and sigh At ev - 'ning, morn - ing,
I in peace may be From all the war a-
sits en - throned of old; For them there is no
and at noon, And He will hear my cry.
gainst me waged, For man - y strive with me.
change of heart; No fear of God they hold.

12. [20] He raised his hands against the ones
Who were at peace with him.
The covenant which he had sworn
He broke at his own whim.

13. [21] Though smooth as butter was his speech,
Within his heart was war;
Though soft as oil the words he spoke,
A naked sword they bore.

14. [22] Cast thou thy burden on the LORD,
And He shall thee sustain;
Yes, He makes sure that still unmoved
The righteous shall remain.

15. [23] But Thou, O God, wilt bring them down
The pit of woe to see.
False killers live not half their days.
But I will trust in Thee.

PSALM 56

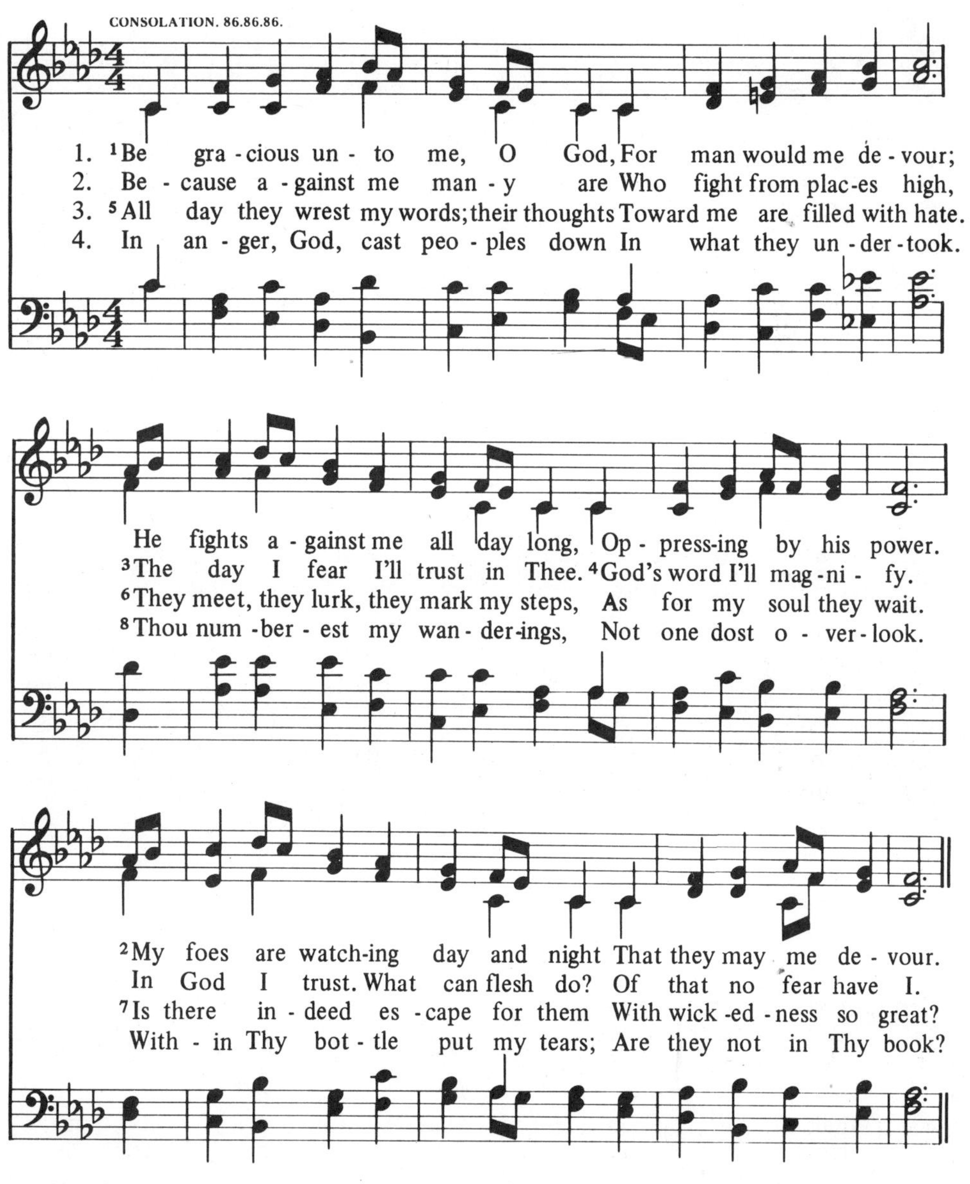
CONSOLATION. 86.86.86.
1. [1]Be gra-cious un-to me, O God, For man would me de-vour;
2. Be-cause a-gainst me man-y are Who fight from plac-es high,
3. [5]All day they wrest my words; their thoughts Toward me are filled with hate.
4. In an-ger, God, cast peo-ples down In what they un-der-took.
He fights a-gainst me all day long, Op-press-ing by his power.
[3]The day I fear I'll trust in Thee. [4]God's word I'll mag-ni-fy.
[6]They meet, they lurk, they mark my steps, As for my soul they wait.
[8]Thou num-ber-est my wan-der-ings, Not one dost o-ver-look.
[2]My foes are watch-ing day and night That they may me de-vour.
In God I trust. What can flesh do? Of that no fear have I.
[7]Is there in-deed es-cape for them With wick-ed-ness so great?
With-in Thy bot-tle put my tears; Are they not in Thy book?

5. [9]My foes shall, when I cry, turn back,
I know; God is for me.
[10]In God I'll praise His word; the LORD—
His word my praise shall be!
[11]In God I've trusted, I'll not fear
What man can do to me.

6. [12]My vows to Thee I'll pay, O God;
Thankoff'rings bring to Thee.
[13]For Thou from death didst save my soul,
My feet from falling free;
I'll walk before God in the light
Of those that living be.

PSALM 57:1-4

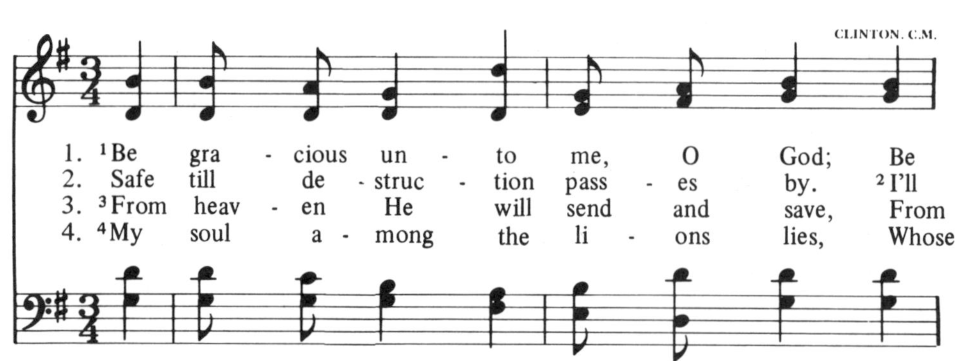
CLINTON. C.M.
1. ¹Be gra - cious un - to me, O God; Be
2. Safe till de - struc - tion pass - es by. ²I'll
3. ³From heav - en He will send and save, From
4. ⁴My soul a - mong the li - ons lies, Whose

gra - cious un - to me. My soul its ref - uge
cry to God Most High, To God, Who does all
slan - der - ers de - fend. His lov - ing - kind - ness
breath a flame af - fords, Men's sons, whose teeth are

finds in You; Your wings will shel - ter me,
things for me Ac - com - plish per - fect - ly.
and His truth God will di - rect - ly send.
spears and darts, Whose tongues are sharp - ened swords.

PSALM 57:5-11

SUNDERLAND. C.M.
5. [5]O be ex - alt - ed high, O God! A - bove the heav - ens stand, And let Your glo - ry be a - bove All earth, both sea and land.
6. [6]They spread a net be - fore my steps, My soul bowed down with dread. But though they dug a pit for me, In it they fell in - stead.
7. [7]My heart is fixed, my heart is fixed, O God. I'll sing. I'll praise. [8]My glo - ry, wake! Wake, harp and lyre! At dawn my song I'll raise.
8. [9]And I will ren - der thanks to You A - mong the peo - ples, Lord; And I a - mong the na - tions will In psalms my praise re - cord.

9. [10]Your steadfast love and mercy great
Above the heavens rise,
And Your unfailing faithfulness
Extends unto the skies.

10. [11]O be exalted high, O God!
Above the heavens stand,
And let Your glory be above
All earth, both sea and land.

58A PSALM 58

ST. MICHEL'S. C.M.D.
1. 1You may be gods, but can you claim That you speak right- eous - ness?
2. 3The wick- ed from their day of birth Are stran-gers to the way;
3. 6O God, in - side their o - penedmouths Break off their cru - el teeth;
And do you judge the sons of men In truth and up - right - ness?
They from the womb come speak- ing lies; They wan- der far a - stray.
The fangs of these young li - ons, LORD, Tear out by roots be- neath.
2No, e - ven in your ver - y heart You wick - ed-ness pro - duce;
4They have the ven - om of a snake; They have an ad - der's ear
7Let them like run - off wa - ters be That leave the ground soon dry.
On earth you weigh out with your hands Your vi - o - lent a - buse.
Which they have closed 5to charm-ers' songs; Skilled charm-ers they'll not hear.
Let ar - rows that he aims be - come Like head - less shafts that fly.

4. 8Let them be like the snails that melt
Along the course they run;
Or like one prematurely born
Who never sees the sun.
9They are like blazing thorns which you
Beneath your kettles lay,
Whose heat is scarcely felt before
A wind sweeps them away.

5. 10The just rejoices when he sees
That vengeance is complete,
For in the blood of wicked men
He then will wash his feet.
11They'll say, "There surely is reward
For righteous ones of worth;
There surely is a living God
Who judges in the earth."

PSALM 58

WORCESTER. C.M.D.
1. 1You may be gods, but can you claim That you speak right-eous-ness?
2. 3The wick-ed from their day of birth Are stran-gers to the way;
3. 6O God, in-side their o-pened mouths Break off their cru-el teeth;
Melody
And do you judge the sons of men In truth and up-right-ness?
They from the womb come speak-ing lies; They wan-der far a-stray.
The fangs of these young li-ons, LORD, Tear out by roots be-neath.
Melody
2No, e-ven in your ver-y heart You wick-ed-ness pro-duce;
4They have the ven-om of a snake; They have an ad-der's ear
7Let them like run-off wa-ters be That leave the ground soon dry.
Melody
On earth you weigh out with your hands Your vi-o-lent a-buse.
Which they have closed 5to charm-ers' songs; Skilled charm-ers they'll not hear.
Let ar-rows that he aims be-come Like head-less shafts that fly.
Melody

4. 8Let them be like the snails that melt
Along the course they run;
Or like one prematurely born
Who never sees the sun.
9They are like blazing thorns which you
Beneath your kettles lay,
Whose heat is scarcely felt before
A wind sweeps them away.

5. 10The just rejoices when he sees
That vengeance is complete,
For in the blood of wicked men
He then will wash his feet.
11They'll say, "There surely is reward
For righteous ones of worth;
There surely is a living God
Who judges in the earth."

59A PSALM 59:1-9

NOMINA. C.M.
1. [1]Save me, my God! Protect from foes Now rising like a flood. [2]Deliver me from evil men; Save me from men of blood.
2. [3]Behold, they for my life lay wait; Fierce men against me run; But not for my transgression, LORD, Nor sin that I have done.
3. [4]Though I am guiltless, still they run And preparation make. Arouse Thyself to help, and see! [5]LORD God of hosts, awake!
4. Arise to punish nations all, Thou God of Israel. No mercy show to any who Deceitfully rebel.

5. [6]At night they come; they snarl like dogs
That round the city stray.
[7]Their mouths stretch wide; their lips are swords:
"For who will hear?" they say.

6. [8]But Thou, O LORD, dost laugh at them;
Thou dost all nations mock.
[9]O Thou my Strength, I'll hold to Thee;
God is my fortress-rock.

PSALM 59:10-17 59B

CREDITON. C.M.
7. 10 In all His lov - ing - kind - ness great My God will meet with me. God will per - mit me on my foes To look tri - um - phant - ly.
8. 11 But lest my peo - ple should for - get, Do not the wick - ed slay, But bring them down, O Lord, our Shield, And scat - ter them a - way.
9. 12 Be - cause of sin with - in their mouths, And words their lips let fly, Let them be caught in their own pride, Be - cause they curse and lie.

10. [13]Destroy them in Thy wrath; destroy,
That they may be no more.
Make known that God in Jacob rules,
To earth's most distant shore.

11. [14]At night they come; they snarl like dogs
That round the city stray.
[15]They search for food but are not filled,
And, hungry, there they stay.

12. [16]But of Thy strength I'll sing aloud,
At morn Thy mercy praise;
For Thou hast been my refuge high,
My fort in evil days.

13. [17]O Thou Who art my strength, I will
Sing praises unto Thee;
For God is my defense, the God
Of grace He is to me.

60A PSALM 60:1-5

DOWNS. C.M.
1. [1]O God, Thou hast re - ject - ed us, Hast brok - en us once more. As Thou with us hast an - gry been, O once a - gain re - store.
2. [2]For Thou hast made the earth to quake, Hast torn it fear - ful - ly. O heal its gap - ing cracks, for, lo, It shakes in ag - o - ny!
3. [3]For Thou hast made the peo - ple see The hard - ness of dis - tress, And Thou hast made them drink the wine Of reel - ing drunk - en - ness.

4. [4]But those that fear Thee Thou didst give
A banner in their sight,
That they might rally and be firm,
Made strong by truth and right.

5. [5]O grant that Thy belovèd ones
May safe delivered be.
O save them with Thy strong right hand,
And do Thou answer me.

PSALM 60:6-11

60B

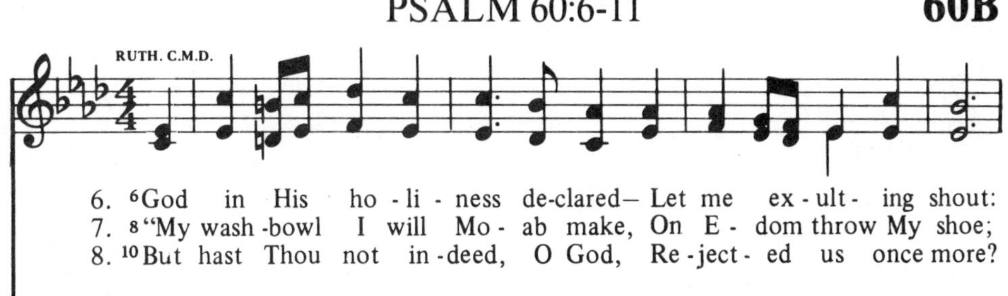
RUTH. C.M.D.
6. 6God in His ho-li-ness de-clared— Let me ex-ult-ing shout:
7. 8"My wash-bowl I will Mo-ab make, On E-dom throw My shoe;
8. 10But hast Thou not in-deed, O God, Re-ject-ed us once more?

"The land of She-chem I'll di-vide, And Suc-coth meas-ure out.
O Pal-es-tine, be-cause of Me Let shouts break forth from you!"
And wilt Thou not a-gain, O God, Go forth with us to war?

7For all of Gil-e-ad is Mine; Man-as-seh, too, I own;
9O who will bring me in the town Be-sieged and for-ti-fied?
11Give help a-gainst the en-e-my, For man no help be-stows.

My head's de-fense is E-phra-im; I Ju-dah made My throne.
And who as far as E-dom's walls Will there my foot-steps guide?
Through God we shall do val-iant-ly, For He treads down our foes.

61 PSALM 61

JOSEPHINE. 886.886.

1. 1My voice and prayer, O God, at - tend; 2From ends of earth to
2. 3In Thee my soul has shel - ter found, And Thou hast been from
3. 5For Thou, O God, my vows hast heard, On me the her - it -
4. 7Be - fore his God he shall a - bide; O do Thou truth and
Thee I send My sup - pli - cat - ing cry, When
foes a - round The tower to which I flee. 4With -
age con - ferred Of him Thy name that fears. 6Long
grace pro - vide To keep him in the way. 8So
trou - bles o - ver - whelm my breast; Then lead me on the
in Thy house I will a - bide, And un - der - neath Thy
life Thou to the king wilt give; Through gen - er - a - tions
I Thy name will ev - er sing, A song of praise will
rock to rest That high - er is than I.
wings will hide, For - ev - er safe in Thee.
he shall live, From age to age his years.
dai - ly bring, That I my vows may pay.

PSALM 62:1-7 **62A**

JERUSALEM. C.M.

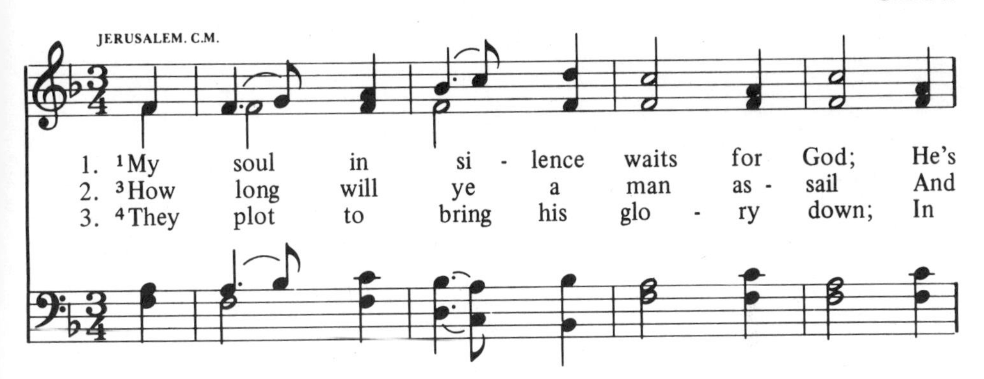

1. [1]My soul in si - lence waits for God; He's
2. [3]How long will ye a man as - sail And
3. [4]They plot to bring his glo - ry down; In

my sal - va - tion proved. [2]He is my strong - hold
seek to make him fall As though he were a
lies they take de - light; And while they bless him

and my rock; I'll not be great - ly moved.
tot - t'ring fence Or like a lean - ing wall?
with their mouth, They curse with in - ward spite.

4. [5]My soul, in silence wait for God,
For He my hope has proved.
[6]He's my salvation, stronghold, rock,
And I shall not be moved.

5. [7]In God alone my glory is
And my salvation sure;
My rock of strength is found in God,
My refuge most secure.

(The rest of this version of Psalm 62 is 62C).

62B PSALM 62

PAVANAS. 10.8.10.8.12.12.13.13.
1. 1 Sure - ly in si - lence my soul waits on God,
2. 5 Sure - ly in si - lence, my soul, wait for God!
3. 9 Sure - ly all men are a breath and a lie,
For my sal - va - tion comes from Him. 2 Sure - ly He
My ex - pec - ta - tion comes from Him. 6 Sure - ly He
Light - er than breath up - on the scales. 10 Then do not
is my sal - va - tion and rock, So I will
is my sal - va - tion and rock, And there - fore
trust in op - pres - sion and force, And do not
not be great - ly moved. 3 Yet how long will your fu - ry
I will not be moved! 7 For on God does my glo - ry
long for stol - en wealth! In your hearts do not hope that

rush a - gainst a man? You would all slay and crush him
and sal - va - tion rest; And with God is my ref - uge
pow - er will suc -ceed, 11 For in truth God de - clares that
like a fall - ing wall. 4 Sure - ly they con - spire to drive him
and my rock of strength. 8 In each time and cir - cum-stance, O
strength be-longs to Him. 12 So to You, my Lord, be - longs the
from his loft - y height; Lov - ing lies, they
peo - ple, trust in Him. Pour your hearts out
mer - cy of Your grace; For You will re -
feign to bless, but in - ward - ly they curse!
to Him, for our ref - uge is in God.
pay to man ac - cord - ing to his deeds.

62C PSALM 62:8-12

PHUVAH. C.M.
6. 8 On Him, O peo - ple, ev - er more Re - ly with con - fi - dence; Be - fore Him pour ye out your heart, For God is our de - fense.
7. 9 The sons of man are van - i - ty, The best of men a lie; To - geth - er in the bal - ance they Are light - er than a sigh.
8. 10 Then in op - pres - sion do not hope; Nor yet for plun - der lust; Though power and force may seem to thrive; In this build not your trust.

9. [11] For truly God has spoken once;
He twice to me made known:
That strength and power belong to God
And unto Him alone;

10. [12] For so it is that sovereign grace
Belongs to Thee, my Lord;
For Thou according to his work
Dost every man reward.

PSALM 63

COOLING. C.M.
1. [1]God, Thee, my God, I'll ear - ly seek; My
2. [2]Thus have I looked for Thee be - fore With -
3. [3]Be - cause Thy grace is more than life My
4. [5]My soul with rich, a - bun - dant food Shall
soul's a - thirst for Thee. On dry land, wea - ry,
in Thy ho - ly place That there I might be -
lips Thee praise shall give; [4]I in Thy name will
be well sat - is - fied; With shouts of joy up -
wa - ter - less, My flesh has longed for Thee.
hold Thy strength And glo - ry of Thy face.
lift my hands And bless Thee while I live.
on my lips My mouth shall praise pro - vide.

5. [6]And when I turn my thoughts to Thee
   Upon my bed at night,
   As watches pass I meditate
   On Thee with great delight.

6. [7]Thou art my help; I sing for joy
   In shadow of Thy wings.
   [8]For Thy right hand has held me fast;
   To Thee my spirit clings.

7. [9]But they go down to depths of earth
   Who would my soul destroy;
   [10]They are delivered to the sword
   For jackals to enjoy.

8. [11]The king shall then rejoice in God
   And all that by Him swear;
   For stopped shall be the mouths of those
   Who do a lie declare.

63B
PSALM 63
TE DEUM. 687.687.10.10.87.
1. [1]O God, You are my God, And ear - ly will I
2. [4]I'll bless You while I live, And I will ev - er
3. [8]My soul clings fast to You; Your right hand holds me
seek for You; My soul is a - thirst for You. My
lift my hands To praise and con - fess Your name. [5]My
safe - ly up. [9]When men would de - stroy my life, To
flesh cries out for You From out a dry and
soul will be made full As with all choice and
depths of earth they go; [10]They are de - liv - ered
thirst - y land, A land where no wa - ter is.
heart - y meats; I'll praise You with joy - ful lips.
to the sword, To jack - als be - come a prey.

2 For thus to be - hold You in splen - did strength
6 I think of You thus as I lie in bed
11 The king will re - joice and be glad in God,
I gazed af - ter You in the ho - ly place.
And bring You to mind in the hours of night.
And they boast a - loud who have sworn in Him,
3 Since Your grace is much more than life,
7 Since You ev - er have been my help,
But the mouth will be made to stop
My lips will give praise to You.
Your wings are my shield and joy.
Of those who de - clare a lie.

64A PSALM 64

CULROSS. C.M.

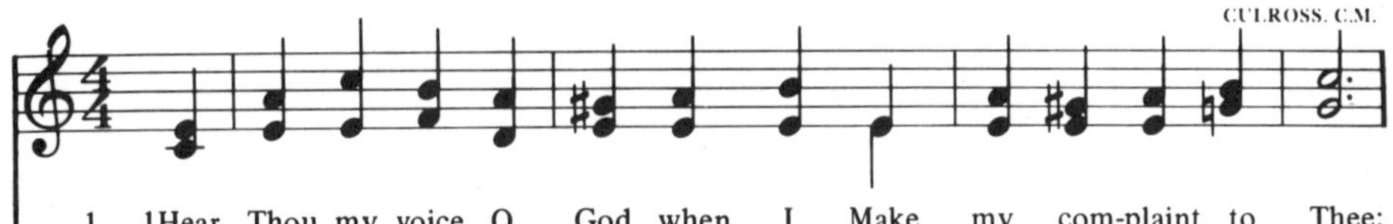

1. [1]Hear Thou my voice, O God, when I Make my com-plaint to Thee;
2. [2]Hide me from se - cret plots of men That e - vil - do - ers be,
3. [3]Their tongues they have al - read - y whet To make them sharp as swords;

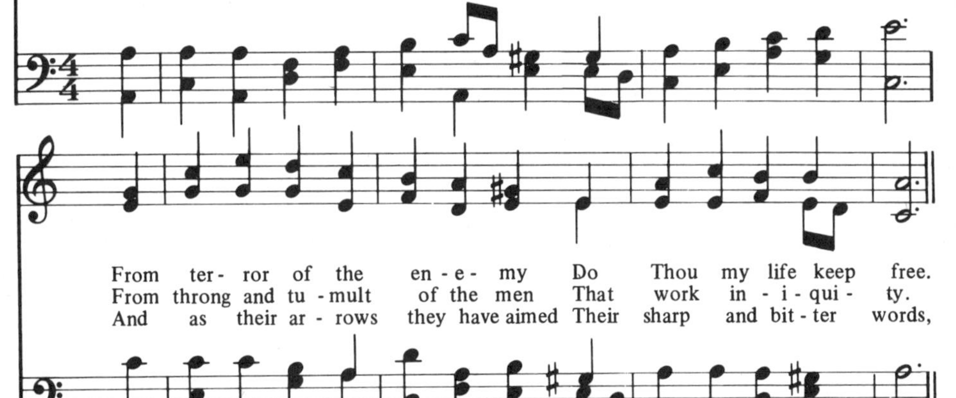
From ter- ror of the en - e - my Do Thou my life keep free.
From throng and tu - mult of the men That work in - i - qui - ty.
And as their ar - rows they have aimed Their sharp and bit - ter words,

4. [4]That they may at the innocent
 From ambush aim their shot;
 They without warning shoot at him,
 And, feeling safe, fear not.

5. [5]In all their evil purposes
 They bid themselves be bold;
 They talk of laying hidden snares,
 And say, "Who shall behold?"

6. [6]They have devised injustices;
 A cunning plot they keep;
 Because the inward thought of man,
 His very heart, is deep.

7. [7]But God will shoot a shaft at them
 And wound them suddenly;
 [8]For their own tongue shall them confound,
 And all who see shall flee.

8. [9]And then all men will stand in awe,
 The work of God declare;
 And they will thoughtfully observe
 What these His doings are.

9. [10]The righteous in the LORD will joy,
 In Him will refuge take;
 And all who are upright in heart
 Will boasts of triumph make.

64B PSALM 64

SCHMÜCKE DICH. 99.99.D.

1. [1]Hear my voice, O God, in my com-plaint; Guard my life from ter-ror
2. [5]They a - gree to form an e - vil plot; Se - cret - ly they talk of
3. [8]They will all be made to trip them-selves; They'll un- do them - selves by

of the foe. 2 Hide me from the plots of wick - ed men, From the
lay - ing snares, Say- ing, "Who shall see them or de-tect?" 6 They plan
their own tongue. All who see them then shall shake their heads. 9 Then shall
nois- y mob of e-vil ones, 3 Men who whet their tongues as sharp as swords,
care-ful-ly their wick-ed schemes; They are read-y with a cun -ning plot;
all men liv - ing be a-fraid, Pub - lish what God does and learn His work.
Who like ar - rows aim their bit - ter words, 4 Shoot from am-bush at the
For man's in- ward thought and heart are deep. 7 God will shoot an ar - row
10 In the LORD the right-eous shall be glad; He will al-ways put his
in - no - cent With - out warn - ing, with no fear of harm.
straight at them; With- out warn - ing they will wound-ed be.
trust in Him. All the right in heart will boast with joy.

65A PSALM 65:1-5

WEBB. 76.76.D.
1. [1]Praise waits for Thee in Zi - on! To Thee vows paid shall be.
2. [4]How blessed the man Thou choos - est And bring-est near to Thee,
3. [5]O God of our sal - va - tion, Thou in Thy right - eous - ness
[2]O God, of prayer the hear - er, All flesh shall come to Thee.
That in Thy courts for - ev - er His dwell - ing place may be.
With awe - some deeds and won - ders Thine an - swer wilt ex - press,
[3]In - i - qui - ties are dai - ly Pre - vail - ing o - ver me,
We shall with - in Thy tem - ple Be whol - ly sat - is - fied
O Thou in Whom con - fid - ing All ends of earth a - gree,
But all of our trans-gres - sions Are cov - ered o'er by Thee.
And filled with all the good - ness Thy sa - cred courts pro - vide.
And peo - ple who are sail - ing Up - on the far - thest sea.

PSALM 65:6-13

65B

COMMEMORATION. 76.76.D.
4. 6Thy might has built the moun - tains; Power clothes Thee ev - er - more,
5. 9Thy vis - its bring the show - ers; Thou dost en - rich the field.
6. 11Thou crown-est years with good - ness; Thy steps en - rich the ground.
7To calm the na - tions' clam - or And still the o - cean's roar.
God's riv - er brims with wa - ter; Thou dost pre - pare earth's yield.
12The de - sert pas - tures blos - som; The hills with joy re - sound.
8Thine awe-some signs and won - ders Fill dis - tant lands with fear.
10Thou wa - ter - est earth's fur - rows; Clods break down 'neath Thy rain.
13The fields with flocks are cov - ered; The vales with grain are clad.
Thou mak - est dawn and sun - set For joy to shout and cheer.
Thou soft - 'nest earth with show - ers, To bless each sprout - ing grain.
They all re - joice with shout - ing! They all with songs are glad!

66A PSALM 66:1-9

MILES LANE. C.M.
1. [1]All lands to God in joy- ful sounds A - loft your voic- es
2. [3]Say un- to God, How ter- ri - ble In all Thy works art
3. [4]Yes, all the earth shall wor - ship Thee, And un - to Thee shall
raise; [2]Sing forth the hon- or of His name, And glo - rious
Thou! Through Thy great power Thy foes to Thee Shall be con -
sing; And to Thy name most glo - ri - ous Their songs of
make His praise, And glo - rious make His praise.
strained to bow, Shall be con- strained to bow.
praise shall bring, Their songs of praise shall bring.

4. [5]O come, behold the works of God,
   His mighty doings see;
   In dealing with the sons of men
   Most terrible is He.

5. [6]He turned the sea into dry land,
   So they a pathway had;
   They through the river went on foot;
   There we in Him were glad.

6. [7]He ruleth ever by His might;
   His eyes the nations try;
   Let not the proud rebellious ones
   Exalt themselves on high.

7. [8]O all ye people, bless our God;
   Aloud proclaim His praise,
   [9]Who holdeth safe our soul in life,
   Our feet from sliding stays.

PSALM 66:10–20

CLARENDON. C.M.
8. 10 For Thou, O God, hast test - ed us As
9. 12 Thou mad - est men ride o'er our heads; Through
10. 13 I'll bring burnt - of - f'rings to Thy house; To
sil - ver is re - fined; 11 Didst take us in a
fire and flood we passed; But Thou didst bring us
Thee my vows will pay, 14 As I gave pro - mise
net; on us A heav - y load didst bind.
out to share A boun - teous place at last.
with my lips When trou - ble on me lay.

11. [15] Burnt sacrifice of fattened beasts
With smoke of rams I'll take,
And from the bullocks and the goats
To Thee an off'ring make.

12. [16] All ye that fear Him, come and hear
What God did for my soul;
[17] I with my mouth have cried to Him;
My tongue did Him extol.

13. [18] If in my heart I sin regard,
The Lord will never hear;
[19] But surely God has heard my voice;
He to my prayer gave ear.

14. [20] Forever blessed be our God;
My prayer He has not spurned,
Nor has He ever yet from me
His lovingkindness turned.

66C PSALM 66

WIE SCHÖN LEUCHTET. 887.887.48.48.
1. [1]All earth to God raise joy - ful song! [2]Sing forth the
2. [5]O come and see what God has done. He's ter - ri-
3. [8]Bless God, O peo - ples, sound His praise, [9]His, Who pre-
glo - ry of His name! To Him give prais - es glo - rious.
ble in all His deeds Per-formed a - mong the peo - ple.
serves our souls a - live And keeps our feet from slip - ping.
[3]Tell God, "How dread - ful are Your deeds! Such power You
[6]He turned the sea in - to dry land; His peo - ple
[10]As sil - ver, God, You test - ed us, [11]De - liv - ered
show Your en - e - mies, They cringe in fear be - fore You."
crossed the riv - er bed; There we in Him ex - ult - ed.
us in - to the net, Laid on our backs a bur - den.

[4]All earth wor -ships! You they fear and You they're prais - ing,
[7]He rules ev - er In His might; He sees the na - tions,
[12]Men rode o'er us – We have gone through fire and wa - ter –

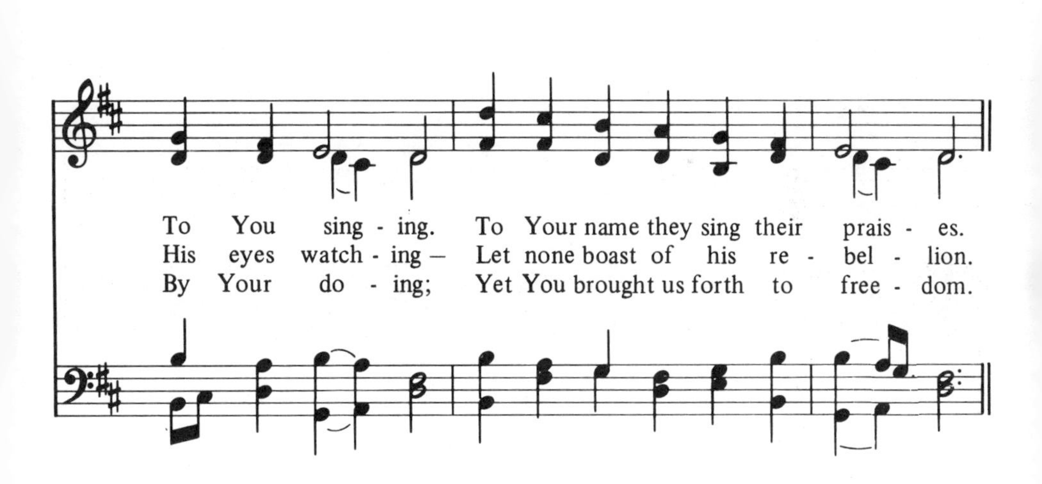
To You sing - ing. To Your name they sing their prais - es.
His eyes watch - ing – Let none boast of his re - bel - lion.
By Your do - ing; Yet You brought us forth to free - dom.

4. [13]I enter will into Your house;
I'll bring burnt offerings with me;
To You I will my vows pay.
[14]These things my lips and mouth resolved:
I promised many offerings
When I was in deep trouble.
[15]I will offer
Burning sacrifice of fatlings,
With ram's incense;
I'll make bulls and goats an off'ring.

5. [16]Come listen, all who fear the LORD;
I'll tell what He has done for me:
[17]I cried to Him and praised Him.
[18]If in my heart I sin regard
The LORD will not give heed to me;
[19]But truly God has listened;
He has heard me.
[20]God be blessed, for He has not
Scorned my praying;
He took not His mercy from me.

67A
PSALM 67
MISSIONARY HYMN. 76.76.D.
1. [1]O God, to us show mer - cy, And bless us in Thy grace;
2. [3]O God, let peo - ples praise Thee; Let all the peo - ple sing;
3. [5]O God, let peo - ples praise Thee; Let all the peo - ple sing;
Cause Thou to shine up - on us The bright - ness of Thy face;
[4]Let na - tions now be joy - ful; Let songs of glad - ness ring;
[6]For earth in rich a - bun - dance To us her fruit will bring.
[2]That so Thy way most ho - ly On earth may soon be known,
For Thou wilt judge the peo - ples In truth and right - eous - ness;
God, our own God, will bless us; [7]Yea, God will bless - ing send;
And un - to eve - ry peo - ple Thy sav - ing grace be shown.
And o'er the earth shall na - tions Thy lead - er - ship con - fess.
And all the earth shall fear Him To its re - mot - est end.

PSALM 67

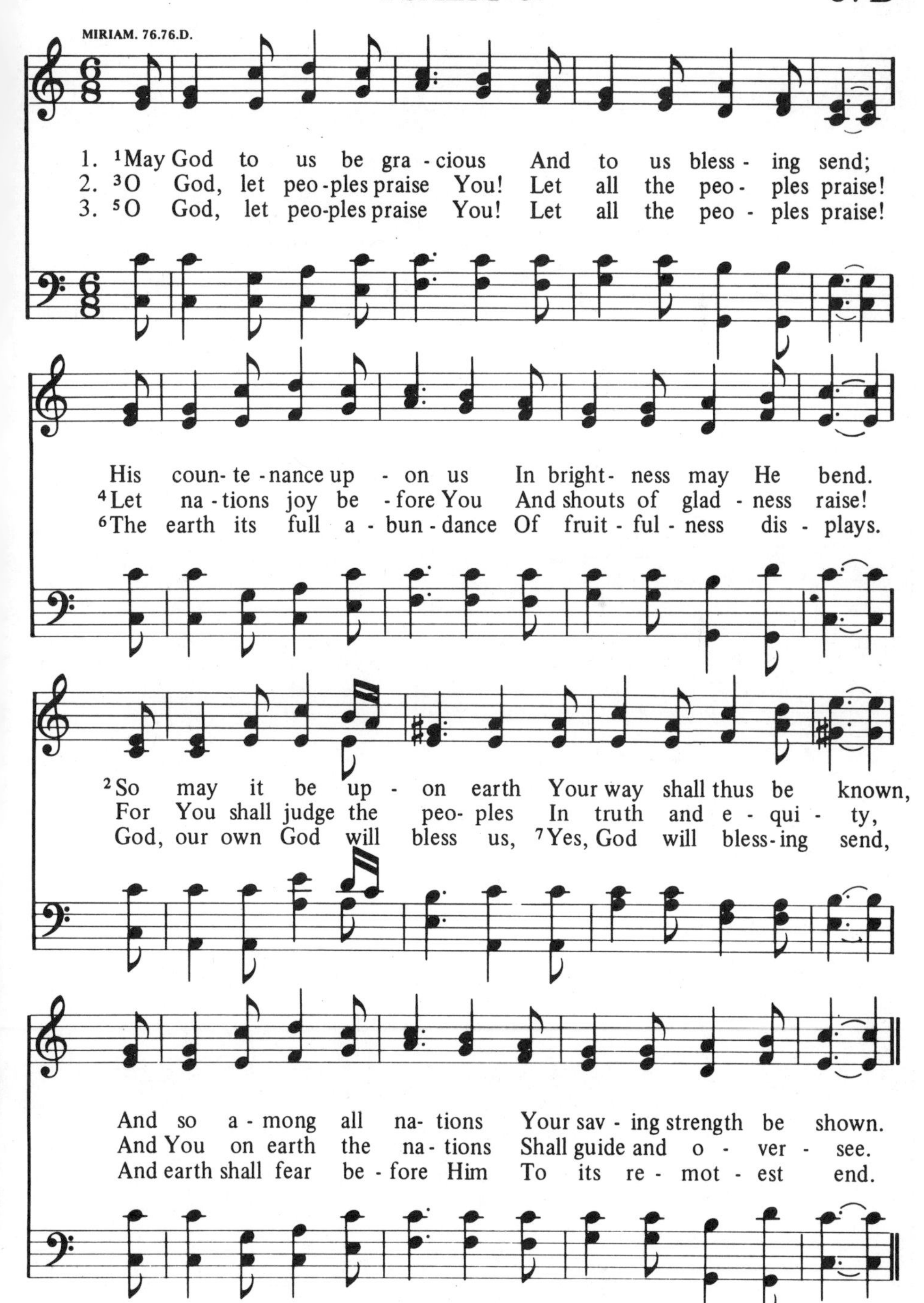
MIRIAM. 76.76.D.
1. [1]May God to us be gra - cious And to us bless - ing send;
2. [3]O God, let peo-ples praise You! Let all the peo - ples praise!
3. [5]O God, let peo-ples praise You! Let all the peo - ples praise!
His coun- te - nance up - on us In bright- ness may He bend.
[4]Let na - tions joy be - fore You And shouts of glad - ness raise!
[6]The earth its full a - bun - dance Of fruit - ful - ness dis - plays.
[2]So may it be up - on earth Your way shall thus be known,
For You shall judge the peo- ples In truth and e - qui - ty,
God, our own God will bless us, [7]Yes, God will bless-ing send,
And so a - mong all na- tions Your sav - ing strength be shown.
And You on earth the na- tions Shall guide and o - ver - see.
And earth shall fear be - fore Him To its re - mot - est end.

68A

PSALM 68:1–6

LAIGHT STREET. 86.866.

1. ¹Let God a - rise, and scat - tered far Be all His
2. As melt - ing wax be - fore a fire, Be - fore God
3. ⁴O sing to God! O praise His name! A high - way
4. ⁵The or - phans' fath - er, wid - ows' help, God's in His

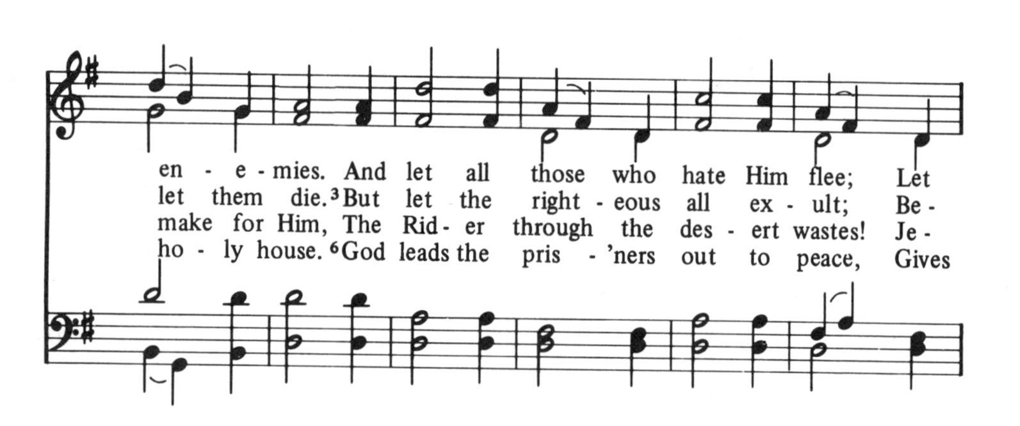
en - e - mies. And let all those who hate Him flee; Let
let them die. ³But let the right - eous all ex - ult; Be -
make for Him, The Rid - er through the des - ert wastes! Je -
ho - ly house. ⁶God leads the pris - 'ners out to peace, Gives

none be - fore Him stay. ²Like smoke drive them a - way!
fore God let them joy; Let them shout loud for joy!
ho - vah is His name! Be - fore Him joy pro - claim!
need - y ones a home; But reb - els des - erts roam.

BELIEVE. C.M.
5. ⁷O God, the time Thy go - ing forth Was at Thy peo - ple's head, The time when Thy ma- jes - tic march In - to the des - ert led,
6. ⁸Then at God's pres - ence trem - bled earth; The melt - ing heav - ens fell; This Si - nai quaked, for God was there, The God of Is - ra - el.
7. ⁹A shower of fresh, a - bun - dant rain, O God, Thou send - est then; Thine her - it - age, when it was faint, Thou didst re - vive a - gain.

8. [10] Thy congregation found their home;
Thy people settled there.
O God, Thou with Thy goodness didst
For all the poor prepare.

9. [11] The LORD will give the word which He
Commanded to be shown;
The women are a mighty host
To make the tidings known.

68C

PSALM 68:12-24

HERBERT. C.M.Tr.

10. [12] The kings of might- y hosts shall flee, Shall flee in haste a - way;
11. [16] Why look a - skance, ye moun - tain peaks, Up - on the ho - ly hill
12. [19] O bless - ed be the Lord, Who doth Each day our bur - den bear;
13. [22] The Lord has said, "From Ba - shan range I will bring back these foes,

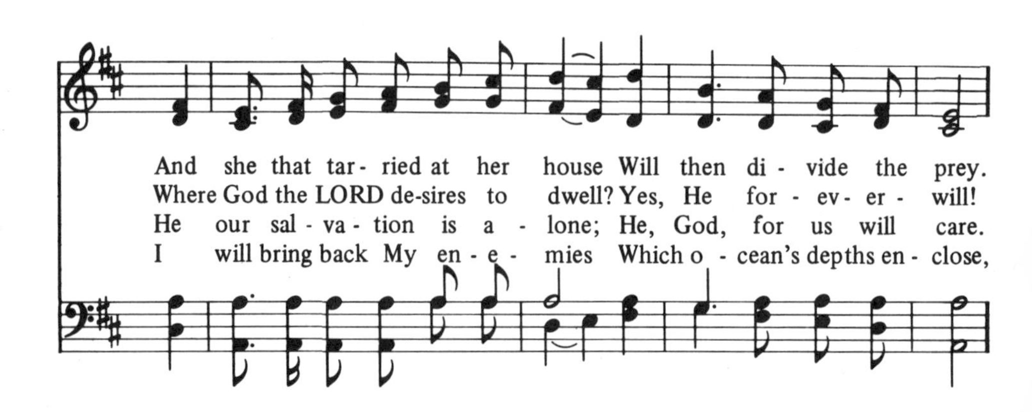
And she that tar - ried at her house Will then di - vide the prey.
Where God the LORD de-sires to dwell? Yes, He for - ev - er - will!
He our sal - va - tion is a - lone; He, God, for us will care.
I will bring back My en - e - mies Which o - cean's depths en - close,

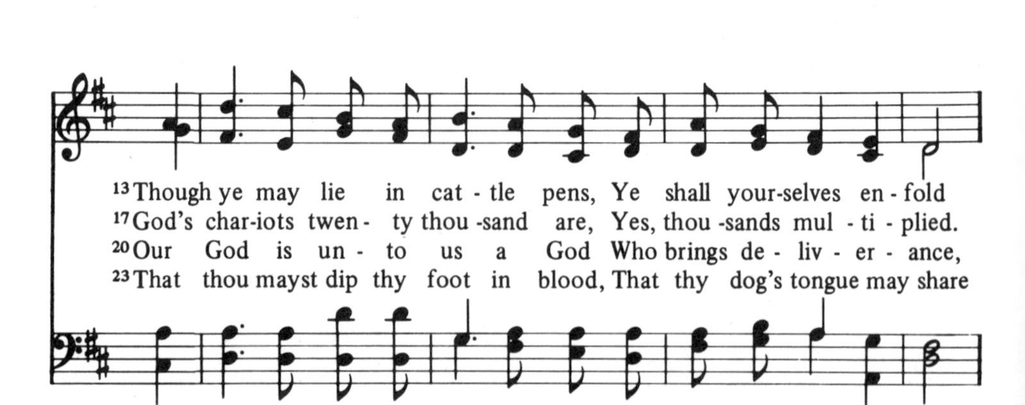
13 Though ye may lie in cat - tle pens, Ye shall your-selves en - fold
17 God's char-iots twen - ty thou -sand are, Yes, thou -sands mul - ti - plied.
20 Our God is un - to us a God Who brings de - liv - er - ance,
23 That thou mayst dip thy foot in blood, That thy dog's tongue may share

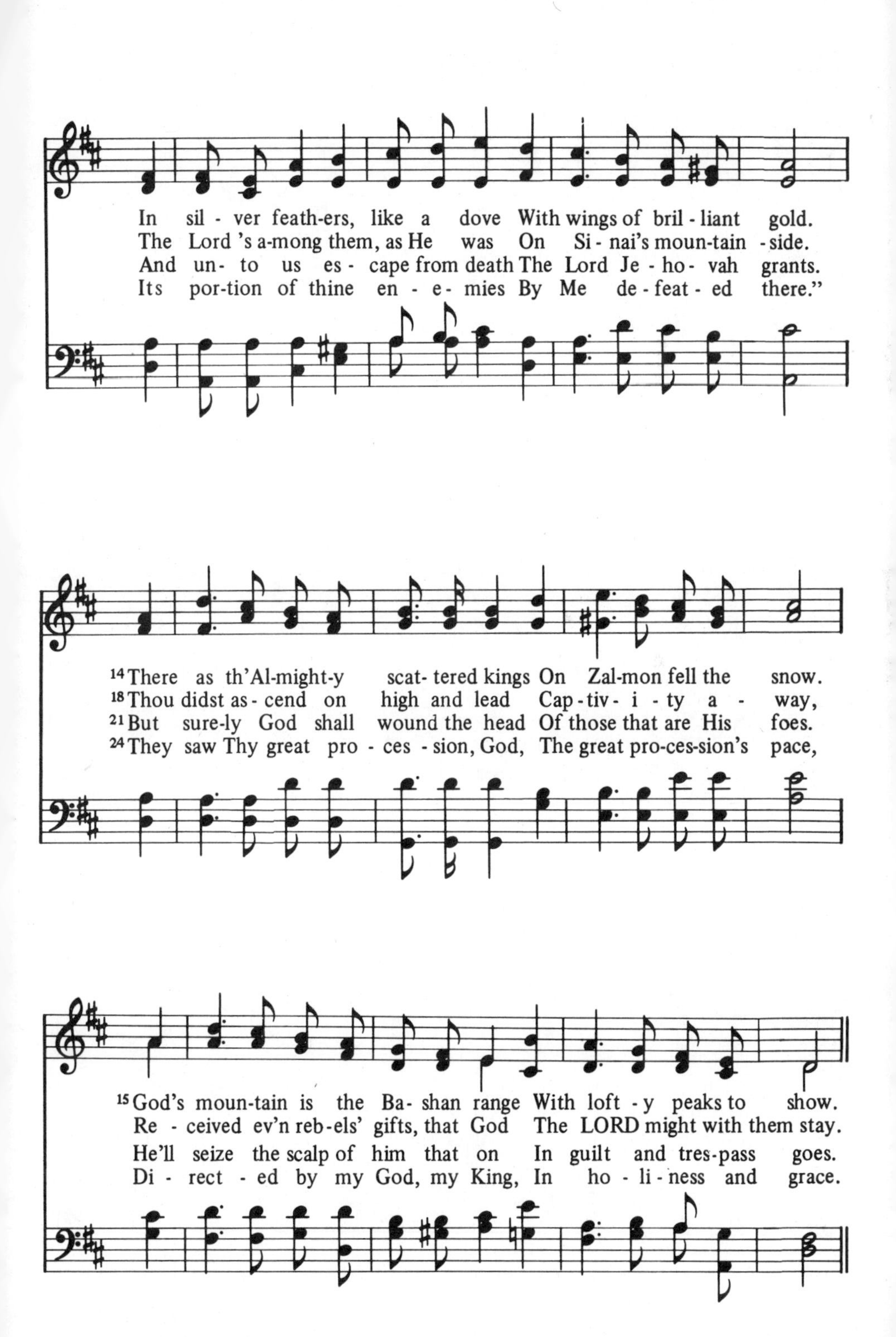
In sil - ver feath-ers, like a dove With wings of bril - liant gold.
The Lord 's a-mong them, as He was On Si - nai's moun-tain - side.
And un- to us es - cape from death The Lord Je - ho- vah grants.
Its por-tion of thine en - e- mies By Me de - feat - ed there."
14 There as th'Al-might-y scat- tered kings On Zal-mon fell the snow.
18 Thou didst as - cend on high and lead Cap - tiv- i - ty a - way,
21 But sure-ly God shall wound the head Of those that are His foes.
24 They saw Thy great pro - ces - sion, God, The great pro-ces-sion's pace,
15 God's moun-tain is the Ba- shan range With loft - y peaks to show.
Re - ceived ev'n reb-els' gifts, that God The LORD might with them stay.
He'll seize the scalp of him that on In guilt and tres-pass goes.
Di - rect - ed by my God, my King, In ho - li - ness and grace.

68D PSALM 68:24–31

WEYMOUTH. C.M.D.
14. 24 They saw Thy great pro - ces- sion, God, The great pro- ces- sion's pace,
15. 26 With - in the con - gre - ga -tions all Bless God with one ac - cord;
16. 28 Thy God com-mands thy strength; for us Thy work, God, strength-ened be.
17. That all may hum- bly bow them- selves, Bring bars of sil - ver ore.
Di - rect - ed by my God, my King, In ho - li - ness and grace.
All ye who come from Is - rael's fount, O do ye bless the LORD.
29 For Thy house in Je - ru - sa - lem Let kings bring gifts to Thee.
For He has scat -tered peo - ples all Who take de - light in war.
25 Be - fore went sing- ers; af - ter them The min - strels mu-sic made,
27 Their prince, young Ben-ja-min, is there, And Ju - dah's prin-ces high;
30 Re - buke the beasts a - mong the reeds, Those tram- pling bulls of might,
31 Then shall the prin - ces proud and great Come out of E- gypt's lands,
And bands of maid- ens all a-round Their ring-ing tim-brels played.
The chiefs of Zeb -u - lon are there, And those of Naph-ta - li.
With all the oth- er peo - ples who But calves are in their sight,
And E - thi- o -pi - a to God Shall soon stretch forth her hands.

PSALM 68:32–35

CROYDON. C.M.
18. 32O all ye king - doms of the earth, Sing prais - es un - to God; And Him Who is the Lord of all With prais - es do ye laud,
19. 33To Him that rides on heav'n of heav'ns Which He of old did found; Lo, He sends out His voice, a voice In might that doth a - bound,
With prais - es do ye laud, With prais - es do ye laud.
In might that doth a - bound, In might that doth a - bound.

20. 34All strength to God do ye ascribe,
Because His majesty
Is over Israel; His strength
Is in the heavens high.

21. 35Thou, God, art dreadful from Thy place;
Isr'el's own God is He,
Who gives His people strength and power;
O let God blessed be.

69A PSALM 69:1–4

SILOAM. C.M.

1. [1]Save me, O God, be - cause the floods Come
2. [3]I with my cry - ing wea - ry am; My
3. [4]The men that with no cause at all Bear
4. Those wrong - ful - ly my en - e - mies Who

in up - on my soul; [2]I sink in mire where
throat is parched and dried; My eyes grow dim while
ha - tred un - to me More than the hairs up -
seek my soul to slay Are ver - y strong; I

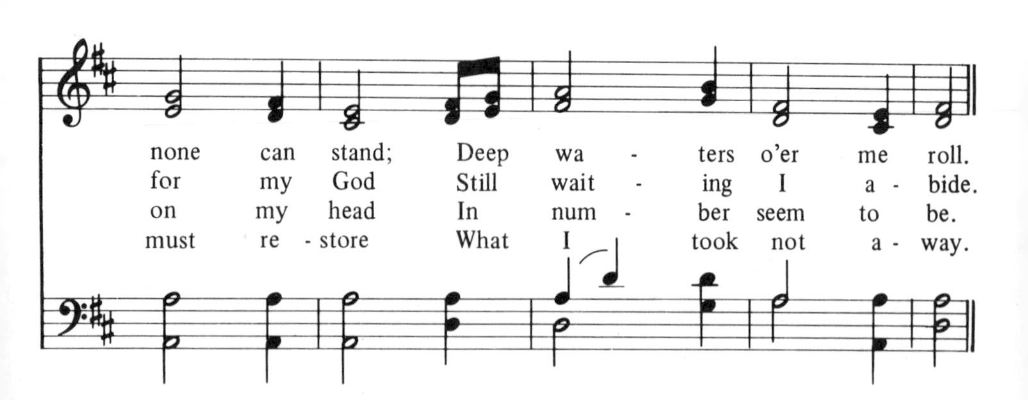
none can stand; Deep wa - ters o'er me roll.
for my God Still wait - ing I a - bide.
on my head In num - ber seem to be.
must re - store What I took not a - way.

PSALM 69:5–12

AGAWAM. C.M.
5. [5]O God, my fool - ish - ness and sins Are sure - ly known to Thee. [6]Let none that wait on Thee be shamed, Lord GOD of hosts, through me.
6. O Thou, the God of Is - ra - el, Let none that seek Thy face Be ev - er made to suf - fer shame For my acts of dis - grace.
7. [7]For I have borne re - proach for Thee; My face is veiled with shame. [8]To broth - ers strange, to moth - er's sons An al - ien, I be - came.
8. [9]For zeal with - in me for Thy house Has been con - sum - ing me, And all re - proach - es cast at Thee Have fal - len now on me.

9. [10]When I was weeping in my soul,
My fasting was my shame;
[11]When I in sackcloth clothed myself,
Their byword I became.

10. [12]The men who sit within the gate
Have talked about me long;
And those who gave themselves to drink
About me made a song.

PSALM 69:13–21

EPHRATAH. C.M.D.
11. 13But in a time ac - cept-ed, LORD, To Thee my prayers as-cend;
12. 15Let not the flood me o - ver - flow; Let me not swal-lowed be
13. 17Ne'er from Thy serv-ant hide Thy face; I'm pressed; soon an- swer me.
14. 20My heart is brok-en by re- proach, And I am sick and weak.
In Thine a- bound- ing love and truth, O God, sal- va- tion send.
By gap - ing deep; let not the pit Close up its mouth on me.
18Draw near to me; re - deem my soul; My foes come; ran- som me.
I nev - er find the sym - pa - thy And com -fort - ers I seek.
14De - liv - er me from out the mire, And me from sink-ing keep;
16Be - cause Thy mer - cy, LORD, is good, O an - swer Thou my plea;
19Well known to Thee is my re - proach, My shame and my dis - grace;
21They al - so gave me bit - ter gall In all the food I ate;
De - liv- er me from those that hate, And from the wa - ters deep.
In all of Thy com- pas - sion great, O turn Thou un -to me.
The ad- ver - sar - ies of my soul Are all be - fore Thy face.
They gave me vin- e- gar to drink The time my thirst was great.

PSALM 69:22–28 69D

LAFAYETTE. C.M.
15. 22 O let their peace become a trap; A snare their table make; 23 In darkness let their eyesight fail, And cause their loins to shake.
16. 24 On them Thine indignation pour; In wrath them overtake; 25 And let their camp be desolate; Their tents let all forsake.
17. 26 For they have persecuted him Whom Thou Thyself didst smite; They advertise the pain of those On whom Thy wounds did light.

18. [27] Keep adding their iniquities;
Sum up their wickedness;
And let them never enter in
To share Thy righteousness.

19. [28] And from the record book of life
O let them be erased;
Upon the roll of righteous men
Let not their names be placed.

69E PSALM 69:29–36

SABBATH EVENING. C.M.
20. 29 But as for me, af - flict - ed, poor, And deep in pain am I; By Thy sal - va - tion, O my God, Let me be set on high.
21. 30 The name of God I with a song Most cheer - ful - ly will praise; And I in giv - ing thanks to Him His name will high - ly raise.
22. 31 For this will please the LORD far more Than will the of - fer - ing Of an - y ox with horns and hoofs, Or bull - ock, which I bring.

23. [32] The humble ones have seen all this,
And are with gladness thrilled.
All ye who seek for God, O let
Your heart with life be filled.

24. [33] Because Jehovah hears the prayers
That from the needy rise,
And those that are His prisoners
He never will despise.

25. [34] Let heav'n and earth give praise, and all
With which the sea is filled;
[35] For God will Zion surely save,
And Judah's cities build.

26. They'll dwell in their inheritance,
[36] Their children's heritage;
His servants, those who love His name,
Dwell there from age to age.

PSALM 70

70A

ST. BRIDE. S.M.
1. 1O God, de - liv - er me. LORD, speed Your help to me;
2. Turned back be they, dis-graced, That in my hurt de - light;
3. 4Let all who seek Thee joy And glad in Thee a - bide.
4. 5In need am I and poor; O God, make haste I pray;
2And let all those who seek my life A- shamed and hum - bled be.
3Ap - palled by their own shame be they Who say, "A - ha", in spite.
Let those who Thy sal - va - tion love Say, "God be mag - ni - fied."
My Help and my De - liv - er - er, O LORD, do not de - lay.
PSALM 70
70B
STATE STREET. S.M.
1. 1O God, de - liv - er me. LORD, speed Your help to me;
2. Turned back be they, dis- graced, That in my hurt de - light;
3. 4Let all who seek Thee joy And glad in Thee a - bide.
4. 5In need am I and poor; O God, make haste I pray;
2And let all those who seek my soul A - shamed and hum - bled be.
3Ap - palled by their own shame be they Who say, "A - ha", in spite.
Let those who Thy sal - va - tion love Say, "God be mag- ni - fied."
My Help and my De - liv - er - er, O LORD, do not de - lay.

70C PSALM 70

PSALM TONE. 86.86.
1. 1 Has - ten, O God, to my res - cue!
2. Turned back be they and dis - hon - ored
3. 4 Let those who seek You be joy - ful;
4. 5 But I am poor and af - flict - ed.
Has - ten my help, O LORD! 2 Let there be shame and con-
Who in my hurt de - light. 3 By their dis - grace be they
Let them in You be glad. Let those who love Your sal-
Has - ten to me, O God! You are my help and my
fu - sion On those who seek my life.
cov - ered Who jeer, "A - ha! A - ha!"
va - tion Say, "God be mag - ni - fied!"
Sav - ior. O LORD, do not de - lay!

PSALM 71:1-8

71A

CONTEMPLATION. C.M.
1. [1]In Thee, O LORD, I ref - uge take; A -
2. [3]Be Thou my rock, my dwell - ing place, My
3. [4]Free me, my God, from wick - ed hands, Hands

shamed let me not be; [2]O save me in Thy
con - stant safe re - sort. Thou my sal - va - tion
cru - el and un - just; [5]Thou, Lord Je - ho - vah,

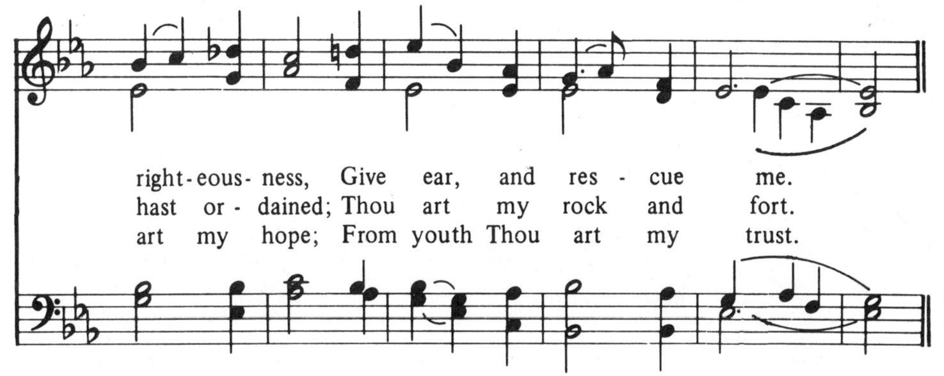
right-eous-ness, Give ear, and res - cue me.
hast or - dained; Thou art my rock and fort.
art my hope; From youth Thou art my trust.

4. [6]For I have been sustained by Thee
Through birth and early days;
Brought from my mother's womb by Thee,
I'll give Thee constant praise.

5. [7]To many I a wonder am;
Thou art my refuge strong.
[8]My mouth is brimming with Thy praise
And honor all day long.

71 B PSALM 71:9-13

THIS ENDRIS NYGHT. C.M.

6. 9 Do not re - ject me in the time When
7. 10 For those who are my en - e - mies A -
8. 11 They say, "God has for - sak - en him! Pur -
9. 13 Let ad - ver - sar - ies of my soul Dis -

old age I shall see; And in my days of
gainst me e - vil speak; Those who are watch - ing
sue him! None will save!" 12 O God, do not be
graced and wast - ed be, All cov - ered with re -

fail - ing strength Do not a - ban - don me.
for my life U - nit - ed coun - sel seek.
far from me; My God, Thy help I crave.
proach and shame Who seek to in - jure me.

PSALM 71:14–19

POLITZ. C.M.D.
10. 14 But I with last-ing con - fi - dence Will hope con - tin - ual - ly,
11. 16 For I will go forth in the strength Of Thee, Je - ho - vah Lord;
12. 18 So now, when I am old and gray, O God, for - sake me not,
And I will add still more and more To all the praise of Thee.
Thy right-eous-ness, and Thine a- lone, A - broad I will re - cord.
Un - til Thy strength and power I have Each gen - er - a - tion taught.
15 All day my mouth Thy right - eous-ness And Thy sal - va - tion show,
17 O God, I have been taught by Thee Ev'n from my days of youth;
19 For, God, Thy right- eous - ness ex- tends In - to in - fin - i - ty;
For proofs of them are far be-yond The num- bers which I know.
And all the won-ders Thou hast done I still de - clare as truth.
And Thou hast wrought such mir-a-cles, O God, who is like Thee?

71D

PSALM 71:20-24

WILTSHIRE. C.M.

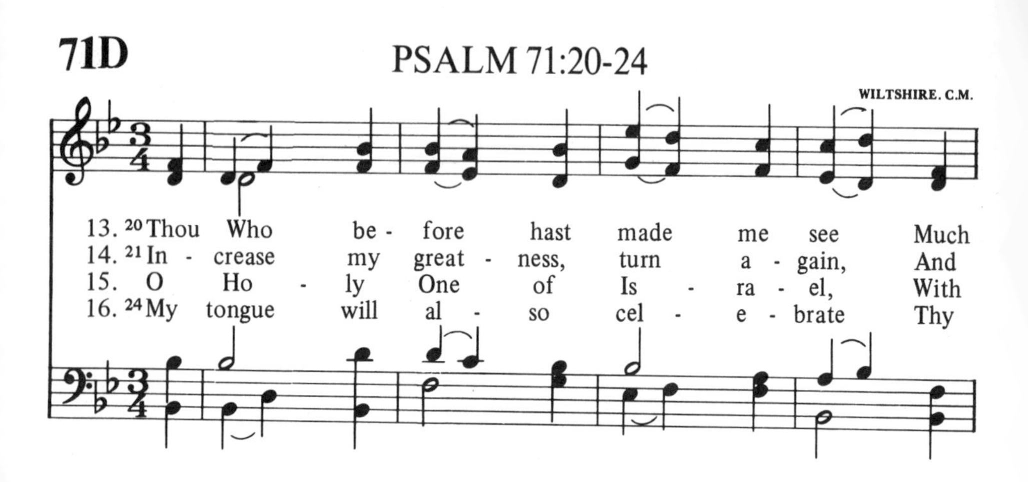
WILTSHIRE. C.M.
13. 20 Thou Who be - fore hast made me see Much
14. 21 In - crease my great - ness, turn a - gain, And
15. O Ho - ly One of Is - ra - el, With
16. 24 My tongue will al - so cel - e - brate Thy

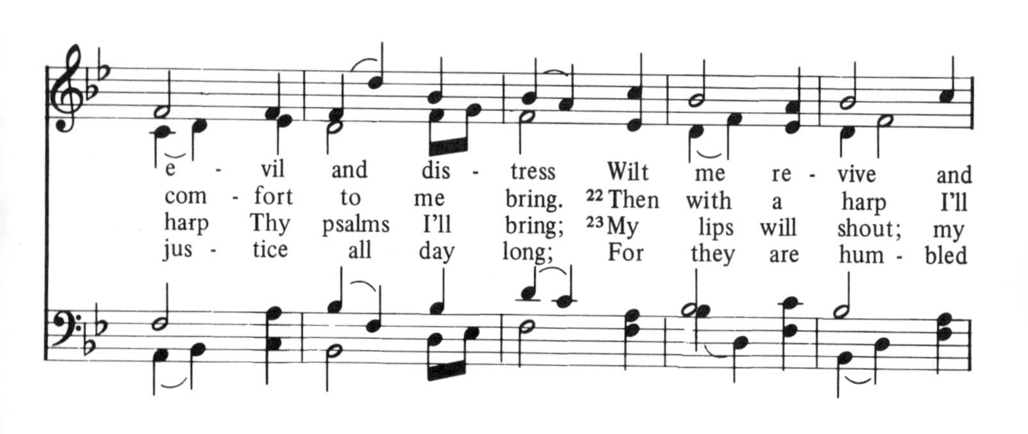
e - vil and dis - tress Wilt me re - vive and
com - fort to me bring. 22 Then with a harp I'll
harp Thy psalms I'll bring; 23 My lips will shout; my
jus - tice all day long; For they are hum - bled

bring me up From depths which me de - press.
give Thee thanks; My God, Thy truth I'll sing.
ran - somed soul In psalms to Thee will sing.
and a - shamed Who seek to do me wrong.

PSALM 72:1–8

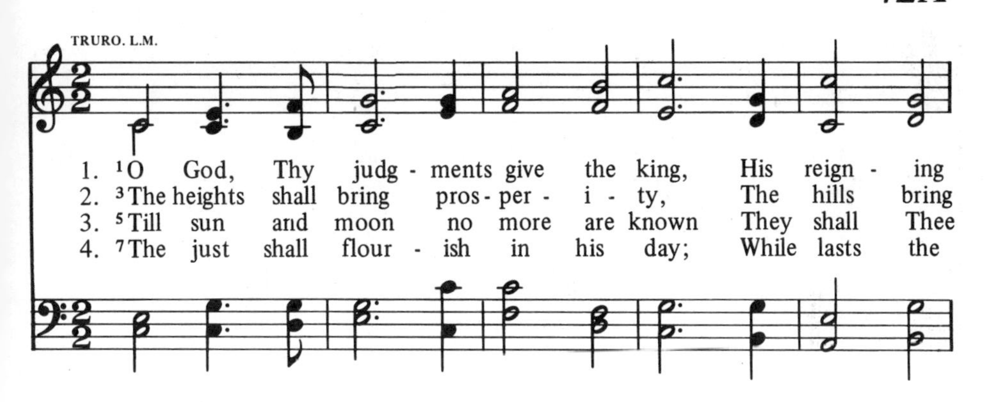
TRURO. L.M.
1. [1]O God, Thy judg - ments give the king, His reign - ing
2. [3]The heights shall bring pros - per - i - ty, The hills bring
3. [5]Till sun and moon no more are known They shall Thee
4. [7]The just shall flour - ish in his day; While lasts the

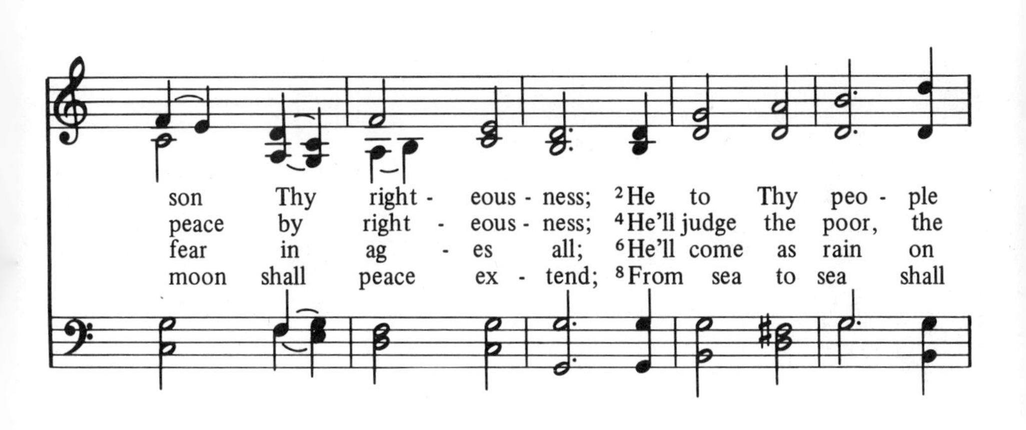
son Thy right - eous - ness; [2]He to Thy peo - ple
peace by right - eous - ness; [4]He'll judge the poor, the
fear in ag - es all; [6]He'll come as rain on
moon shall peace ex - tend; [8]From sea to sea shall

right shall bring, With jus - tice shall Thy poor re - dress.
wronged set free, And crush the men who them op - press.
mead - ows mown And showers up - on the earth that fall.
be his sway, And from the Riv - er to earth's end.

72B PSALM 72:9-15

ROCKINGHAM NEW. L.M.
5. 9The no - mads bow to him as king, And
6. 11All kings shall down be - fore him fall, All
7. 13He'll show the poor his sym - pa - thy, And
8. 15So he shall live; a gift of gold From

to the dust his foes de - scend; 10The isles and Tar - shish
na - tions his com - mands o - bey. 12He'll save the need - y
save the need - y by his might; 14From fraud and force he'll
She - ba they'll be - fore him lay. They'll him in con - stant
trib - ute bring, And She - ba, Se - ba gifts shall send.
when they call, The poor, and those that have no stay.
set them free; Their blood is pre - cious in his sight.
prayer up - hold, Their bless - ings on him chant all day.

PSALM 72:16–19

ANDRE. L.M.
9. [16]On hill - tops sown a lit - tle grain,
10. [17]Long as the sun his name shall last.
11. [18]Now bless - ed be our God a - lone.
12. [19]And bless - ed be His glo - rious name,
Like Leb - a - non with fruit shall bend; New
It shall en - dure through ag - es all; And
Je - ho - vah, God of Is - ra - el; For
Long as the ag - es shall en - dure. O'er
life the cit - y shall at - tain; She shall like grass grow
men shall still in him be blessed; Blessed all the na - tions
on - ly He has won - ders done; His deeds in glo - ry
all the earth ex - tend His fame; A - men, a - men, for
and ex - tend, She shall like grass grow and ex - tend.
shall him call, Blessed all the na - tions shall him call.
far ex - cel, His deeds in glo - ry far ex - cel.
ev - er - more, A - men, a - men, for ev - er - more.

72D
PSALM 72:18,19
BETA. Irregular.
18 Bless - ed be the LORD, the God of Is - ra - el, Who a - lone does won - drous things.
19 Bless-ed be His glo - rious name for - ev - er. Let His glo - ry fill the whole earth. A - men, and A - men.

BOOK III
PSALMS 73–89
PSALM 73:1–12
73A
RAKEM. 88.88.88.
1. 1 God's sure - ly good to Is - ra - el, To eve - ry
2. 4 For in their death no pangs they know; Their strength is
3. 7 Their eyes are bulg - ing from ex - cess; Their hearts o'er -
4. 10 Their peo - ple there - fore this way turn And drink their
one whose heart is pure. 2 But as for me, I near - ly fell;
firm from day to day; 5 They have no part in oth - ers' woe,
flow with dreams they seek. 8 They scoff; they threat-en to op - press;
streams that o - ver -flow. 11 "For how," they say, "can God dis - cern?
My foot - steps were no long - er sure. 3 For I was
Nor plagued as mor - tal men are they. 6 They make their
Dis - dain - ful words they proud - ly speak. 9 Their mouth the
And does the Most High real - ly know?" 12 Be - hold, un-
en - vious of the proud And wick-ed ones with wealth en - dowed.
neck-lace ar - ro - gance, And clothe them-selves with vi - o - lence.
heights of heav- en raids; Their tongue a-round the world pa - rades.
god - ly men are these, Who gain in wealth and live at ease.

73B PSALM 73:13–22

PETERSBURG. 88.88.88.

5. [13]Then surely I have toiled in vain
To cleanse my heart from all offense,
And vainly from each guilty stain
Have washed my hands in innocence.
[14]Still grievous plagues all day I've borne
And have been chastened every morn.

6. [15]If I would let my thoughts lead me
To speak with doubting words this way,
Behold, the children called by Thee
I certainly would then betray.
[16]But though the facts I tried to see
The problem deeply troubled me.

7. [17]Then came I to God's sanctuary
And there considered well their end.
[18]They're set on slipp'ry ground by Thee,
And them to ruin Thou dost send.
[19]How rapidly destroyed are they,
By sudden terrors swept away!

8. [20]As one who from a dream awakes,
Their form, O Lord, Thou wilt despise.
[21]So when my heart with grieving breaks
And bitter thoughts within me rise,
[22]I senseless am, and blind within;
A beast before Thee I have been.

PSALM 73:23-28

TRUST. 88.88.88.
9. 23 Yet ev - er - more I am with Thee: Thou hold - est me by my right hand. 24 And Thou, ev'n Thou, my guide shalt be; Thy coun - sel shall my way com - mand; And af - ter - ward in glo - ry bright Shalt Thou re - ceive me to Thy sight.
10. 25 For whom have I in heav'n but Thee? None else on earth I long to know. 26 My flesh may faint and wea - ry be; My heart may fail and heav - y grow; With strength doth God my heart re - store; He is my por - tion ev - er - more.
11. 27 They per - ish that are far from Thee; Lo, in their lewd-ness they shall die. 28 But sure - ly it is good for me That un - to God I should draw nigh. I ref - uge take in GOD the Lord, That all Thy works I may re - cord.

74A PSALM 74:1-11

LEAF. 86.866.

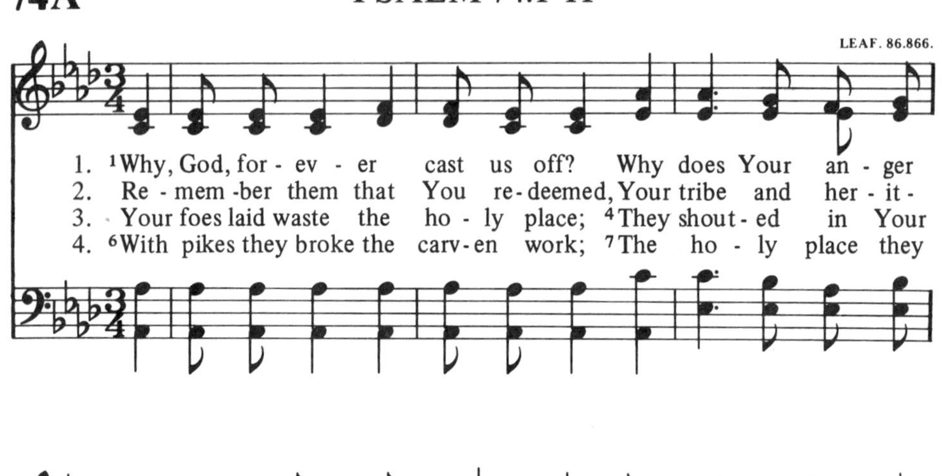
1. [1]Why, God, for - ev - er cast us off? Why does Your an - ger
2. Re - mem -ber them that You re- deemed, Your tribe and her - it -
3. Your foes laid waste the ho - ly place; [4]They shout - ed in Your
4. [6]With pikes they broke the carv- en work; [7]The ho - ly place they

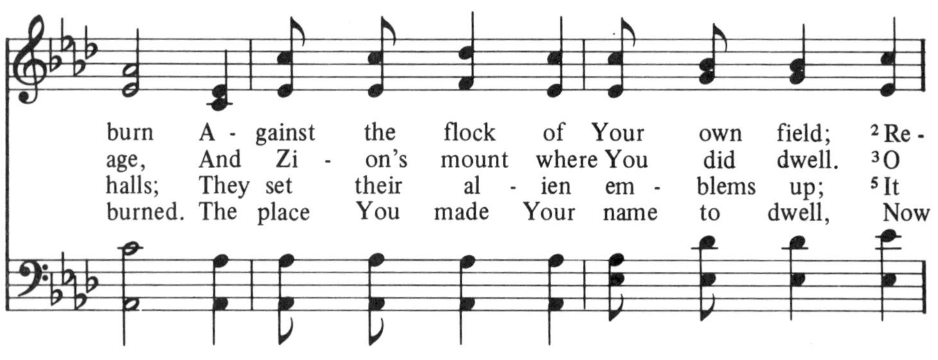
burn A - gainst the flock of Your own field; [2]Re -
age, And Zi - on's mount where You did dwell. [3]O
halls; They set their al - ien em - blems up; [5]It
burned. The place You made Your name to dwell, Now

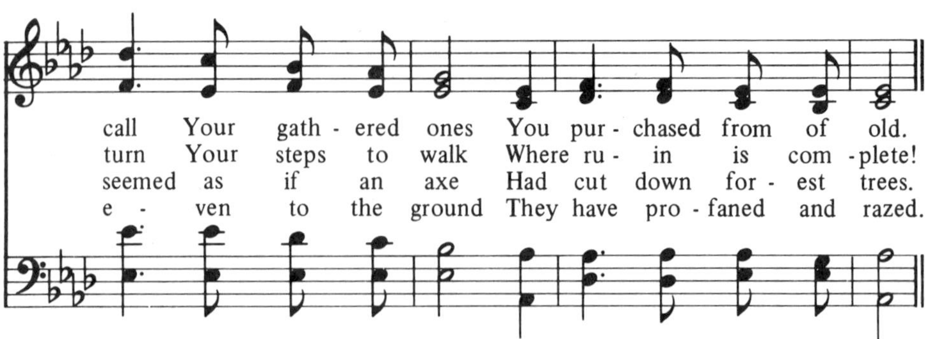
call Your gath - ered ones You pur - chased from of old.
turn Your steps to walk Where ru - in is com -plete!
seemed as if an axe Had cut down for - est trees.
e - ven to the ground They have pro - faned and razed.

5. [8]"O let us bring their strength to naught!" –
So did their hearts declare.
They burned each God-appointed place.
[9]No prophet now, no signs,
And none who knows how long!

6. [10]How long, O God, will foes insult
And scorn Your name always?
[11]O why do You hold back Your hand?
Your right hand O reach forth
To end and to destroy!

PSALM 74:12-23

74B

BROOMSGROVE. 86.866.
7. 12 Yet God my King brings forth of old Sal - va - tion
8. 15 You o- pened springs; You dried the streams; 16 Both day and
9. 18 Re - mem-ber, LORD, how foes in - sult! How fools have
in the earth. 13 The sea You part - ed by Your strength;
night are Yours. You have or-dained both light and sun;
scorned Your name! 19 Your dove O give not to the beasts!
You smote Le - vi - a - than 14 And fed him to the beasts.
17 You gave the earth its bounds, And made the heat and cold.
Your meek ones' lives re - gard And not al - ways for - get!

10. 20 O look upon the covenant!
The darkness of the land
Is with the dens of plunder filled.
21 O do not shame the meek,
But let them praise Your name!

11. 22 Arise, O God! Take up Your strife!
Recall the scorn of fools!
23 Recall Your adversaries' cries,
The raging noise of foes
Which rises endlessly!

75 PSALM 75

KATHRINE. C.M.

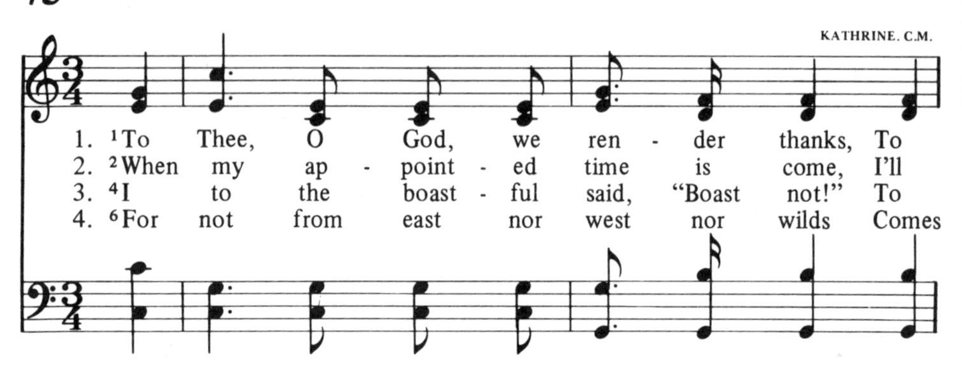
1. 1 To Thee, O God, we ren - der thanks, To
2. 2 When my ap - point - ed time is come, I'll
3. 4 I to the boast - ful said, "Boast not!" To
4. 6 For not from east nor west nor wilds Comes

Thee give thanks sin - cere, Be - cause Thy won - drous
judge with e - ven hand. 3 Though earth and all its
vile men, "Lift no horn! 5 Do not lift up your
ex - al - ta - tion nigh, 7 For God is judge, de -

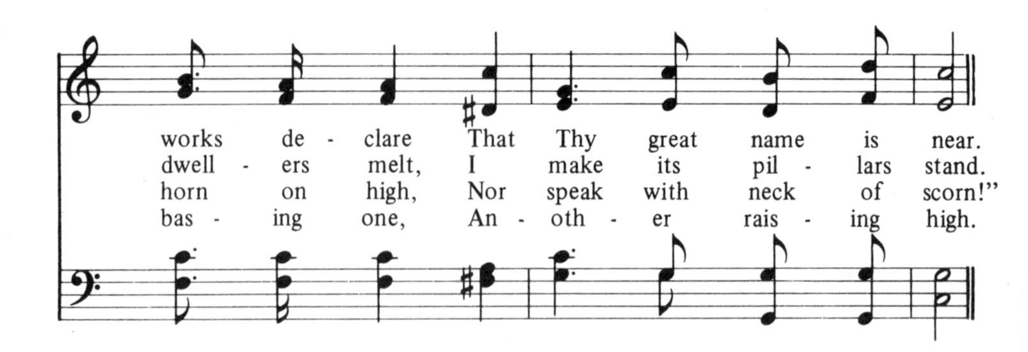
works de - clare That Thy great name is near.
dwell - ers melt, I make its pil - lars stand.
horn on high, Nor speak with neck of scorn!"
bas - ing one, An - oth - er rais - ing high.

5. [8] The LORD pours out a foaming cup
Which well-mixed wine contains,
And every wicked one on earth
Must drink; the dregs he drains.

6. [9] But I will tell it evermore,
To Jacob's God sing praise;
[10] And horns of sinners I'll cut off,
But just men's horns I'll raise.

PSALM 76

76A

NEANDER. 87.87.87.
1. 1God the Lord is known in Ju - dah; Great His name in
2. 4Ex - cel - lent art Thou and glo - rious Com - ing from the
3. 6Horse and char - iot low are ly - ing In the sleep of
Is - ra - el; 2His pa - vil - ion is in Sa - lem;
hills of prey. 5Thou hast spoiled the val - iant - heart - ed;
death's dark night. Ja - cob's God, Thou didst re - buke them;
His a - bode on Zi - on hill. 3There He broke the
Wrapt in sleep of death are they. Might - y men have
7Thou art fear - ful in Thy might. When Thine an - ger
bow and ar - rows, Bade the sword and shield be still.
lost their cun - ning; None are read - y for the fray.
once is ris - en, Who may stand be - fore Thy sight?

4. 8When from heav'n Thy sentence sounded,
All the earth in fear was still,
9While to save the meek and lowly
God in judgment wrought His will.
10Ev'n the wrath of man shall praise Thee;
What remains is kept from ill.

5. 11Make your vows now to Jehovah;
Pay your God what is His own.
All men, bring your gifts before Him;
Fear is due to Him alone;
12He brings low the pride of princes;
Kings shall tremble at His frown.

76B PSALM 76

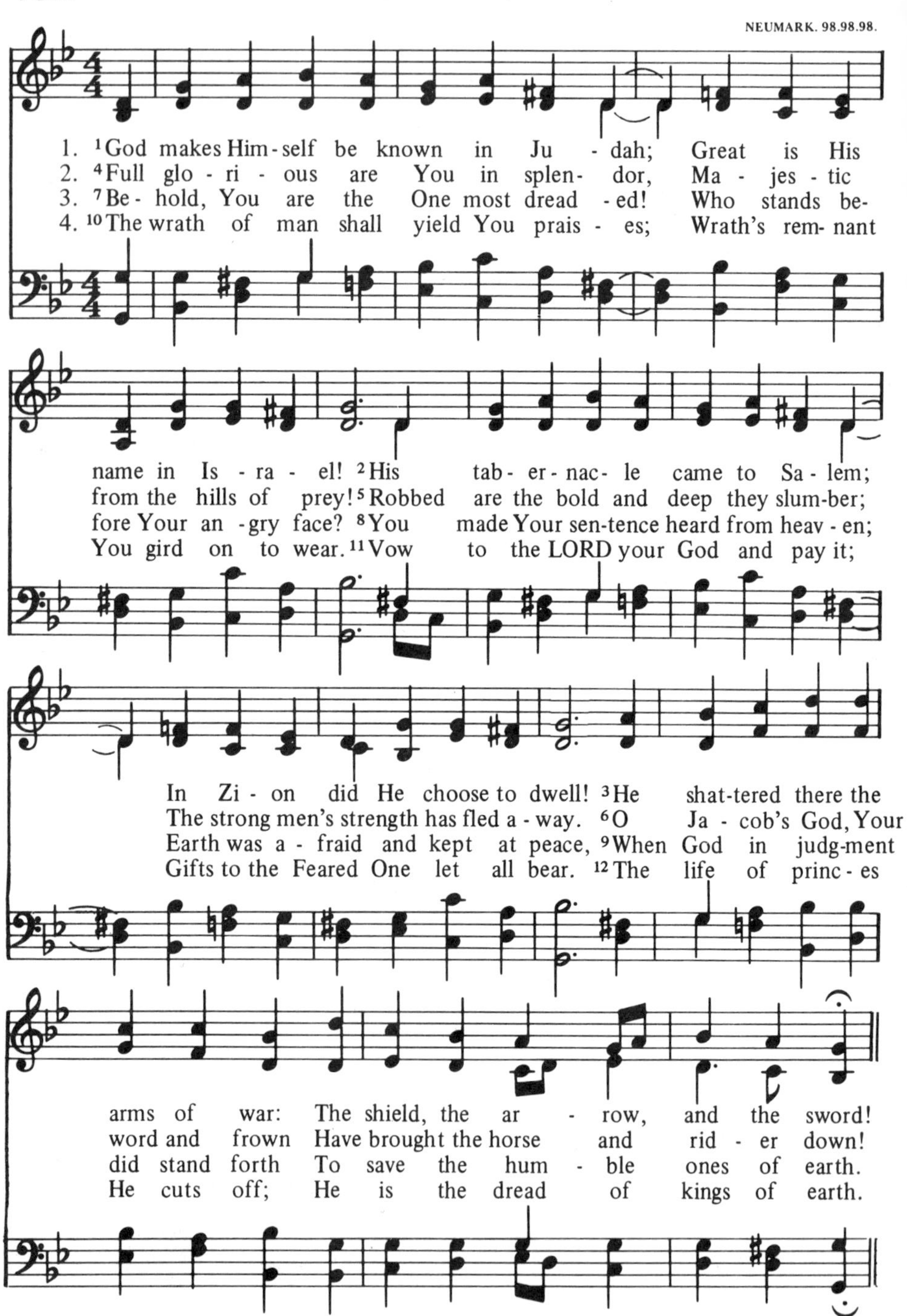
NEUMARK. 98.98.98.
1. [1]God makes Him-self be known in Ju - dah; Great is His
2. [4]Full glo - ri - ous are You in splen- dor, Ma - jes - tic
3. [7]Be - hold, You are the One most dread - ed! Who stands be-
4. [10]The wrath of man shall yield You prais - es; Wrath's rem- nant
name in Is - ra - el! [2]His tab - er - nac - le came to Sa - lem;
from the hills of prey! [5]Robbed are the bold and deep they slum-ber;
fore Your an - gry face? [8]You made Your sen-tence heard from heav - en;
You gird on to wear. [11]Vow to the LORD your God and pay it;
In Zi - on did He choose to dwell! [3]He shat-tered there the
The strong men's strength has fled a - way. [6]O Ja - cob's God, Your
Earth was a - fraid and kept at peace, [9]When God in judg-ment
Gifts to the Feared One let all bear. [12]The life of princ - es
arms of war: The shield, the ar - row, and the sword!
word and frown Have brought the horse and rid - er down!
did stand forth To save the hum - ble ones of earth.
He cuts off; He is the dread of kings of earth.

PSALM 77:1-6

PALESTRINA. C.M.
1. [1]With sup - pli - cat - ing cry to God My
2. [2]Through all the day I sought the Lord, When
3. [3]A - gain, as I re - mem - ber God, Dis -
voice shall lift - ed be; Yes, un - to God I
trou - bles on me pressed; Through all the night I
qui - et - ness pre - vails; And as I deep - ly
lift my voice, And He will an - swer me.
stretched my hands; My soul re - fused to rest.
med - i - tate, My sigh - ing spir - it fails.

4. [4]For Thou hast held my eyelids so
That they are open wide;
Yet I so deeply troubled am
To speak I have not tried.

5. [5]I've thought on days and years gone by,
Recalled my song at night;
[6]I've meditated with my heart;
My spirit searched for light.

77B PSALM 77:7-15

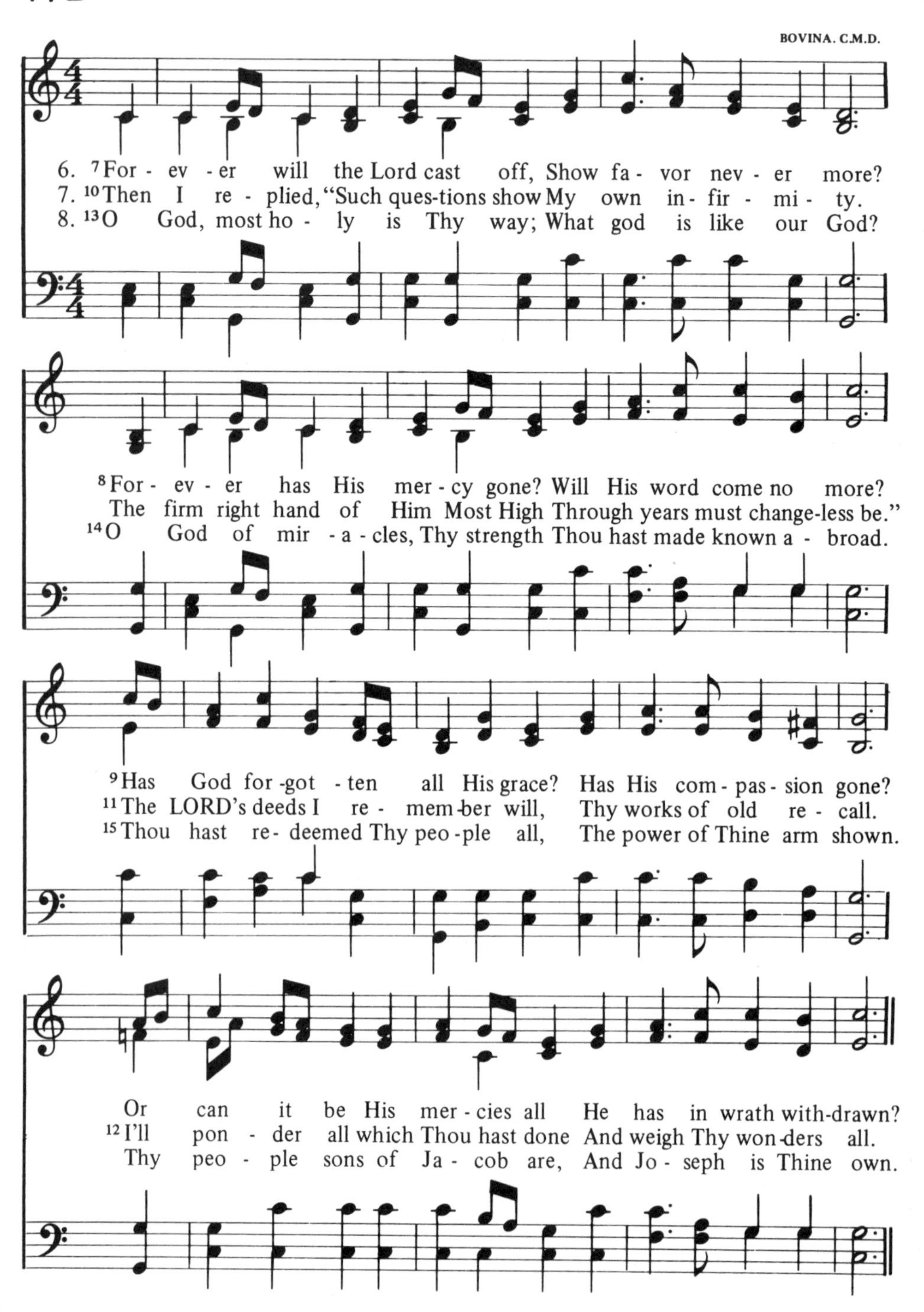
BOVINA. C.M.D.
6. 7For - ev - er will the Lord cast off, Show fa - vor nev - er more?
7. 10Then I re - plied, "Such ques-tions show My own in - fir - mi - ty.
8. 13O God, most ho - ly is Thy way; What god is like our God?
8For - ev - er has His mer - cy gone? Will His word come no more?
The firm right hand of Him Most High Through years must change-less be."
14O God of mir - a - cles, Thy strength Thou hast made known a - broad.
9Has God for -got - ten all His grace? Has His com - pas - sion gone?
11The LORD's deeds I re - mem -ber will, Thy works of old re - call.
15Thou hast re - deemed Thy peo -ple all, The power of Thine arm shown.
Or can it be His mer - cies all He has in wrath with-drawn?
12I'll pon - der all which Thou hast done And weigh Thy won -ders all.
Thy peo - ple sons of Ja - cob are, And Jo - seph is Thine own.

PSALM 77:16-20

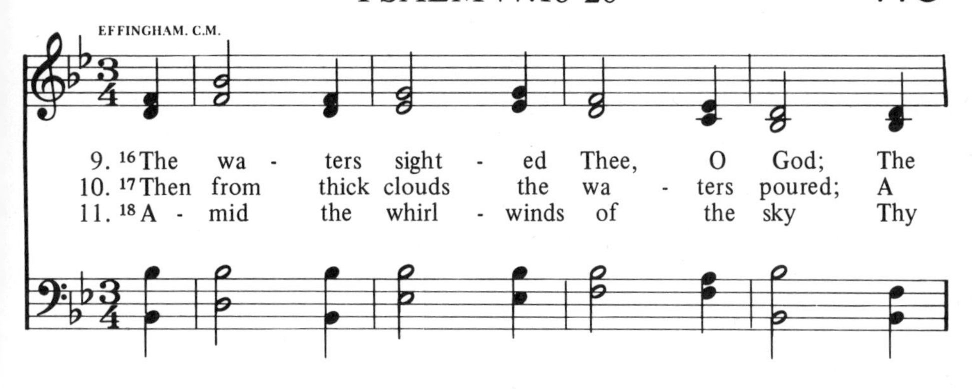
EFFINGHAM. C.M.
9. 16 The wa - ters sight - ed Thee, O God; The
10. 17 Then from thick clouds the wa - ters poured; A
11. 18 A - mid the whirl - winds of the sky Thy

wa - ters sight - ed Thee. They were in an - guish,
sound came from the sky. Thine ar - rows flash - ing
voice in thun - der pealed; Thy light - nings light - ened

and the deeps Then trem - bled fear - ful - ly.
here and there A - broad be - gan to fly.
up the world; The earth with trem - bling reeled.

12. 19 Thy way was in the troubled sea,
Thy path in waters deep.
Thy footprints have remained unknown;
None can their record keep.

13. 20 Thy people like a flock of sheep
Were led at Thy command,
By Moses and by Aaron kept,
And guided by their hand.

78A PSALM 78:1-8

ILLA. C.M.D.
1. [1]O ye my peo-ple, to my law At - ten - tive - ly give ear;
2. [4]We will not hide them from their sons But tell the race to come
3. That chil-dren yet un-born might know And their de - scend - ants lead
The words that from my mouth pro-ceed In - cline your-selves to hear.
Je - ho -vah's prais-es and His strength, The won-ders He has done.
[7]To trust in God, re-call God's works, And His com-mand-ments heed,
[2]My mouth shall speak a par- a - ble, The say - ings dark of old,
[5]His word He un - to Ja-cob gave, His law to Is - ra - el,
[8]And not be like their fa-thers were, A race of stub-born mood,
[3]Which we have lis-tened to and known As by our fa-thers told.
And bade our fa-thers teach their sons [6]The com-ing race to tell,
Which nev- er would pre - pare its heart Nor keep its faith with God.

PSALM 78:9-16

78B

WINCHESTER OLD. C.M.
4. 9 The sons of E - phra - im were armed; For bows they did not lack; But when the day of bat - tle came, Faint - heart - ed they turned back.
5. 10 They did not keep God's cov - e - nant, Nor walk in His com- mands. 11 His won - ders shown them they for - got, The deeds done by His hands.
6. 12 Great mir - a - cles He brought to pass Be - fore their fa - thers' sight; In E - gypt's land, in Zo - an's field He showed His won - drous might.

7. [13] He split the sea to let them pass;
The waters stood aside;
[14] By day He led them with a cloud;
All night a flame was guide.

8. [15] He split the rocks and gave them drink,
As from great deeps below;
[16] He from the rock brought running streams,
Like floods made waters flow.

78C PSALM 78:17-33

ELLACOMBE. C.M.D.
9. 17Yet in the des- ert still they sinned, Pro - vok - ing the Most High;
10. 20"Be - hold, He struck the rock, and out Gushed streams of wa - ter sweet;
11. 22For they did not be - lieve in God Nor trust His sav- ing love;
18For in their heart they test - ed God, Urged Him their lust sup- ply.
But can He give His peo - ple bread And send them flesh to eat?"
23But still he o - pened heav - en's doors, Com - mand- ed clouds a- bove,
19They spoke a-gainst their God; they said, "Can e - ven God pro - vide
21Be - cause the LORD heard this, His wrath Was kind - led in - to flame;
24And rained His man-na down on them; He gave them grain from heav'n;
A ta - ble in the wil - der - ness That we may be sup- plied?
On Ja- cob, and on Is - ra - el His in - dig - na-tion came.
25And man par - took of an- gels' food, In His a - bun-dance giv'n.

12\. [26]In heav'n He made the east wind blow;
The south wind felt His hand;
[27]So He rained meat on them like dust,
Winged fowl like ocean's sand.
[28]He let them fall amid their camp,
By tents on every side.
[29]And so they ate till they were filled;
Their greed He satisfied.

13\. [30]They craved still more, mouths filled with food;
[31]God's wrath then on them fell
And killed their stout ones, and subdued
Choice men of Israel.
[32]Yet still they sinned; they disbelieved
His wonders in the way;
[33]So in a breath He closed their days,
Their years in deep dismay.

PSALM 78:34-39 **78D**

PRINCE. C.M.
14. 34 But when He killed them, they de - sired To
15. 35 They then re - mem - bered God to be Their
16. 36 But they en - ticed Him with their mouth, And
seek Him ea - ger - ly; So they re - turned and
rock e - ter - nal - ly, And knew that on - ly
with their tongue they lied; 37 Their heart was not sin -
searched for God With sense of ur - gen - cy.
God Most High Could their re - deem - er be.
cere toward Him; His cov - 'nant they de - nied.

17. [38] But He forgave iniquity
In mercy, did not slay,
Aroused not all His wrath, but oft
His anger turned away.

18. [39] Thus He remembered they were flesh,
That they were only men,
A breath that swiftly goes away
And never comes again.

78E PSALM 78:40-51

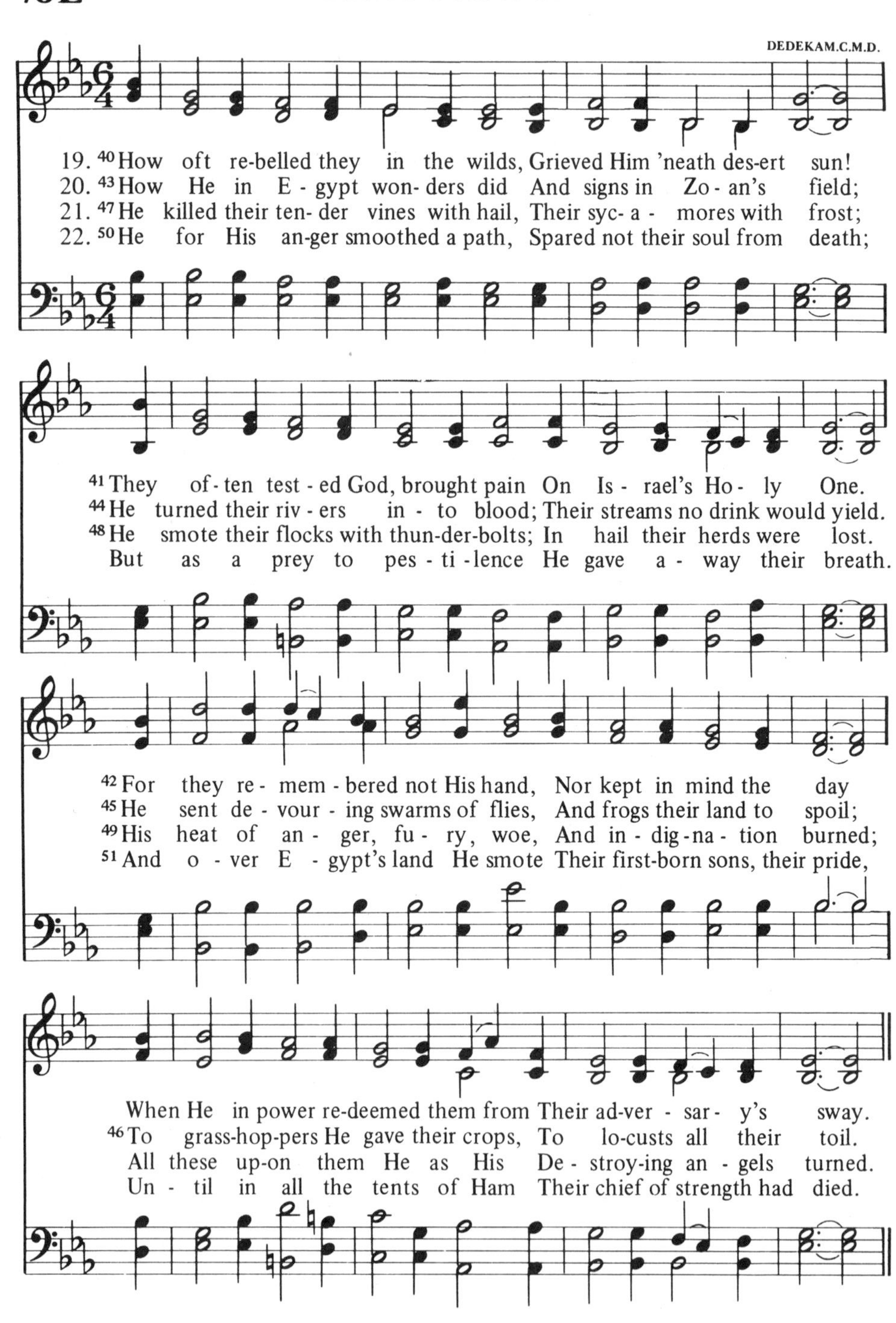
DEDEKAM.C.M.D.
19. 40 How oft re-belled they in the wilds, Grieved Him 'neath des-ert sun!
20. 43 How He in E - gypt won- ders did And signs in Zo - an's field;
21. 47 He killed their ten- der vines with hail, Their syc- a - mores with frost;
22. 50 He for His an-ger smoothed a path, Spared not their soul from death;
41 They of- ten test - ed God, brought pain On Is - rael's Ho - ly One.
44 He turned their riv - ers in - to blood; Their streams no drink would yield.
48 He smote their flocks with thun-der-bolts; In hail their herds were lost.
But as a prey to pes - ti - lence He gave a - way their breath.
42 For they re - mem - bered not His hand, Nor kept in mind the day
45 He sent de - vour - ing swarms of flies, And frogs their land to spoil;
49 His heat of an - ger, fu - ry, woe, And in - dig - na - tion burned;
51 And o - ver E - gypt's land He smote Their first-born sons, their pride,
When He in power re-deemed them from Their ad-ver - sar - y's sway.
46 To grass-hop-pers He gave their crops, To lo-custs all their toil.
All these up-on them He as His De - stroy-ing an - gels turned.
Un - til in all the tents of Ham Their chief of strength had died.

PSALM 78:52-57

78F

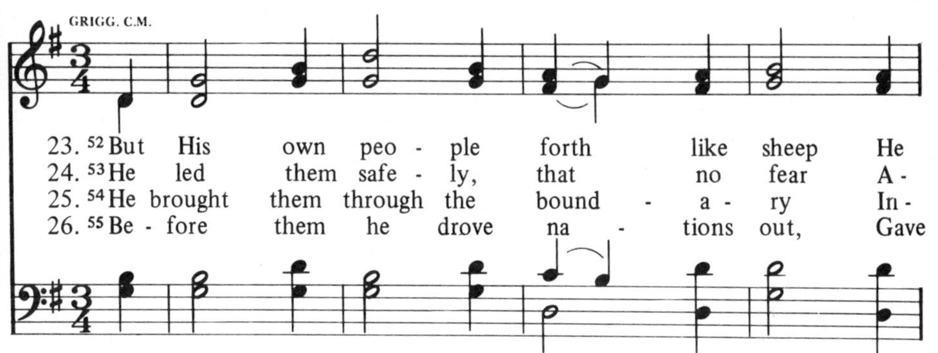
GRIGG. C.M.
23. 52 But His own peo - ple forth like sheep He
24. 53 He led them safe - ly, that no fear A -
25. 54 He brought them through the bound - a - ry In -
26. 55 Be - fore them he drove na - tions out, Gave

brought with guid - ing hand, And led his peo - ple
mong them might be found, But in the o - ver -
to His ho - ly land, This ver - y moun - tain
them in - her - i - tance By meas - ured lot, caused

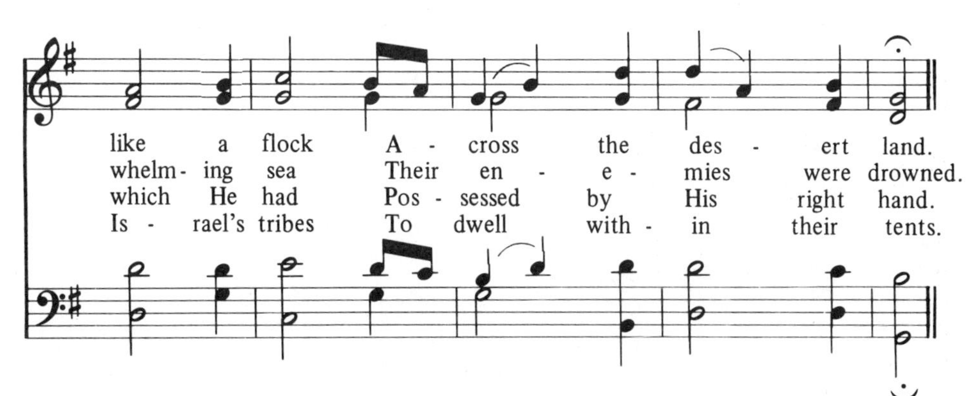
like a flock A - cross the des - ert land.
whelm - ing sea Their en - e - mies were drowned.
which He had Pos - sessed by His right hand.
Is - rael's tribes To dwell with - in their tents.

27. 56 And yet they tempted God Most High,
Rebelled against His will;
The testimonies He proclaimed
They disregarded still.

28. 57 They like their fathers backward turned
In treachery and pride;
Like shafts from a deceitful bow
They all did turn aside.

78G PSALM 78:58-64

ST. GREGORY. C.M.
29. 58 With their high plac - es they to wrath Pro -
30. 59 God heard, and in His an - ger great Re -
31. 61 So He de - liv - ered up His strength In -

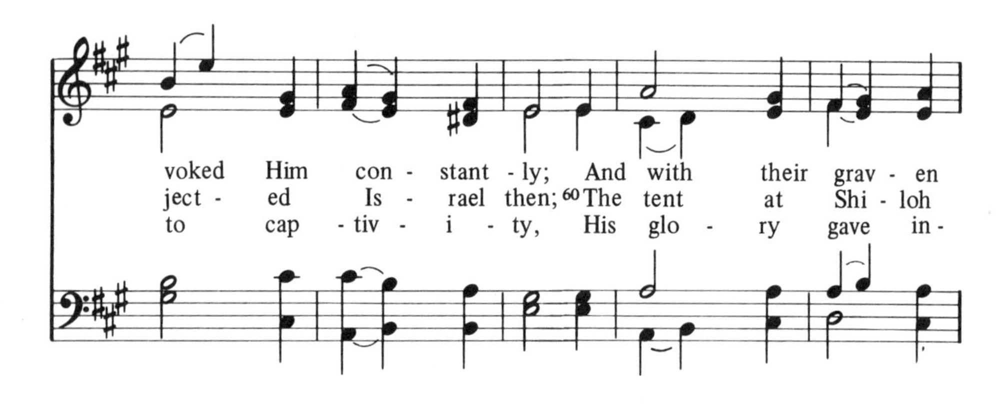
voked Him con - stant - ly; And with their grav - en
ject - ed Is - rael then; 60 The tent at Shi - loh
to cap - tiv - i - ty, His glo - ry gave in -

im - ag - es A - roused His jeal - ous - y.
He for - sook Where He had dwelt with men.
to the hand Of His proud en - e - my.

32. [62] And He His people to the sword
Delivered to be killed.
Against His own inheritance
With anger He was filled.

33. [63] Their young men were devoured by fire;
Their maidens were unwed;
[64] And when their priests fell by the sword
No tears their widows shed.

PSALM 78:65-72 78H

ST. AMBROSE. C.M.
34. 65 The Lord a - woke as from a sleep, Like
35. 67 Then Jo - seph's tent re - ject - ed He, On
36. 69 And there ex - alt - ed like the heights He
37. 70 He for His serv - ant Da - vid chose, Took
war - rior cheered by wine; 66 He drove His ad - ver -
E - phraim would not count; 68 But He the tribe of
built His sanc - tu - 'ry, And like the earth He
him from guard - ing sheep, 71 Brought him from where the
sar - ies back, Made their re - proach a sign.
Ju - dah chose, For He loved Zi - on's Mount.
found - ed it For all e - ter - ni - ty.
ewes with lambs It was his task to keep,

38. That He might shepherd Jacob then
And lead His people well,
Watch over His inheritance,
His chosen Israel.

39. [72] So with integrity of heart
Them faithfully he fed,
And with his understanding hands
He guided as he led.

79A PSALM 79:1-8

HOLY CROSS. 86.84
1. [1]O God, to Thine in - her - it - ance
2. [2]Thy serv - ants' bod - ies they have cast
3. [3]Their blood a - bout Je - ru - sa - lem
The heath - en en - trance made; They have de -
To fowls of heav'n for meat; The flesh of
Like wa - ter they have shed; And there was
filed Thy house, in heaps Have Sa - lem laid.
Thy dear saints they gave Wild beasts to eat.
none to bur - y them When they were dead.

4. [4]To all our neighbors we've become
A scorn and a reproach,
A laughingstock to all who now
On us encroach.

5. [5]How long, O LORD? Thy wrath toward us
Wilt Thou forever turn?
And will Thy fire-like jealousy
Forever burn?

6. [6]On heathen kingdoms pour Thy wrath,
Who call not on Thy name,
[7]For Jacob they devour, and waste
His fields with flame.

7. [8]Remember not our fathers' sins,
Which guilt on us bestow.
Let Thy compassion soon meet us,
Brought very low.

PSALM 79:9-13 **79B**

FAIR HAVEN. 86.84.
8. 9 O God of our sal - va - tion, help! Thy name the glo - ry take! De - liv - er us; for - give our sins, For Thy name's sake.
9. 10 Should na - tions say, "Where is their God?" Let us and them be shown Thou dost a - venge Thy serv - ants' blood Shed for Thine own.
10. 11 O let the pris' - ner's sighs as - cend Be - fore Thee there on high; Ac - cord - ing to Thy might pre - serve Those doomed to die.

11. [12] And to our neighbors' bosom turn,
In sevenfold reward,
All their reproach which they have cast
On Thee, O Lord.

12. [13] So we Thy people, Thine own flock,
Forever thank Thy name;
And to all generations we
Thy praise proclaim.

80A

PSALM 80

UNDE ET MEMORES. 10.10.10.10.10.10.
1. [1]O Shep - herd of all Is - ra - el, give ear,
2. [4]LORD God of hosts, how long dis - dain our prayer?
3. [8]A vine You brought up out of E - gypt's land;
Who like a flock of sheep leads Jo - seph on.
[5]Your peo - ple You have fed with bread of tears.
[9]You drove the na - tions out to give it room.
En - throned be - tween the cher - u - bim ap - pear.
A - bun - dant tears for drink You them pre - pare.
It took deep root; it spread on eve - ry hand;
[2]To E - phra - im, Ma - nas - seh, Ben - ja - min
[6]You've made us strife of foes and neigh - bors' jeers.
[10]It cov - ered moun - tains with its shade and bloom.

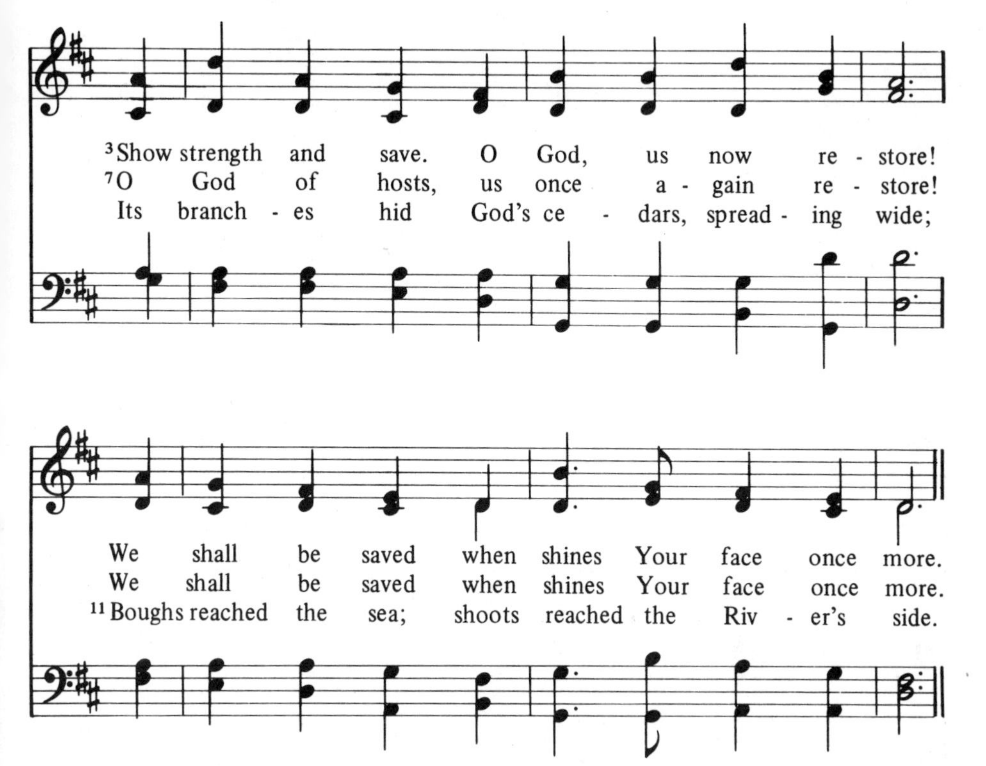
[3]Show strength and save. O God, us now re - store!
[7]O God of hosts, us once a - gain re - store!
Its branch - es hid God's ce - dars, spread - ing wide;
We shall be saved when shines Your face once more.
We shall be saved when shines Your face once more.
[11]Boughs reached the sea; shoots reached the Riv - er's side.

4. [12]Why have You broken down its circling wall,
   That all may pluck who pass along the way?
[13]The boar from out the woods roots round it all;
   The untamed beasts devour it as they stray.
[14]O God of hosts, return to us, we pray!
Look down from heaven and behold this day!

5. O visit and protect this vine of Yours,
   [15]The root You planted with Your own right hand,
This son whom You have strengthened for Yourself.
   [16]Burned up with fire, Your people cannot stand.
They are cut down; they perish when You look,
Because with Your appearance comes rebuke.

6. [17]Your hand be on the man of Your right hand,
   The son of man You've strengthened for Your own.
[18]Then we shall never turn away from You.
   Revive us! We will call Your name alone.
[19]LORD God of hosts, us once again restore!
We shall be saved when shines Your face once more.

80B
PSALM 80
BRYN CALFARIA. 88.88.88.98.
1. [1]Hear, O hear us, Is - rael's Shep-herd, Who drives forth Jo- seph
2. [4]O how long, LORD God of Ar -mies, Burns Your wrath at Your
3. [8]You brought forth a vine from E - gypt, And to plant it drove
like a flock! From the cher - u - bim, O shine forth!
peo - ple's prayer! [5]With the bread of tears You feed them,
na - tions out. [9]You made room to root it deep - ly,
Rise in val - or that we be saved! [2]So a - rise in
And full meas - ure of tears they drink! [6]Strife You make us
And it flour - ished and filled the land. [10]Then its shad - ow
sight of E - phraim, And Ma - nas - seh and Ben - ja - min!
to our neigh - bors, And our foes laugh at us in scorn!
wrapped the moun - tains, And its boughs hid the ce - dars tall!

³God, we pray, O turn us! Bring us back!
⁷God of Ar - mies, turn us! Bring us back!
¹¹To the sea it thrust great branch - es forth.

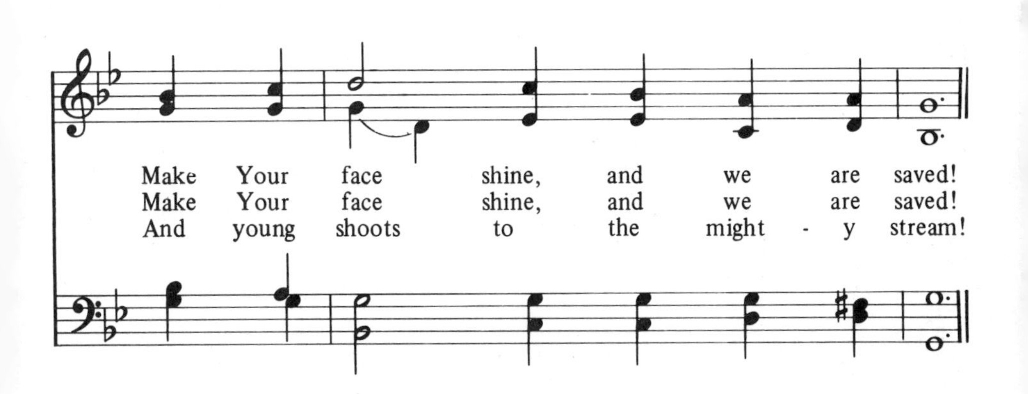
Make Your face shine, and we are saved!
Make Your face shine, and we are saved!
And young shoots to the might - y stream!

4. [12]Why have You torn down its fences?
It is plucked by each passing hand!
[13]Forest boars have gnawed upon it,
And wild creatures have pastured there!
[14]Turn again, O God of Armies!
Look from heav'n! Visit this Your vine!
[15]So uphold what Your right hand did plant,
And the son You raised up in strength!

5. [16]It is burned and hewn in pieces –
By Your frown will they be destroyed!
[17]Lay Your hand on him You favored,
Son of man that You raised in strength!
[18]Then from You we will not wander;
Make us live! We will call Your name!
[19]O LORD God of Armies, turn us back!
Make Your face shine, and we are saved!

81A PSALM 81:1-7

O JESU. 86.86.86.
1. [1]To God our Strength, to Ja - cob's God, A
2. [4]This is the law of Ja - cob's God, For
3. [6]I from his shoul - der took the load, His
song and shout now raise! [2]With psalm and tim-brel, harp and lute, A -
Is - rael His com- mand.[5]This wit-ness He for Jo - seph set When
hands from bur- dens freed. [7]You called Me when in trou - ble sore; I
wake to joy - ous praise![3]At each new moon the
smit - ing E - gypt's land. When there I heard a
saved you in your need, Tried you at streams of
trum - pets blow For sol - emn fes - tal days.
for - eign tongue I could not un - der - stand.
Mer - i - bah; In thun - der I gave heed.

PSALM 81:8-16 81B

KEOKUK. 86.86.86.
4. 8 Hear, O my peo - ple! Is - ra - el: 'Gainst
5. I brought you up from E - gypt's land; Your
6. 13 O that My peo - ple would Me hear And
7. 15 Then all who hate the LORD would cringe, In
you I'll tes - ti - fy. If on - ly you would hear Me now! 9 On
o - pened mouth I'll fill. 11 My peo-ple would not hear My voice; My
Is - rael choose My way! 14 How soon I would their foes sub-due! My
fear and dread a - bide. 16 But Is- rael with the fin - est wheat He'd
no strange god re - ly; Have none near you; don't
Is - rael spurned Me still. 12 I left them to their
out - stretched hand I'd lay Up - on their ad - ver -
al - ways keep sup - plied. And I with hon - ey
wor - ship them. 10 The LORD your God am I.
stub - born heart, To walk by their own will.
sar - ies all, To fill them with dis - may.
from the rock Would keep you sat - is - fied.

PSALM 82

OMNI DIE. 87.87.

1. [1]God is in His con - gre - ga - tion; Judge a- mong the gods He stands. [2]How long will you judge un - just - ly, Fa - vor - ing the wick - ed hands?
2. [3]Judge the des - ti - tute and or - phan, And the poor, dis - tressed de - -fend; [4]Free the des - ti - tute and need - y; Save them from the wick - ed's hand.
3. [5]These are they who have no know - ledge, To per - ceive no ef - fort make; They walk on in ut - ter dark - ness; All of earth's foun - da - tions shake.

4. [6]Gods you are, I have declared it,
Sons now of the Highest, all;
[7]Yet you'll die as common men die
And like any prince shall fall.

5. [8]Now, O God, arise we pray You,
And the earth to judgment call;
For You, as Your own possession,
Shall inherit nations all.

PSALM 83:1-12

83A

MONORA. C.M.D.
1. 1Rest not, O God, nor si - lent be! O God, hold not Thy peace!
2. 5A - gainst Thee they with one ac - cord In cov - e - nant u - nite:
3. 9Deal with them as with Mid - i - an, With Ja - bin, Sis - e - ra,
2Those hat - ing Thee ex - alt them - selves; Thy foes their roars in - crease.
6The tents of E - dom, Ish - ma - el, Mo - ab, the Hag - a - rite,
At Ki - shon's flood, 10at En - dor killed, And left as dung and straw.
3A - gainst Thy peo - ple they con - spire, A - gainst Thy loved ones plot:
7And Ge - bal, Am - mon, Am - a - lek, Phi - lis - tines, men of Tyre,
11Their chiefs like Or - eb, Ze - eb be, Zal - mun - na, Ze - bah proud:
4"Come, let us wipe their na - tion out! Is - rael re - mem - ber not!"
8And joined with them As - syr - i - a, To help Lot's race con - spire.
12"Let's take the pas - ture lands of God For ours!" they shout - ed loud.

83B PSALM 83:13-18

IRISH. C.M.

4. [13]O Thou my God, make them to be Like whirl - ing dust that flies,
5. [14]As fire a for - est burns, as flames That blaze on moun - tains high.
6. [16]With shame their fac - es fill, O LORD, That they may seek Thy name;
7. [18]So they shall know that Thou a lone – Je - ho - vah is Thy name –

Like stub - ble blown be - fore the wind When win - ter storms a - rise.
[15]So with Thy tem - pest them pur - sue, With Thy storm ter - ri - fy.
[17]Dis - graced and ter - ri - fied be they And per - ish in their shame.
That Thou art the Most High, the One O'er all the earth su - preme.

83C PSALM 83

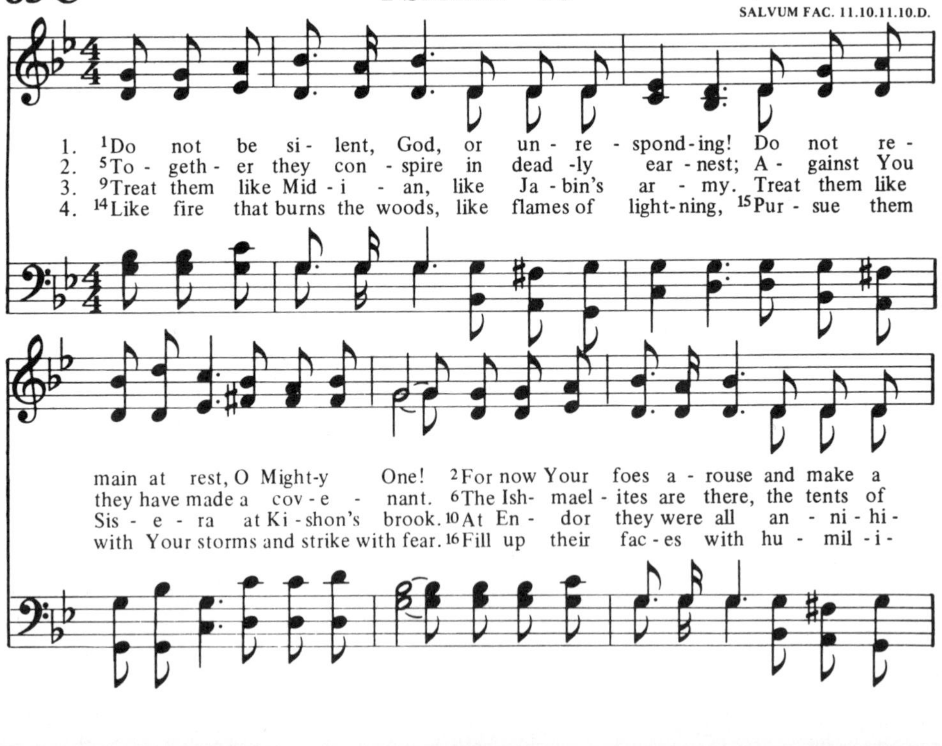

SALVUM FAC. 11.10.11.10.D.

1. [1]Do not be si - lent, God, or un - re - spond - ing! Do not re -
2. [5]To - geth - er they con - spire in dead - ly ear - nest; A - gainst You
3. [9]Treat them like Mid - i - an, like Ja - bin's ar - my. Treat them like
4. [14]Like fire that burns the woods, like flames of light - ning, [15]Pur - sue them

main at rest, O Might - y One! [2]For now Your foes a - rouse and make a
they have made a cov - e - nant. [6]The Ish - mael - ites are there, the tents of
Sis - e - ra at Ki - shon's brook. [10]At En - dor they were all an - ni - hi -
with Your storms and strike with fear. [16]Fill up their fac - es with hu - mil - i -

clam - or; Your bit-ter en - e - mies lift up the head. 3 A - gainst Your
E - dom, The men of Mo- ab with the Hag- a - renes. 7 See Ge- bal,
lat - ed, And they be- came as dung up - on the ground. 11 Like O - reb
a - tion, And let them seek Your name, Je- ho-vah, then. 17 Let them be
peo - ple now they plot in se - cret; They meet to work a - gainst
Am -a - lek, with men of Am - mon; Be- hold Phi - lis - ti - a
make their chiefs, their lords like Ze - bah! 12 Who thought they would pos-sess
ter - ri -fied and shamed for - ev - er, And let them be dis- mayed
Your hid - den ones. 4 They say, "Let us go up and end their
and them of Tyre. 8 For As - shur too has come and joins their
the land of God. 13 My God, O make them be like whirl -ing
and be de - stroyed! 18 Let them know You a - lone–You are Je -
na - tion. The name of Is - ra - el shall be no more!"
forc - es; They are the pow - er of the sons of Lot.
dust - clouds; Make them like bits of chaff be - fore the wind.
ho - vah – You are the One Most High o'er all the earth.

84A PSALM 84:1-6

STELLA. 88.88.88.

1. [1]How love - ly, LORD of hosts, to me The tab - er - nac - les
2. [3]The spar - row has her place of rest; The swal - low through Thy
3. [4]Blest they who in Thy house a - bide; To Thee they ev - er

of Thy grace! [2]O how I long, yes, faint to see Je-
kind - ly care Has found where she may build her nest And
ren - der praise. [5]Blest they who in Thy strength con - fide, And

ho - vah's courts, His dwell - ing place! My heart and flesh with
brood her young in safe - ty there. Thine al - tars as my
in whose heart are pil - grims' ways. [6]They make the vale of
joy draw nigh As to the liv - ing God I cry.
rest I sing, O LORD of hosts, my God, my King.
tears a spring, With showers of bless - ings cov - er - ing.

PSALM 84:7-12

MELITA. 88.88.88.
4. 7Ad - vanc-ing still from strength to strength They go where oth - er
5. 9Look Thou, O God, up - on our Shield; The face of Thine A-
6. 11For God the LORD is shield and sun; The LORD will grace and
pil - grims trod, Till each to Zi - on comes at length And
noint - ed see; 10One day with - in Thy courts will yield More
glo - ry give. No good will He with - hold from one Who
stands be - fore the face of God. 8LORD God of hosts, my
good than thou - sands with - out Thee. I'd rath - er stand near
does up - right - ly walk and live. 12O LORD of hosts, how
plead - ing hear; O Ja - cob's God, to me give ear.
my God's house Than dwell in tents of wick - ed - ness.
blest is he Who plac - es all his trust in Thee!

84C PSALM 84

CHANT E.

1. [1]How amiable are Thy / taber/nacles, //
   O / LORD / of / hosts! //

   [2]My soul longeth, yea, even fainteth, for the / courts · of the / LORD: //
   My heart and my flesh crieth / out · for the / living / God.

2. [3]Yea, the sparrow has found a house, and the swallow a nest for herself, where she may / lay her / young, //
   Even Thine altars, O LORD of / hosts, my / King, · and my / God. //

   [4]Bless-ed are they that / dwell · in Thy / house: //
   They will / be still / praising / Thee.

3. [5]Bless-ed is the man whose / strength · is in / Thee; //
   In whose / heart · are the / ways of / them, //

   [6]Who passing through the valley of Baca / make · it a / well; //
   The / rain also / filleth the / pool.

4. [7]They go from / strength to / strength; //
   Every one of them in / Zion ap/peareth before / God. //

   [8]O LORD God of hosts, / hear my / prayer: //
   Give / ear, O / God of / Jacob.

5. [9]Behold, O / God our / Shield, //
   And look upon the / face of / Thine a/nointed. //

   [10]For a day in Thy courts is better / than a / thousand. //
   I had rather be a doorkeeper in the house of my God, than to / dwell · in the / tents of / wickedness.

6. [11]For the LORD God is a sun and shield: the LORD will give / grace and / glory. //
   No good thing will He withhold from / them that / walk up/rightly. //

   [12]O / LORD of / hosts, //
   Bless-ed is the / man who / trusteth in / Thee.

For "AN INTRODUCTION TO CHANTING" please turn to page 440.

PSALM 85:1-7

BERA. L.M.

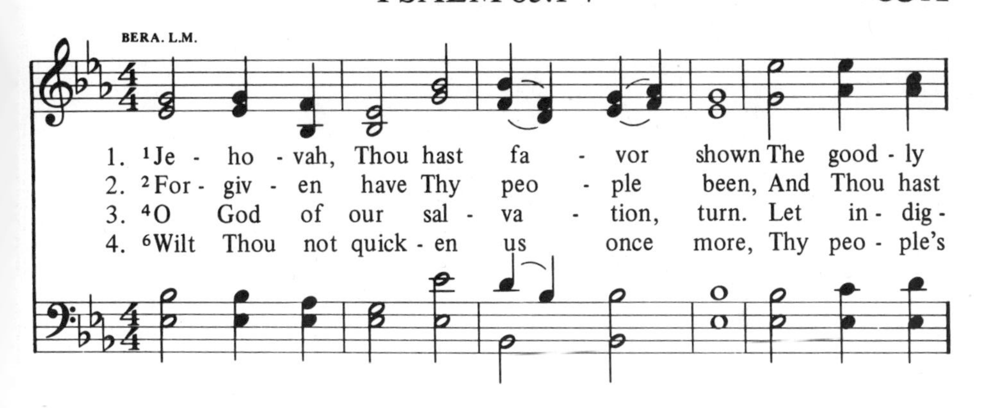
1. ¹Je - ho - vah, Thou hast fa - vor shown The good - ly
2. ²For - giv - en have Thy peo - ple been, And Thou hast
3. ⁴O God of our sal - va - tion, turn. Let in - dig -
4. ⁶Wilt Thou not quick - en us once more, Thy peo - ple's

land which is Thine own; And Ja - cob from his
cov - ered all their sin; ³A - way hast tak - en
na - tion cease to burn. ⁵Wilt Thou for - ev - er
joy in Thee re - store? ⁷O LORD, to us Thy

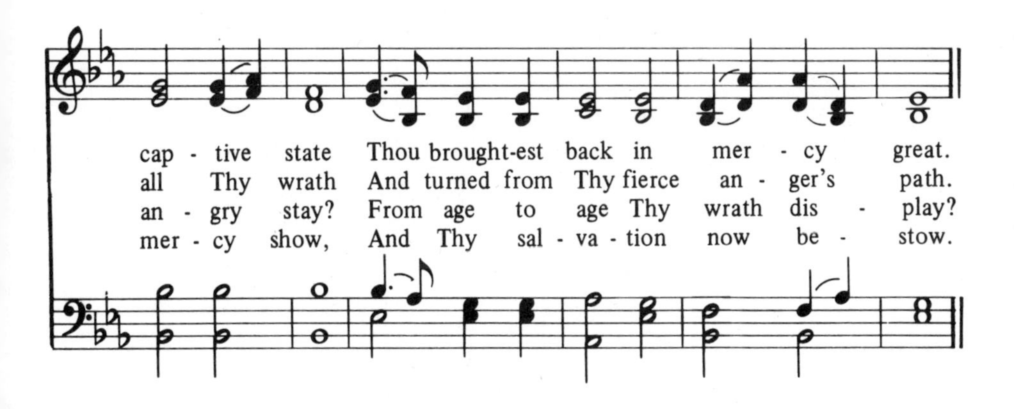
cap - tive state Thou brought-est back in mer - cy great.
all Thy wrath And turned from Thy fierce an - ger's path.
an - gry stay? From age to age Thy wrath dis - play?
mer - cy show, And Thy sal - va - tion now be - stow.

85B

PSALM 85:8-13

BRADBURY. L.M.
5. 8 I'll hear what God the LORD will speak, Ev'n peace to
6. 9 His sav - ing help is sure - ly near To those who
7. 10 To - geth - er met are truth and grace, While right - eous -
8. 12 The LORD will give us what is good; Our land shall

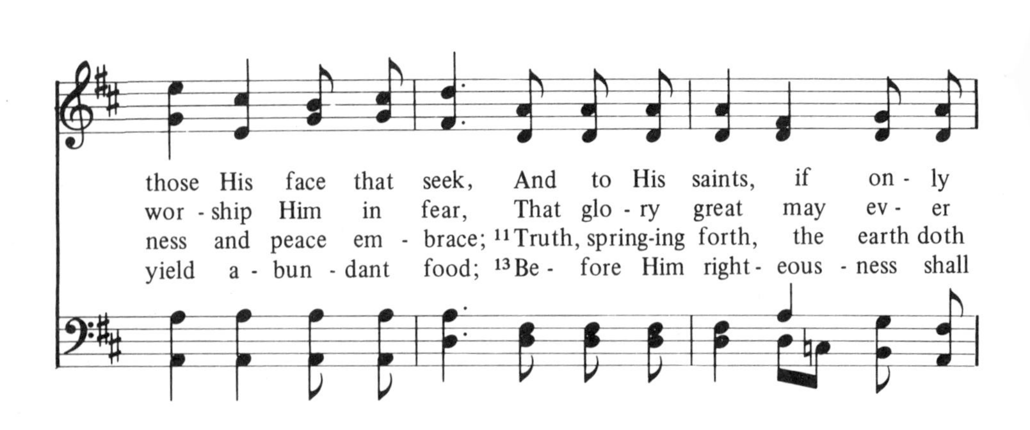
those His face that seek, And to His saints, if on - ly
wor - ship Him in fear, That glo - ry great may ev - er
ness and peace em - brace; 11 Truth, spring-ing forth, the earth doth
yield a - bun - dant food; 13 Be - fore Him right - eous - ness shall

they No more in fol - ly's path will stray.
dwell With - in the land of Is - ra - el.
crown, And right - eous - ness from heav'n looks down.
go, And in His steps our path - way show.

PSALM 86:1-10

86A

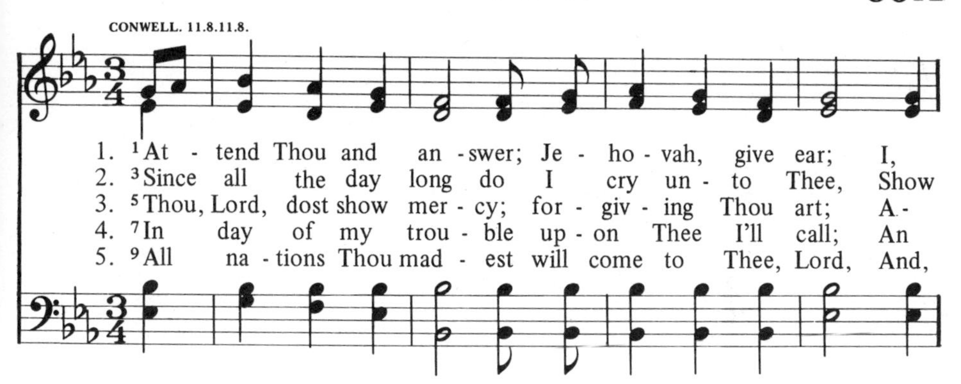

CONWELL. 11.8.11.8.
1. [1]At - tend Thou and an - swer; Je - ho - vah, give ear; I,
2. [3]Since all the day long do I cry un - to Thee, Show
3. [5]Thou, Lord, dost show mer - cy; for - giv - ing Thou art; A -
4. [7]In day of my trou - ble up - on Thee I'll call; An
5. [9]All na - tions Thou mad - est will come to Thee, Lord, And,

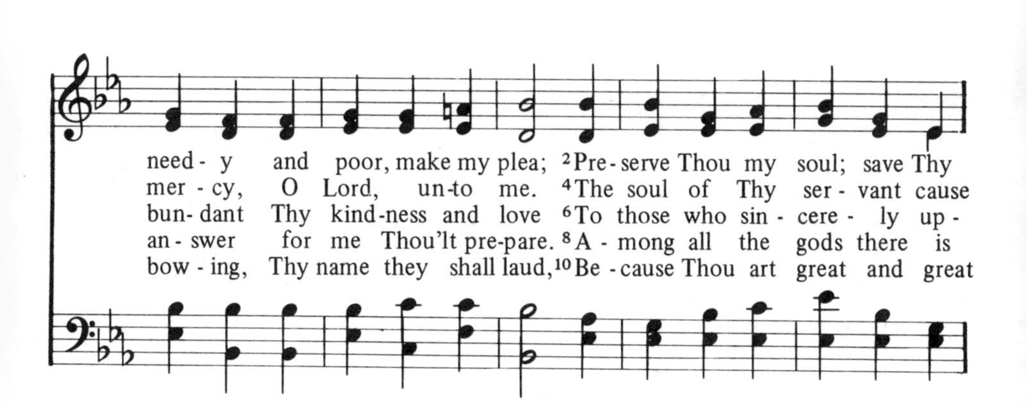

need - y and poor, make my plea; [2]Pre - serve Thou my soul; save Thy
mer - cy, O Lord, un-to me. [4]The soul of Thy ser - vant cause
bun - dant Thy kind-ness and love [6]To those who sin - cere - ly up -
an - swer for me Thou'lt pre-pare. [8]A - mong all the gods there is
bow - ing, Thy name they shall laud, [10]Be - cause Thou art great and great

ser - vant, O God, For god - ly and trust - ing is he.
Thou to re - joice; I lift up my soul un - to Thee.
on Thee do call. My voice, LORD, at - tend from a - bove.
none like to Thee; And no works with Thine can com - pare.
won - ders hast done; For Thou and Thou on - ly art God.

86B PSALM 86:11-17

DELPHINE. 11.8.11.8.
6. 11 Thy way teach me, LORD; I will walk in Thy truth; U-
7. 13 For great are Thy love and Thy kind-ness to me. My
8. 15 But Thou, Lord, art mer - ci - ful; gra - cious Thou art, A-
9. The son of Thy hand - maid re - deem by Thy grace; 17 A

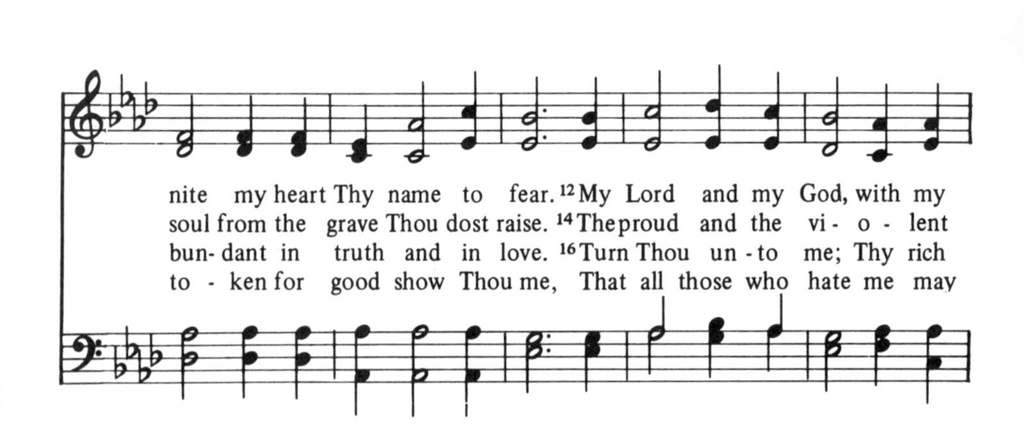
nite my heart Thy name to fear. 12 My Lord and my God, with my
soul from the grave Thou dost raise. 14 The proud and the vi - o - lent
bun- dant in truth and in love. 16 Turn Thou un - to me; Thy rich
to - ken for good show Thou me, That all those who hate me may

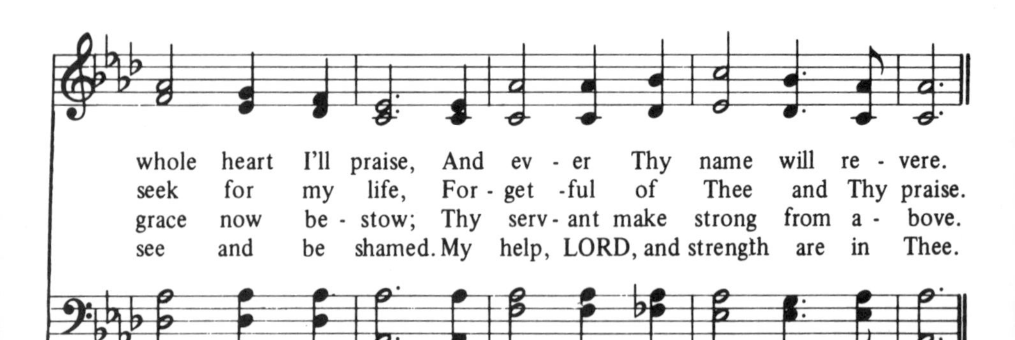
whole heart I'll praise, And ev - er Thy name will re - vere.
seek for my life, For - get -ful of Thee and Thy praise.
grace now be - stow; Thy serv - ant make strong from a - bove.
see and be shamed. My help, LORD, and strength are in Thee.

PSALM 87

ST. LEONARD. C.M.
1. [1]Up - on the ho - ly hills the LORD Has His foun - da - tion laid; [2]He loves the gates of Zi - on more Than dwell - ings Ja - cob made.
2. [3]O cit - y of our God, there are Things glo - rious said of thee. [4]I'll men - tion E - gypt, Bab - y - lon, A - mong those know - ing me.
3. In - clude the land of Pal - es - tine; Let Tyre the sur - vey share, With dis - tant E - thi - o - pi - a: "This is a man born there!"

4. [5]And so of Zion it is said,
"Each one was born in her;"
And He that is Himself Most High,
He has established her.

5. [6]The LORD, when listing peoples, notes,
"This is a man born there!"
[7]And singers with their minstrels say,
"Our fountains in thee are."

88A

PSALM 88:1-9

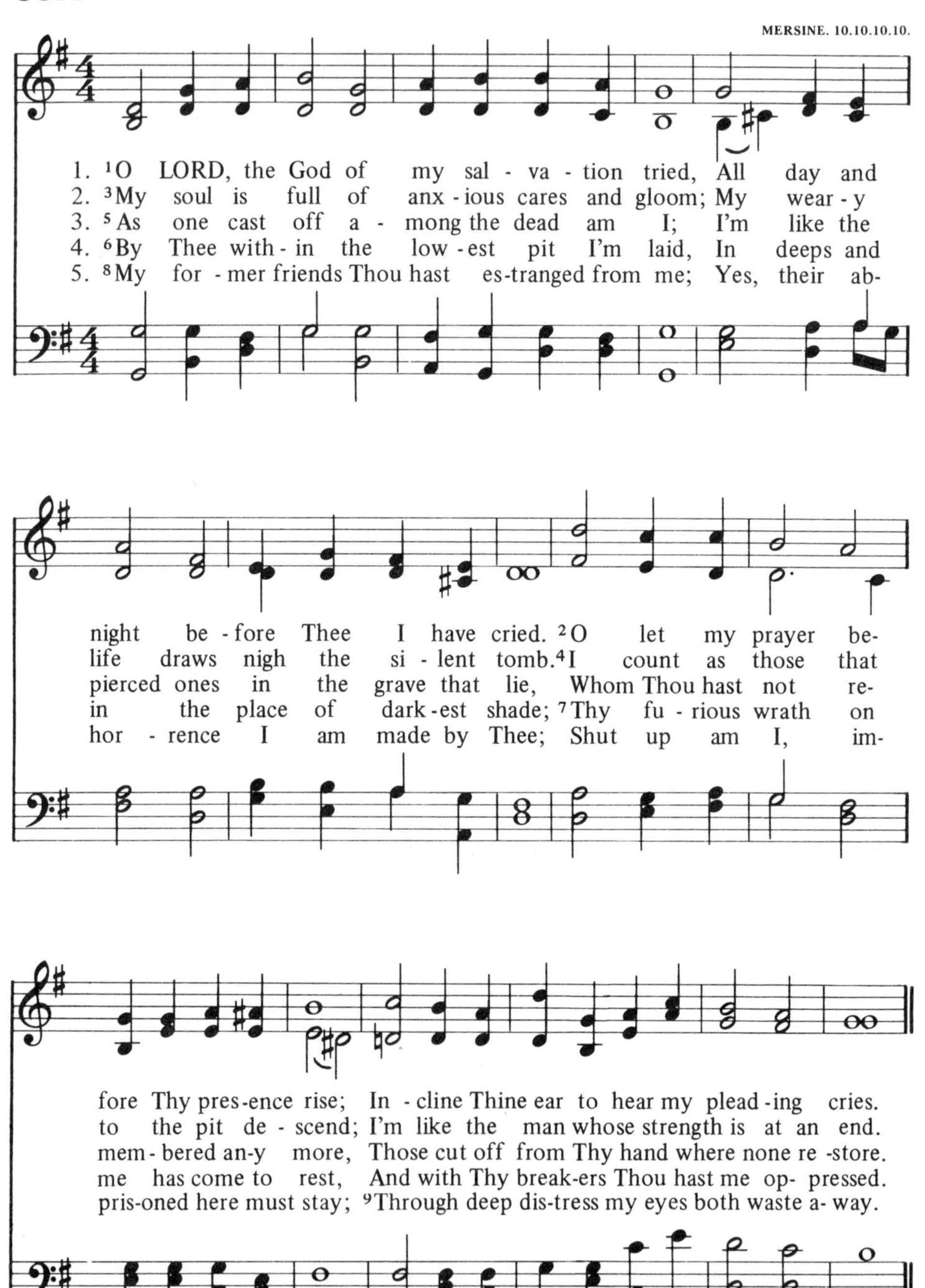
MERSINE. 10.10.10.10.
1. ¹O LORD, the God of my sal - va - tion tried, All day and
2. ³My soul is full of anx - ious cares and gloom; My wear - y
3. ⁵As one cast off a - mong the dead am I; I'm like the
4. ⁶By Thee with - in the low - est pit I'm laid, In deeps and
5. ⁸My for - mer friends Thou hast es-tranged from me; Yes, their ab-
night be - fore Thee I have cried. ²O let my prayer be-
life draws nigh the si - lent tomb.⁴I count as those that
pierced ones in the grave that lie, Whom Thou hast not re-
in the place of dark - est shade; ⁷Thy fu - rious wrath on
hor - rence I am made by Thee; Shut up am I, im-
fore Thy pres-ence rise; In - cline Thine ear to hear my plead - ing cries.
to the pit de - scend; I'm like the man whose strength is at an end.
mem - bered an-y more, Those cut off from Thy hand where none re -store.
me has come to rest, And with Thy break-ers Thou hast me op- pressed.
pris-oned here must stay; ⁹Through deep dis-tress my eyes both waste a- way.

PSALM 88:9-18

88B

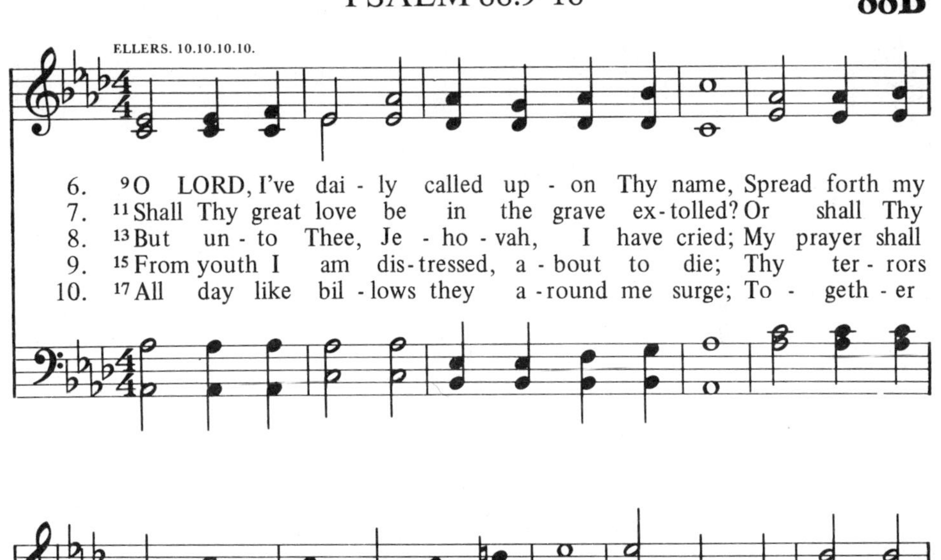
ELLERS. 10.10.10.10.
6. 9 O LORD, I've dai - ly called up - on Thy name, Spread forth my
7. 11 Shall Thy great love be in the grave ex - tolled? Or shall Thy
8. 13 But un - to Thee, Je - ho - vah, I have cried; My prayer shall
9. 15 From youth I am dis - tressed, a - bout to die; Thy ter - rors
10. 17 All day like bil - lows they a - round me surge; To - geth - er

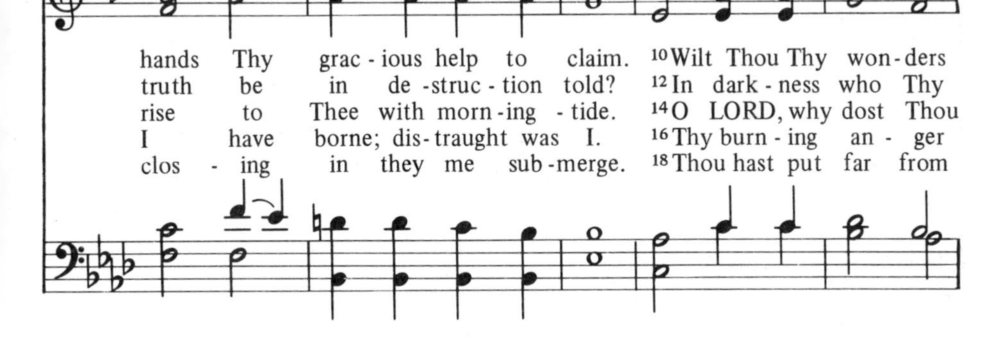
hands Thy grac - ious help to claim. 10 Wilt Thou Thy won - ders
truth be in de - struc - tion told? 12 In dark - ness who Thy
rise to Thee with morn - ing - tide. 14 O LORD, why dost Thou
I have borne; dis - traught was I. 16 Thy burn - ing an - ger
clos - ing in they me sub - merge. 18 Thou hast put far from

make the dead to know? And shall the dead a - rise Thy praise to show?
won - ders will con - fess, Where mem'-ries fade make known Thy right-eous-ness?
cast my soul from Thee? Why dost Thou hide Thy grac - ious face from me?
o - ver me has passed; Thy ter - rors all have cut me off at last.
me each lov - er, friend, And my ac - quaint - anc - es in dark - ness end.

89A PSALM 89:1-5

NEW JERUSALEM. C.M.
1. [1]The lov - ing - kind - ness of the LORD For - ev - er I will sing; Thy faith- ful - ness to eve - ry age My mouth in song shall bring.
2. [2]"For mer - cy shall be built", said I, "For - ev - er to en - dure; And in the heav'ns Thy faith - ful - ness Thou wilt es - tab - lish sure."
3. [3]"I've made a cov - e - nant with him Who is My chos - en one; To Da - vid, who My ser - vant is, What I have sworn be done:

4. [4]"Thy seed I will establish firm,
Forever to remain;
And unto generations all
Thy throne I will maintain."

5. [5]The praises of Thy wonders, LORD,
The heavens shall express,
In the assembly of the saints
Thy faithfulness confess.

PSALM 89:6-14

89B

NOEL. C.M.D.
6. 6Who with the LORD can be com-pared In all the loft - y sky?
7. 8Je - ho- vah, God of hosts, who is Like Thee, the LORD of might?
8. 10And Thou hast Ra - hab bruised like one Be - set with wound-ing blows;
9. 12Thou hast cre - at - ed north and south;From Thee their be - ing came;
And who a-mong the sons of might Is like the LORD Most High?
Sur - round-ing Thee on eve - ry side Are faith - ful - ness and right.
Thou with the arm of Thy great strengthHast scat- tered all Thy foes.
Mount Ta- bor and Mount Her-mon both Re - joice in Thy great name.
7With - in the coun-cil of His saints A God to be re -vered;
9For o'er the swell-ing of the sea Thou ru - lest by Thy will,
11The heav - ens all be - long to Thee; The earth is all Thine own.
13Thou hast an arm of strength; Thy hand Is strong, Thy right hand high.
A - bove all them sur - round - ing Him Most great- ly to be feared.
And when its surg- ing bil - lows rise Thou bid -dest them be still.
The world with all that it con-tains Hast Thou set up a - lone.
14On right and jus - tice rests Thy throne,While grace and truth are nigh.

89C
PSALM 89:6-14
GOD REVERED. C.M.D.
6. [6]Who with the LORD can be com - pared In all the loft - y sky? And who a - mong the sons of might Is like the LORD Most High?
7. [8]Je - ho - vah, God of hosts, who is Like Thee, the LORD of might? Sur- round - ing Thee on eve - ry side Are faith - ful - ness and right.
8. [10]And Thou hast Ra - hab bruised like one Be - set with wound - ing blows; Thou with the arm of Thy great strength Hast scat - tered all Thy foes.
9. [12]Thou hast cre - at - ed north and south; From Thee their be - ing came; Mount Ta - bor and Mount Her - mon both Re- joice in Thy great name.

7 With - in the coun - cil of His saints A
9 For o'er the swell - ing of the sea Thou
11 The heav - ens all be - long to Thee; The
13 Thou hast an arm of strength; Thy hand Is
God to be re - vered; A - bove all them sur-
rul - est by Thy will, And when its surg - ing
earth is all Thine own. The world with all that
strong, Thy right hand high. 14 On right and jus - tice
round - ing Him Most great - ly to be feared.
bil - lows rise Thou bid - dest them be still.
it con - tains Hast Thou set up a - lone.
rests Thy throne, While grace and truth are nigh.

89D PSALM 89:15-18

ST. MAGNUS. C.M.

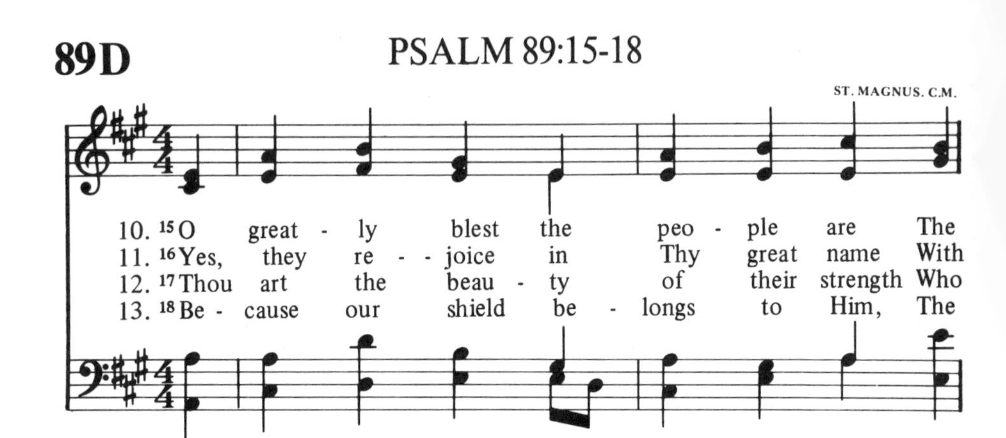
10. 15 O great - ly blest the peo - ple are The
11. 16 Yes, they re - - joice in Thy great name With
12. 17 Thou art the beau - ty of their strength Who
13. 18 Be - cause our shield be - longs to Him, The

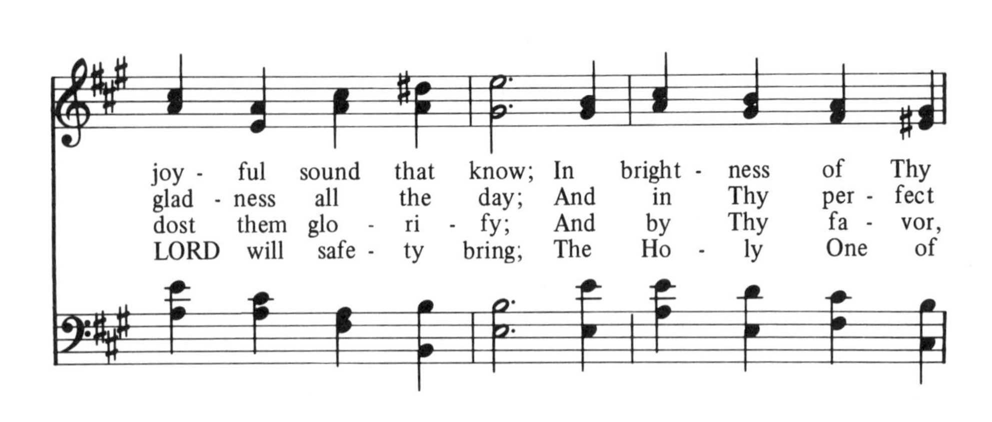
joy - ful sound that know; In bright - ness of Thy
glad - ness all the day; And in Thy per - fect
dost them glo - ri - fy; And by Thy fa - vor,
LORD will safe - ty bring; The Ho - ly One of

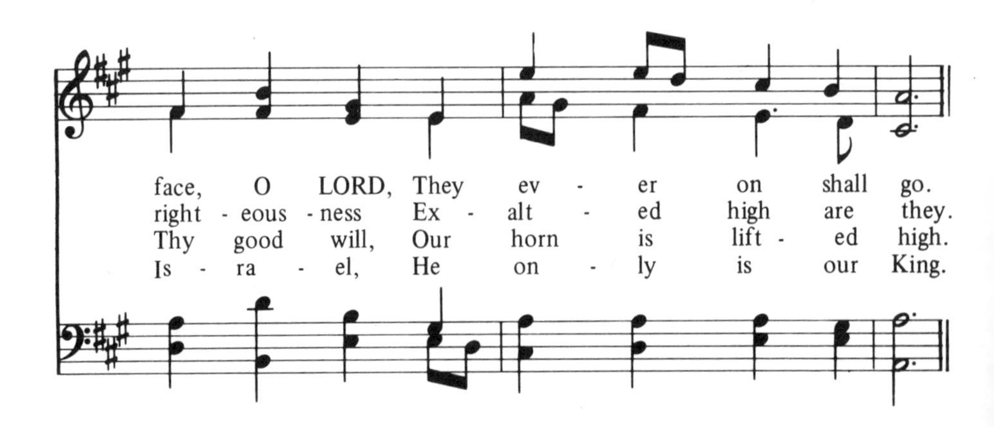
face, O LORD, They ev - er on shall go.
right - eous - ness Ex - alt - ed high are they.
Thy good will, Our horn is lift - ed high.
Is - ra - el, He on - ly is our King.

PSALM 89:19-29

89E

HALIFAX. C.M.D.
14. 19 Thou to Thy saints in dreams didst say, "I have laid help up - on
15. 22 "No foe shall fee ex - tract from him, No wick- ed one him wrong.
16. 25 "I al - so will im - pose his hand Up - on the roll - ing sea;
17. 27 "I'll make him My first - born, a- bove All kings of eve - ry land;
A might - y one; I raised him up, One from the peo - ple drawn.
23 His ad - ver - sar - ies I will crush And smite his hat - ers strong.
And on the might-y riv - ers all I'll make his right hand be.
28 My love for him I'll ev - er keep; My cov - 'nant firm shall stand.
20 My serv - ant Da - vid I have found, With oil a - noint - ed him.
24 My faith - ful - ness and stead-fast love With him shall ev - er be,
26 'Thou art my Fa - ther and my God,' He un - to Me shall cry;
29 And I will al - so make his seed For- ev - er to en - dure;
21 With him My hand es - tab - lished is; My arm will strength-en him.
And in My name his horn, raised up, Shall flour - ish glo - rious - ly.
'The rock of my sal - va - tion sure, On Whom I will re - ly.'
And as the days of heav - en are, His throne shall stand se - cure."

89F PSALM 89:30-37

COVENANTERS. C.M.
18. 30 "But if his sons for - sake My law, Walk not as I or - dain; 31 If My com - mand - ments they'll not keep, My stat - utes will pro - fane;
19. 32 "I'll vis - it their trans - gres - sions then, On them My rod will lay; And I will their in - i - qui - ty With heav - y stripes re - pay.
20. 33 "Yet I'll not take My love from him, Nor break My faith - ful - ness; 34 I'll not pro - fane My cov - e - nant Nor change My prom - is - es.

21. [35] "Once by My holiness I've sworn;
To David I'll not lie;
[36] His seed and throne shall still endure
While lasts the sun on high.

22. [37] "It like the moon shall ever be
Established most secure;
And for a witness in the sky
It ever shall endure."

PSALM 89:38-45

NORWICH. C.M.
23. [38] But Thine a - noint - ed Thou hast spurned, In
24. [40] And Thou hast brok - en all his walls, And
25. [42] Thou hast raised up his foes' right hand And
26. [44] His glo - ry Thou hast made to cease, His

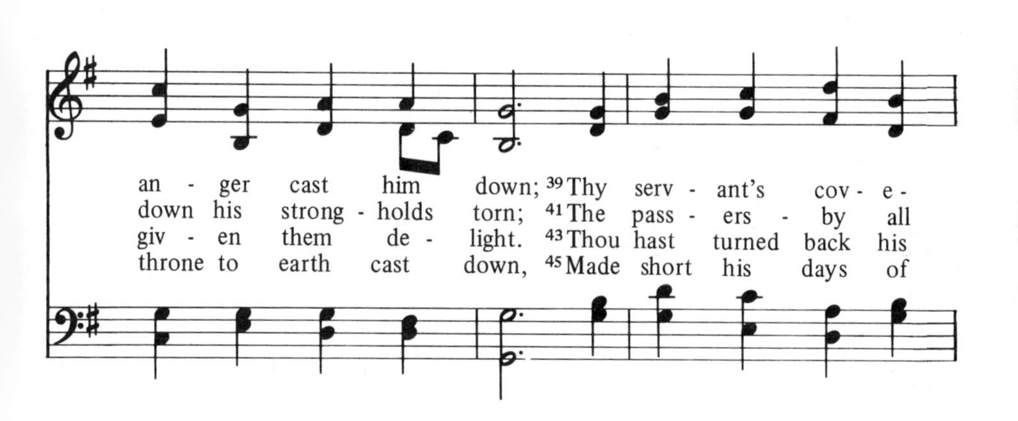
an - ger cast him down; [39] Thy serv - ant's cov - e -
down his strong - holds torn; [41] The pass - ers - by all
giv - en them de - light. [43] Thou hast turned back his
throne to earth cast down, [45] Made short his days of

nant ab - horred, Pro-faned to earth his crown.
plun - der him; He is his neigh - bors' scorn.
sword, no more Hast made him stand to fight.
youth, with shame Hast cov - ered his re - nown.

89H PSALM 89:46-52

EMMANUEL. C.M.
27. 46 How long, LORD, wilt Thou hide Thy - self? Thy wrath still burn - ing be? 47 Re - call my life - span! Why hast Thou Made men for van - i - ty?
28. 48 Who is the man now liv - ing here That death shall nev - er see? Or from the power of neth - er depths Who can his soul set free?
29. 49 Where are Thy lov - ing - kind - ness - es That once, O Lord, were there, When in Thy last - ing faith - ful - ness To Da - vid Thou didst swear?
30. 50 Re - mem - ber, Lord, Thy ser - vants' shame; How in my heart I bear All those re - proach - es cast on them By peo - ples eve - ry - where;

31. [51] Remember the reproaching, LORD,
Thine enemies have done,
How they reproached the very steps
Of Thine anointed one.

32. [52] All blessings to Jehovah be
Ascribed forever then;
For evermore, so let it be.
Amen, yes, and Amen.

89I PSALM 89:52

GAMMA. Irregular.
Bless - ed be the LORD for - ev - er! A - men and A - men.

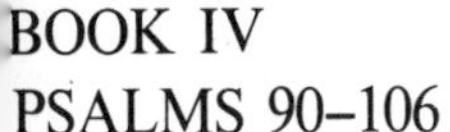

PSALM 90:1–12

90A

MARTYRDOM. C.M.

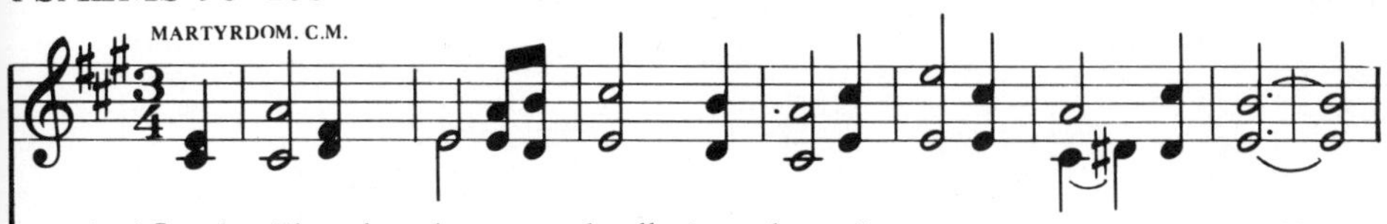

1. [1] Lord, Thou hast been our dwell - ing place In gen - er - a - tions all,
2. Ere ev - er Thou hadst formed the earth, And all the world a - broad;
3. [3] And yet Thou to de - struc - tion dost Man that is mor - tal turn;

[2] Be - fore Thou ev - er hadst brought forth The moun - tains great or small;
Ev'n Thou from ev - er - last - ing art To ev - er - last - ing God.
Thou un - to them dost say, "A - gain, Ye sons of men, re - turn."

4. [4] Because a thousand years appear
No more before Thy sight
Than yesterday when it is past,
Or than a watch by night.

5. [5] As with an overflowing flood
Thou sweepest them away;
They are as sleep, and as the grass
That grows at morn are they.

6. [6] At morn it flourishes and grows,
Cut down at eve doth fade.
[7] For by Thine anger we're consumed;
Thy wrath makes us afraid.

7. [8] All our iniquities Thou dost
Before Thy presence place,
And set our secret faults before
The brightness of Thy face.

8. [9] For in Thine anger all our days
Pass onward to an end;
And as a tale that has been told
So all our years we spend.

9. [10] Threescore and ten years are the sum
Of all the days we see;
Or if by reason of more strength
In some fourscore they be;

10. Their pride is grief and vanity,
Soon gone; we've flown away.
[11] Who knows the power of all Thy wrath
And fears Thy fury's sway?

11. [12] O teach Thou us to think upon
And number all our days,
That we may bring to Thee a heart
Confirmed in wisdom's ways.

90B PSALM 90:13–17

BEATITUDO. C.M.
12. 13 Turn yet a - gain to us, O LORD;
13. 14 Each morn - ing with Thy kind - ly grace
14. 15 Ac - cord - ing as the days have been
How long thus shall it be? Let it re - pent Thee
Us ear - ly sat - is - fy, That we may shout for
Where - in we grief have had, The years where- in we
now for those That serv - ants are to Thee.
joy and sing As all our days pass by.
ill have seen, Now do Thou make us glad.

15. [16] Thy work unto Thy servants done
Again make them to see,
And let Thy majesty and power
Upon their children be.

16. [17] So let the beauty of the LORD
Our God upon us rest.
Our handiworks establish Thou;
Our work by Thee be blest.

ST. CATHERINE. 88.88.88.
1. 1Lord, Thou hast been our dwell-ing place Through all the a - ges of our race.
2. 3Thou turn- est man to dust a - gain, And say'st, "Re-turn, ye sons of men."
3. 5Thou with a flood hast swept men on; They like a sleep are quick - ly gone.
4. 7For by Thine an - ger we're con-sumed, And by Thy wrath to ter - ror doomed.
2Be - fore the moun-tains had their birth, Or ev - er Thou hadst formed the earth,
4As yes-ter - day when past ap - pears, So are to Thee a thou - sand years;
They are like grass which grows each morn; 6Its blades of green the fields a - dorn.
8Our sins Thou in Thy sight dost place, Our se - cret faults be - fore Thy face;
From years which no be - gin-ning had To years un- end- ing, Thou art God.
They like a day are in Thy sight, Yes, like a pass- ing watch by night.
At morn its sprouts and blos-soms rise; At eve, cut down, it with- ered lies.
9So in Thy wrath our days we end, And like a sigh our years we spend.

5. 10For some life's years are seventy;
 Perhaps the strong may eighty see;
 Their best involves but toil and woe;
 All quickly ends. How soon we go!
 11Who has Thine anger understood?
 Who fears Thy fury as he should?

6. 12O teach Thou us to count our days
 And set our hearts on wisdom's ways.
 13How long, O LORD? Return! Repent,
 And toward Thy servants now relent.
 14Each morning fill us with Thy grace;
 We'll sing for joy through all our days.

7. 15According to the days we spent
 Beneath affliction Thou hast sent,
 And all the years we evil knew,
 Now make us glad, our joy renew.
 16Thy work in all Thy servants show;
 Thy glory on their sons bestow.

8. 17On us let there be shed abroad
 The beauty of the LORD our God.
 Our handiwork upon us be
 Established evermore by Thee.
 Yes, let our handiwork now be
 Established evermore by Thee.

90D PSALM 90

ST. CHRYSOSTOM. 88.88.88.

1. [1]Lord, Thou hast been our dwell-ing place Through all the a - ges of our race.
2. [3]Thou turn-est man to dust a -gain, And say'st, "Re -turn, ye sons of men."
3. [5]Thou with a flood hast swept men on; They like a sleep are quick- ly gone.
4. [7]For by Thine an - ger we're con-sumed, And by Thy wrath to ter - ror doomed
[2]Be - fore the moun-tains had their birth, Or ev - er Thou hadst formed the earth,
[4]As yes- ter - day when past ap- pears, So are to Thee a thou -sand years;
They are like grass which grows each morn; [6]Its blades of green the fields a - dorn.
[8]Our sins Thou in Thy sight dost place, Our se - cret faults be - fore Thy face;
From years which no be - gin - ning had To years un - end- ing, Thou art God.
They like a day are in Thy sight, Yes, like a pass-ing watch by night.
At morn its sprouts and blos-soms rise; At eve cut down it with - ered lies.
[9]So in Thy wrath our days we end, And like a sigh our years we spend.

5. [10]For some life's years are seventy;
   Perhaps the strong may eighty see;
   Their best involves but toil and woe;
   All quickly ends. How soon we go!
   [11]Who has Thine anger understood?
   Who fears Thy fury as he should?

6. [12]O teach Thou us to count our days
   And set our hearts on wisdom's ways.
   [13]How long, O LORD? Return! Repent,
   And toward Thy servants now relent.
   [14]Each morning fill us with Thy grace;
   We'll sing for joy through all our days.

7. [15]According to the days we spent
   Beneath affliction Thou hast sent,
   And all the years we evil knew,
   Now make us glad, our joy renew.
   [16]Thy work in all Thy servants show;
   Thy glory on their sons bestow.

8. [17]On us let there be shed abroad
   The beauty of the LORD our God.
   Our handiwork upon us be
   Established evermore by Thee.
   Yes, let our handiwork now be
   Established evermore by Thee.

PSALM 91

91A

HYFRYDOL. 87.87.D.
1. [1]Who with God Most High finds shel- ter In th'Al - might- y's shad - ow hides.
2. God's own truth, your shield and buck- ler: [5]You will fear no ill by night,
3. [9]You have made the LORD your ref - uge, God Most High your dwell - ing - place;
4. [13]You shall tram - ple ser - pents, li - ons, Tread on all your dead - ly foes.
[2]To the LORD I'll say, "My Ref-uge!" In my God my trust a - bides.
Nor the shafts in day- light fly - ing, [6]Nor dis - ease that shuns the light,
[10]Noth-ing e - vil shall be - fall you; In your tent no scourge you'll face.
[14]For his love to Me I'll save him, Keep him, for My name he knows;
[3]From the fowl- er's snare He'll save you, From the dead - ly pes - ti - lence;
Nor the plague that wastes at noon- day. [7]At your side ten thou - sand fall;
[11]He will an - gels charge to keep you, Guard you well in all your ways.
[15]When he calls Me I will an- swer, Save and hon - or him will I.
[4]Cov - er you with out - spread pin - ions, Make His wings your con - fi - dence.
[8]You will on - ly see this judg - ment Which re - wards the wick - ed all.
[12]In their hands they will up - hold you Lest your foot a stone should graze.
[16]I will show him my sal - va - tion, With long life will sat - is - fy.

From THE ENGLISH HYMNAL by permission of the Oxford University Press.

91B PSALM 91:1–4

WOODWORTH. L.M.
1. [1]The man al - lowed to oc - cu - py The se - cret place of God Most High Shall with Al - might - y God a - bide, And in His shad - ow safe - ly hide.
2. [2]I there - fore of the LORD will say, "He is my ref - uge and my stay; My cit - a - del of strength is He – My God in Whom my trust shall be."
3. [3]For He shall with His watch - ful care Pre - serve thee from the fowl - er's snare; Yes, He shall be thy sure de - fense A - gainst the dead - ly pes - ti - lence.
4. [4]His out - spread pin - ions shall thee hide; Be - neath His wings shalt thou con - fide. His faith - ful - ness shall ev - er be A shield and buck - ler un - to thee.
91C
PSALM 91:5–10
O SALUTARIS. L.M.
5. [5]No night-ly ter - rors shall a - larm; No dead-ly shaft by day shall harm,
6. [7]At thy right hand ten thou-sand fall; No harm shall come to thee at all.
7. [9]Be-cause thy home is God Most High, The LORD, Who is my ref-uge nigh,

6Nor pes- ti - lence that walks by night, Nor plagues that waste in noon- day light.
8Thou on - ly with thine eyes shalt see What wick -ed men's re - ward shall be.
10No e - vil shall on thee be sent, Nor an - y plague come nigh thy tent.
PSALM 91:11–16
91D
GARDINER. L.M.
8. 11Be - cause His an - gels He com -mands To bear thee
9. 13Thou shalt tread down the li - on's wrath And crush the
10. 14Be - cause he set his love on Me, From dan - ger
safe - ly in their hands, 12To guard thy ways, lest left a -
ad - der in thy path; On li - ons young, on ser - pents
I will set him free. Be-cause to him My name is
lone, Thou dash thy foot a - gainst a stone.
dread. Thy tram - pling feet un - harmed shall tread.
known, On high I'll set him as Mine own.

11. 15As oft as he shall call to Me,
Most gracious shall My answer be.
I will be with him in distress,
And in his troubles I will bless.

12. Yes, great salvation give will I,
16With length of life will satisfy.
15On him I honor will bestow,
16To him My full salvation show.

92A PSALM 92:1–8

THANKSGIVING. C.M.D.

1. [1]To ren - der thanks to Thee, O LORD, It is a come - ly thing,
2. [3]Up - on a ten - stringed in - stru - ment And on a psal - ter - y,
3. [5]How great, Je - ho - vah, are Thy works! How deep Thine eve - ry thought
And to Thy name, O Thou Most High, Due praise a - loud to sing;
Up - on the harp with sol - emn sound, With grave sweet mel - o - dy.
[6]Un - think-ing man does not know this, And fools ac - knowl-edge not:
[2]Thy lov - ing-kind-ness to show forth When shines the morn - ing light,
[4]For Thou, Je - ho-vah, by Thy works Hast glad - ness to me brought:
[7]That wick-ed men spring up like grass, As blos - soms sin - ners start,
And to de-clare Thy faith-ful - ness With pleas - ure eve - ry night;
And I will tri - umph in the works Which by Thy hands are wrought.
To be de-stroyed for-ev-er - more. [8]But, LORD, Thou ev - er art.

PSALM 92:9–15 **92B**

THANKSGIVING. C.M.D.
4. 9 Thy foes, O LORD, Thy foes will die, All sin - ners scat-tered be.
5. 12 But like the palm- tree flour - ish- ing Shall be the right-eous one;
6. 14 And in old age when oth - ers fade Their boughs with fruit shall bend;
10 But Thou my horn, ox - like, hast raised, With oil a - noint - ed me.
He shall like to the ce - dar grow That is in Leb - a -non.
They shall be green and flour-ish - ing, Their life in vig - or end,
11 My eyes shall look ex-ult-ant - ly On all my dead -ly foes;
13 Those that with-in Je- ho-vah's house Are plant - ed by His grace,
15 To show that up-right is the LORD; He is a rock to me,
My ears shall hear of wick-ed men, Those who a- gainst me rose.
They shall grow up and flour - ish all In our God's ho - ly place.
And He from all un- right-eous - ness Is al - to - geth - er free.

92C PSALM 92

DARWALL'S 148TH. 66.66.4444.
1. [1]It's good to thank the LORD, To praise Your name, Most High! [2]To show Your love at dawn, Your faith-ful - ness all night! [3]The ten- stringed lyre With sweet - voiced lute and rip - pling harp Your praise in - spire.
2. [4]Your deeds, LORD, made me glad. I'll joy in what You've done. [5]How great Your do- ings, LORD! How deep Your thoughts each one! [6]Fools won't be shown; The stu - pid can't ac - cept this truth, To him un - known!
3. [7]Though sin - ners grow like weeds, Ill - do - ers blos- som may, They're doomed to be de - stroyed. [8]You, LORD, ex - alt - ed stay. [9]LORD, Your foes fall. See! How Your foes, vain e - vil men, Are scat - tered all!

4. [10]You've raised, like ox, my horn,
Poured fresh oil on my head.
[11]You made me see the spies
And hear what plotters said.
[12]Like thriving palm
The righteous grows, like cedars tall
On Lebanon.

5. [13]Those planted by the LORD
Shall in God's courts be seen;
[14]When old they'll still bear fruit
And flourish fresh and green,
[15]And loud proclaim
How upright is the LORD, my Rock;
No wrong in Him!

PSALM 93

93A

RIALTO. S.M.
1. 1Je - ho - vah reigns; He's clothed With maj - es - ty most bright;
2. Es - tab - lished is the world, Its stead - fast place to hold.
3. 3The floods, O LORD, lift up, The floods lift up their voice.
4. 4But yet the LORD on high – More might - y far is He
5. 5Thy tes - ti - mo - nies all In faith - ful - ness ex - cel;
Je - ho - vah is ar - rayed with strength; He girds Him - self with might.
2And Thou from ev - er - last - ing art; Thy throne is fixed of old.
The floods are lift - ing up their waves; They make a might - y noise.
Than is the thun - der of the waves Or break-ers of the sea.
And ho - li - ness, for - ev - er, LORD, Thine house be - com - eth well.
CHANT F.

PSALM 93

93B

1. [1]The LORD reigneth, He is / clothed with / majesty; //
The LORD is clothed with strength, wherewith / He hath / girded Him/self:

2. The world / also · is es/tablished, //
That / it can/not be / moved.

3. [2]Thy throne is es/tablished of / old: //
Thou / art from /ever/lasting.

4. [3]The floods have lifted up, O LORD, the floods have / lifted · up their / voice; //
The / floods lift / up their / waves.

5. [4]The LORD on high is mightier than the / noise of · many/ waters, //
Yea, than the / mighty / waves · of the / sea.

6. [5]Thy testimonies are / very / sure: //
Holiness becometh Thine / house, O / LORD, for/ever.

For "AN INTRODUCTION TO CHANTING" please turn to page 440.

94A PSALM 94:1–15

AUSTRIA. 87.87.D.

1. [1]God of venge-ance, O Je - ho - vah, God of venge-ance, O shine forth!
2. [5]They, Je - ho - vah, crush Your peo-ple And Your her- it - age dis- tress;
3. [9]Who the ear made, does He hear not? Who formed eyes, does He not see?
4. [13]Give him rest from days of trou-ble, Till the wick - ed be o'er - thrown
[2]Rise up, O You Judge of Na - tions! Ren-der to the proud their worth.
[6]They kill so -journ - er and wid - ow, Mur - der they the fa - ther - less.
[10]Who warns na-tions, does He smite not? Who men teach-es, knows not He?
[14]Our LORD will not leave His peo - ple, Will a - ban- don not His own.
[3]O LORD, how long shall the wick - ed, How long shall the wick - ed boast?
[7]And they say, "Je - ho - vah sees not; Ja - cob's God does not have eyes."
[11]All the thoughts of men the LORD sees, Knows that but a breath are they.
[15]When to eve- - ry ver - dict giv - en Jus - tice shall come back a - gain,
[4]Ar - ro-gant the words they pour out, Ill men all, a taunt-ing host.
[8]Un - der-stand, O stu - pid peo - ple! When, O fools, will you be wise?
[12]Blessed the man whom You chas-tise, LORD, Whom You teach to know Your Way.
Eve - ry - one whose heart is up - right Will see right- eous judg- ment then.

PSALM 94:16–23

94B

KINGDOM. 87.87.
5. 16Who for me with - stands the wick - ed? Who a-
6. 18If I say, "My foot is slip - ping!" LORD, Your
7. 20Can de - struc - tive rul - ers join You And by
8. 22But the LORD is still my strong - hold; God, my

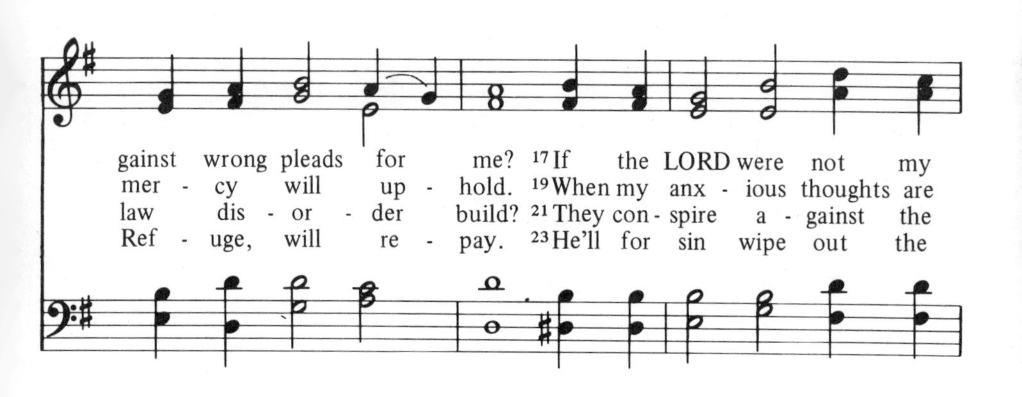
gainst wrong pleads for me? 17If the LORD were not my
mer - cy will up - hold. 19When my anx - ious thoughts are
law dis - or - der build? 21They con - spire a - gainst the
Ref - uge, will re - pay. 23He'll for sin wipe out the

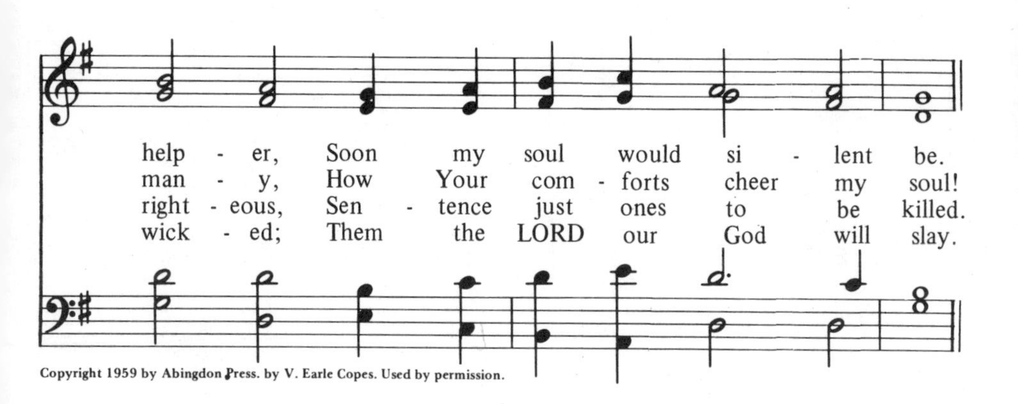
help - er, Soon my soul would si - lent be.
man - y, How Your com - forts cheer my soul!
right - eous, Sen - tence just ones to be killed.
wick - ed; Them the LORD our God will slay.

95A PSALM 95:1–5

ALEXANDRIA. C.M.
1. 1O come and to Je - ho - vah sing; Let us our voi - ces raise;
2. 2Be-fore His pres - ence let us come With praise and thank - ful voice;
3. 3The LORD's a might - y God and King; A - bove all gods He is.
4. 5To Him the spa - cious sea be - longs; 'Twas made by His com - mand;
In joy - ful songs let us the Rock Of our sal - va - tion praise.
Let us sing psalms to Him with grace; With shouts let us re - joice.
4The depths of earth are in His hand; The moun-tain peaks are His.
And by the work - ing of His hands He formed the ris - ing land.
95B
PSALM 95:6–11
REST. C.M.
5. 6O come and let us wor - ship Him; Let us with one ac - cord
6. 7Be - cause He on - ly is our God, And we His chos - en sheep,
7. To day if you will hear His voice, 8Then hard - en not your heart;
In pres - ence of our Mak - er kneel, And bow be - fore the LORD.
The peo - ple of His pas - tur - age, Whom His own hand will keep.
Strive not as those at Mer - i - bah, Nor Mas - sah's test - ing start.

8. 9Your fathers tried and tempted Me,
Though they My work perceived;
10And with that generation I
For forty years was grieved.

9. I said, "They have a wand'ring heart,
And they My ways detest."
11In wrath I swore they should not come
Into My promised rest.

PSALM 95
95C
OLD 95TH. 889.889.
1. 1Come, let us sing un - to the LORD! Let us in hon - or
2. 3Be - cause the LORD is a great God, A might - y King a -
3. 6Come, let us wor - ship and bow down; Let us be - fore our
4. 8God's voice says, "Don't stif - fen your heart The way you did at
5. 10"I grieved with that gen - er - a - tion; They for - ty years dis-
shout for joy To Him, the Rock of our sal - va - tion.
bove all gods. 4The depths of earth are at His fin - gers;
Mak - er kneel, Be - fore the LORD, 7for He is our God.
Mer - i - bah, A time of test - ing in the des - ert.
gust - ed Me. I said, 'They are a folk whose heart strays,
2O let us en - ter His pres - ence With thanks- giv - ing, with
He owns the high - est of moun - tains. 5The sea is His, for
We peo- ple are of His pas - ture, The chos - en flock He
9Your fa - thers test - ed My pa - tience; They tried Me with their
Who have no knowl - edge of My ways.' 11I there - fore prom - ised
joy - ful song. O let us sing with psalms un - to Him.
He made it. His hands have fash - ioned all the dry land.
tends with care. Oh, if to - day you would hear His voice!
dis - con - tent, Though wit-ness - ing the won - ders I did.
in My wrath, 'These shall not ev - er en - ter My rest.' "

96 A PSALM 96:1–8

CORONATION. 86.86.86.
1. [1]O sing a new song to the LORD; All earth sing to the
2. [4]The LORD is great. How great His praise! A - bove all gods He's
3. [7]O fam - i - lies of earth, as - cribe All glo - ry to the
LORD. [2]Sing to the LORD, and bless His name; "He
feared. [5]For hea - then gods are i - dols vain; The
LORD! All strength as - cribe un - to the LORD; [8]The
saves!" each day pro - claim. [3]His glo - ry to all
LORD the heav - ens made. [6]Be - fore Him hon - or,
glo - ry of His name Give to the LORD. To
na - tions show; His deeds let peo - ples know.
maj - es - ty, And strength and splen - dor be!
His courts come And bring an of - fer - ing.

PSALM 96:9–13
96B
MORWELLHAM. 86.86.86
4. 9 In beau - ti - ful and ho - ly robes Bring wor - ship to the
5. 11 Let heav'ns be glad and earth re - joice. In vast ex - panse un -
6. 13 Let all pre-pare to greet the LORD, Be - cause He com - ing
LORD. All earth, be - fore Him stand in awe; 10 Pro -
told Let seas speak out with end - less roar. 12 Let
is. He sure - ly comes to judge the earth. And
claim, "The LORD is King!" Con - trolled by Him, the
fields and all they hold Their glo - ry give; let
right - eous - ness is His. He'll na - tions judge with
world stands firm; His judg - ments jus - tice bring.
trees and woods With rus - tling boughs give praise.
faith - ful - ness, The world with jus - tice bless.

97A PSALM 97:1–7

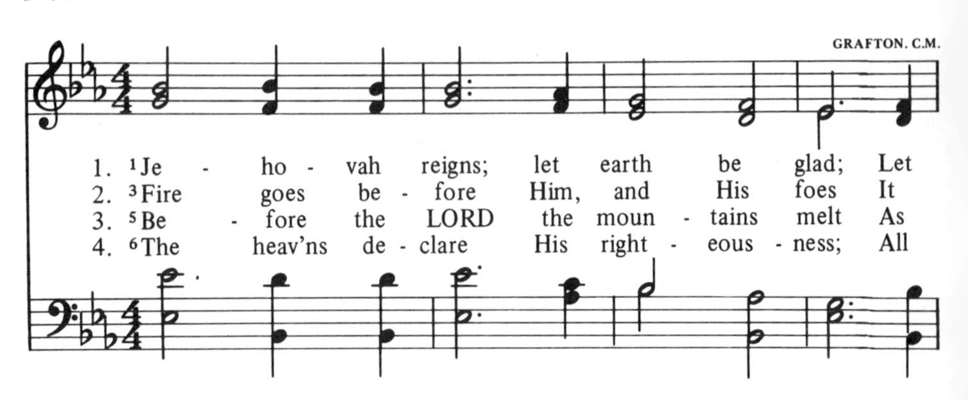
GRAFTON. C.M.
1. [1]Je - ho - vah reigns; let earth be glad; Let
2. [3]Fire goes be - fore Him, and His foes It
3. [5]Be - fore the LORD the moun - tains melt As
4. [6]The heav'ns de - clare His right - eous - ness; All

isles their joy make known; [2]Dark clouds sur- round Him,
burns up round a - bout; [4]His light - nings light- ened
wax be - fore a flame, Be - fore the Lord of
men His glo - ry see. [7]All serv - ing grav - en

and on right And jus - tice rests His throne.
all the world; Earth saw and shook through- out.
all the earth As near His pres - ence came.
im - ag - es Con - fused and shamed shall be.

PSALM 97:7–12
97B
HENRY. C.M.
5. [7]They who of i - dols boast are shamed; To Him gods
6. Be - cause of all Thy judg- ments, LORD.[9]Thou art the
7. [10]Hate e - vil, all who love the LORD; He keeps His
8. [11]For all the right - eous light is sown, And true hearts
wor - ship bring. [8]When Zi - on hears this, she is
LORD Most High A - bove all earth, a - bove all
saints se - cure, And from the hand of wick - ed
glad - ness claim. [12]Ye right - eous, in the LORD re -
glad, And Ju - dah's daugh - ters sing,
gods Ex - alt - ed ver - y high.
men He gives de - liv - 'rance sure.
joice, And thank His ho - ly name.

97C PSALM 97

THRONE. 11.10.11.6.
1. 1 Je - ho - vah reigns; let all the earth be joy - ful.
2. 6 His right - eous - ness the heav - ens are pro - claim - ing;
3. 10 Let all of you that love the LORD hate e - vil.
And let the man - y is - lands all be glad.
His glo - ry all the men of earth be - hold.
He guards the lives of all His faith - ful ones.
2 Bil - low - ing clouds and dark - ness swirl a -
7 Let them be shamed who serve and boast of
And from the hand of men who would do
round Him; His throne is truth and right.
i - dols; Let gods bow down to Him!
e - vil He sure - ly res - cues them.

3 Be - fore Him burns a fire, His foes con - sum - ing.
8 When Zi - on heard these things she was made mer - ry;
11 For light is cast like seed up - on the right - eous,
4 His light - nings lit the world; earth trem - bling saw.
Your judg - ments, LORD, make Ju - dah's daugh - ters glad.
And glad - ness for the firm and true in heart.
5 Be - fore the LORD the hills like wax have
9 For o - ver earth You are the LORD, the
12 Loud - ly re - joice, you right - eous, in Je-
melt - ed — Great Lord of all the earth.
High - est, And far a - bove all gods.
ho - vah! And thank His ho - ly name!

98A PSALM 98

DESERT. C.M.
1. ¹O sing a new song to the LORD For won - ders He has done, For won - - ders He has done; His right hand and His ho - ly arm
The
The vic - to - ry have

vic - to - ry have won, The vic - to - ry have
The vic - to - ry have won, The
The vic - to - ry have
won, The vic - to - ry have won, The
won, The vic - to - ry have won.
vic - - - - to - ry have won.
won, The vic - - to - ry have won.
vic - - - - - - to - ry have won.

2. [2]The great salvation wrought by Him
Jehovah has made known.
His justice in the nations' sight
He openly has shown.

3. [3]He mindful of His grace and truth
To Isr'el's house has been.
The great salvation of our God
All ends of earth have seen.

4. [4]O all the earth, sing to the LORD
And make a joyful sound.
Lift up your voice aloud to Him;
Sing psalms! Let joy resound!

5. [5]With harp make music to the LORD;
With harp a psalm O sing!
[6]With horn and trumpet raise a shout
Before the LORD, the King.

6. [7]Let seas in all their vastness roar,
The world, its living horde.
[8]Let rivers clap, let mountains sing
Their joy [9]before the LORD!

7. Because He comes, He surely comes,
The judge of earth to be!
With justice He will judge the world,
All men with equity.

98B PSALM 98

STUTTGART. 87.87.
1. [1]Sing a new song to Je - ho - vah
2. [2]Lo, Je - ho - vah His sal - va - tion
3. [3]Mind - ful of His truth and mer - cy
For the won - ders He has wrought; His right hand and
Has to all the world made known; In the sight of
He to Is - r'el's house has been; Of our God the
arm most ho - ly Have to Him sal - va - tion brought.
eve - ry na - tion He His right - eous - ness has shown.
great sal - va - tion All the ends of earth have seen.

4. [4]Sing, O earth, sing to Jehovah;
Shout aloud, rejoice, and sing;
[5]With the harp sing to Jehovah,
With melodious voice and string.

5. [6]Sound the trumpet and the cornet;
Shout before the LORD, the King;
[7]Seas and all their fulness, thunder;
Earth with all its people, sing.

6. [8]Let the rivers in their gladness
Clap their hands with one accord;
Let the mountains sing together
And rejoice [9]before the LORD;

7. For behold He surely cometh,
Judge of all the earth to be;
He with right will judge the nations
And the world with equity.

PSALM 99:1–5

99A

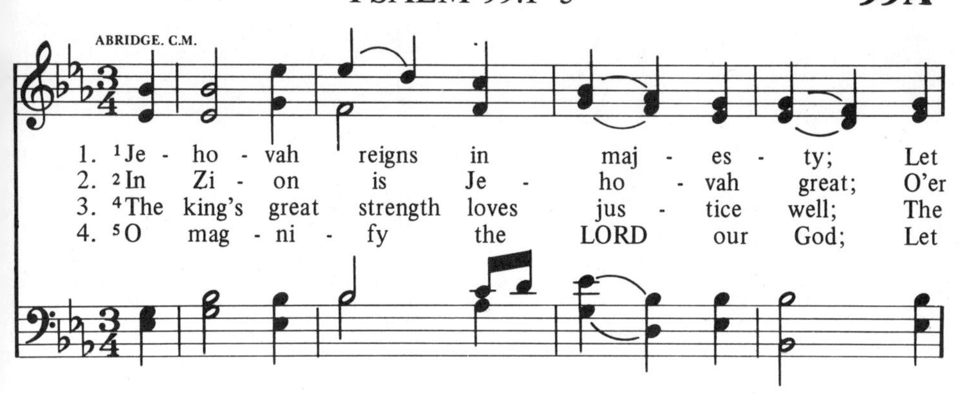
ABRIDGE. C.M.
1. 1 Je - ho - vah reigns in maj - es - ty; Let
2. 2 In Zi - on is Je - ho - vah great; O'er
3. 4 The king's great strength loves jus - tice well; The
4. 5 O mag - ni - fy the LORD our God; Let

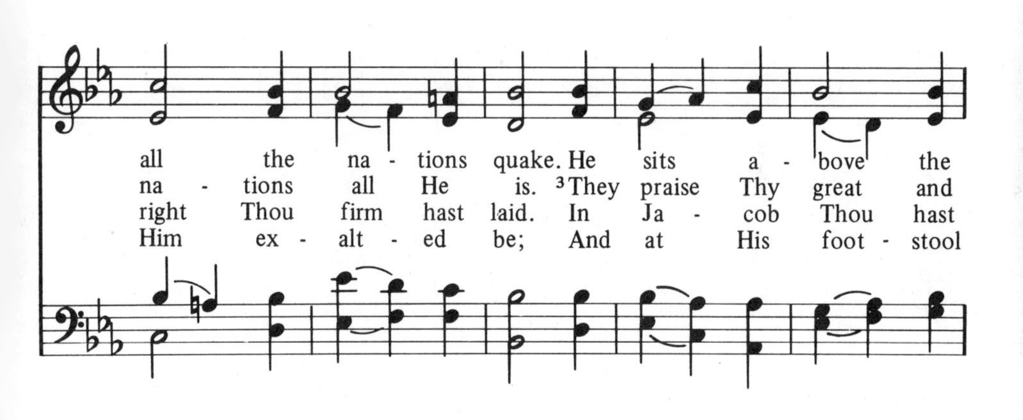
all the na - tions quake. He sits a - bove the
na - tions all He is. 3 They praise Thy great and
right Thou firm hast laid. In Ja - cob Thou hast
Him ex - alt - ed be; And at His foot - stool

cher - u - bim; Let earth's foun - da - tion shake.
awe - some name: The ho - ly name it is.
jus - tice done And right - eous - ness hast made.
wor - ship Him; The Ho - ly One is He.

99B PSALM 99:6–9

ST. LAWRENCE. C.M.

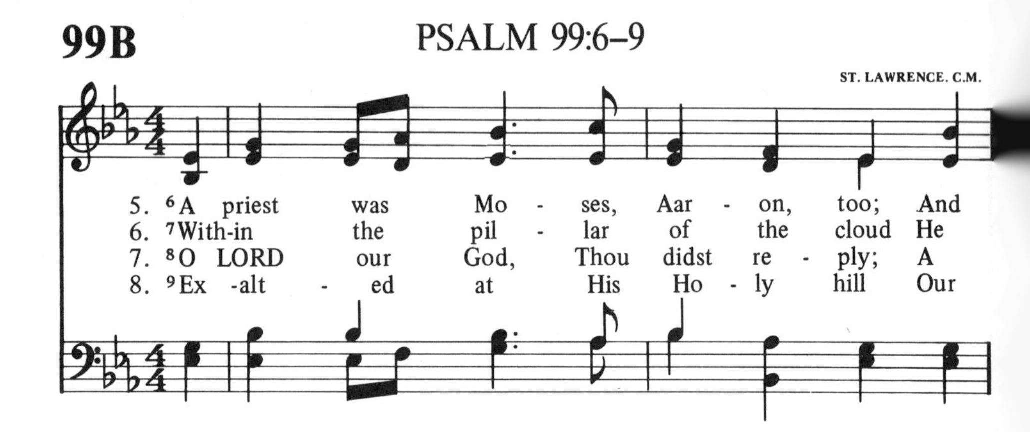
5. 6A priest was Mo - ses, Aar - on, too; And
6. 7With-in the pil - lar of the cloud He
7. 8O LORD our God, Thou didst re - ply; A
8. 9Ex -alt - ed at His Ho - ly hill Our

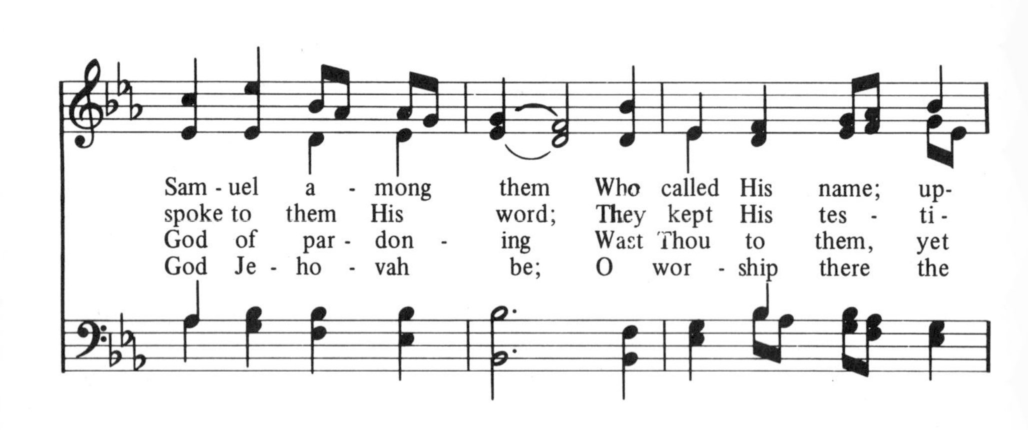
Sam - uel a - mong them Who called His name; up-
spoke to them His word; They kept His tes - ti -
God of par - don - ing Wast Thou to them, yet
God Je - ho - vah be; O wor - ship there the

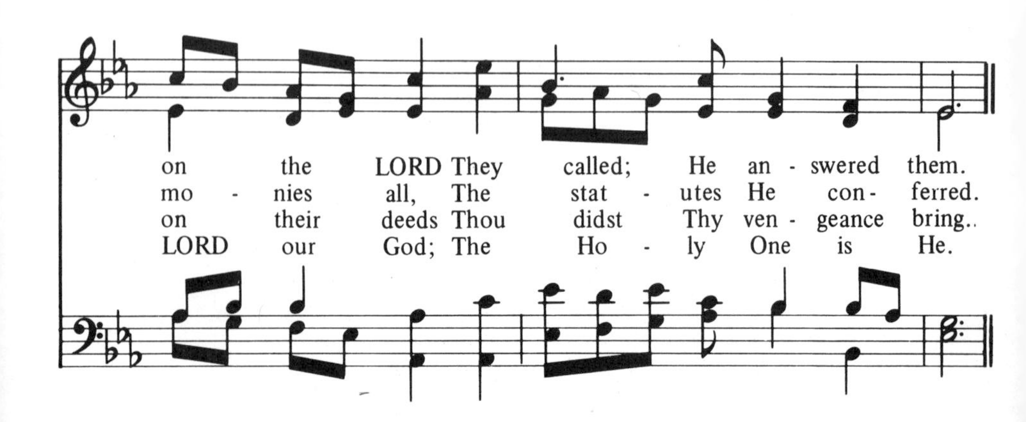
on the LORD They called; He an - swered them.
mo - nies all, The stat - utes He con - ferred.
on their deeds Thou didst Thy ven - geance bring..
LORD our God; The Ho - ly One is He.

PSALM 99
99C
LEONI. 66.84.D.
1. 1The LORD is King in - deed! Let peo - ples quail and fear!
2. 4The pow - er of the King De- lights in e - qui - ty;
3. 6For Mo - ses was His priest, And Aar - on, too, did serve,
4. 8O LORD our God, You heard, And an - swer gave to them;
He sits a - bove the cher - u - bim; Let earth be moved!
In Ja - cob You es - tab - lish law And right - eous - ness.
And Sam - u - el of them who called Up - on His name.
You were a God that bore them up – But judged their works!
2The LORD in Zi - on rules, And o - ver all is high;
5Ex - alt and cel - e - brate The LORD, Who is our God,
The LORD re - ceived their cry; 7He spoke from out the cloud.
9Ex - alt the LORD our God! Bow to His ho - ly hill!
3O praise His great and dread - ful name, The Ho - ly One!
And at His foot - stool wor - ship Him, The Ho - ly One!
His tes - ti - mo - nies they o - beyed; They kept His laws.
Be - hold, He is the Ho - ly One, The LORD our God!

100A

PSALM 100

OLD 100TH. L.M.

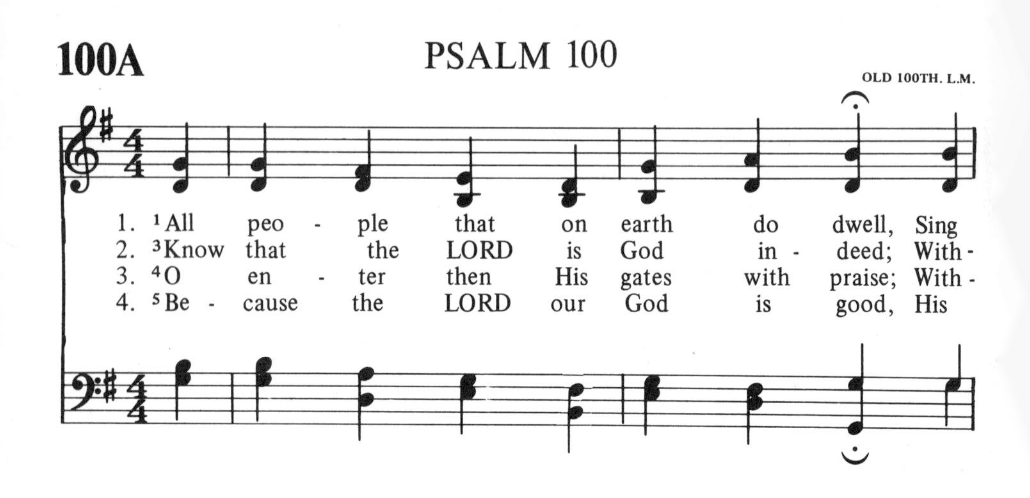
1. [1]All peo - ple that on earth do dwell, Sing
2. [3]Know that the LORD is God in - deed; With -
3. [4]O en - ter then His gates with praise; With -
4. [5]Be - cause the LORD our God is good, His

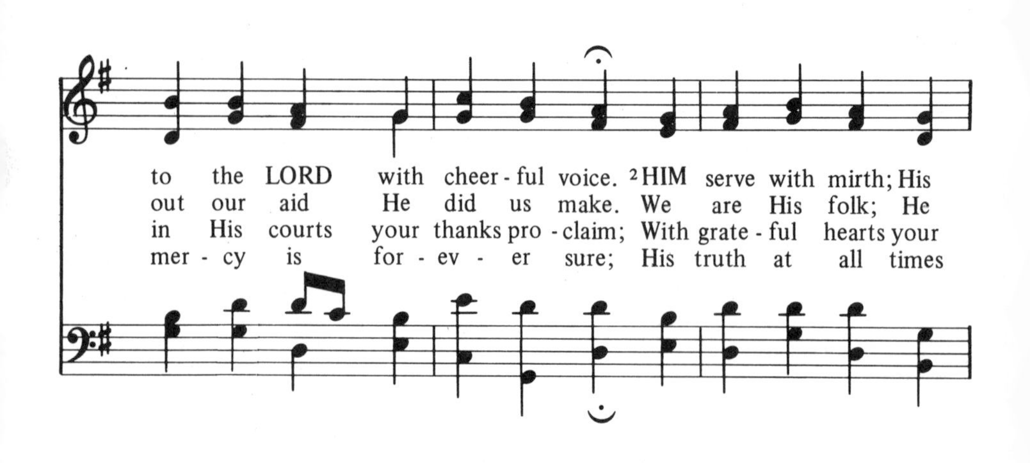
to the LORD with cheer - ful voice. [2]HIM serve with mirth; His
out our aid He did us make. We are His folk; He
in His courts your thanks pro - claim; With grate - ful hearts your
mer - cy is for - ev - er sure; His truth at all times

praise forth tell; Come ye be - fore Him and re - joice.
doth us feed, And for His sheep He doth us take.
voic - es raise To bless and mag - ni - fy His name.
firm - ly stood And shall from age to age en - dure.

PSALM 100
100B
GLASGOW. C.M.
1. 1O shout for joy un - to the LORD, Earth's
2. 3Know that the LORD is God in - deed; He
3. 4O en - ter then His gates with thanks, His
4. 5Be - cause Je - ho - vah is most good, His
peo - ple far and near; 2With glad - ness serve the
made us; we are His. We are His peo - ple,
courts with voice of praise; Give thanks to Him with
mer - cy nev - er ends; And un - to gen - er -
LORD; O come To Him with songs of cheer.
and the sheep Kept where His pas - ture is.
joy - ful - ness. And bless His name al - ways.
a - tions all His faith - ful - ness ex - tends.

100C PSALM 100

ENTER. Irregular.
1Make a joy - ful noise un - to the LORD, all ye lands.
2Serve the LORD with glad - ness! Come be - fore His
pres - ence with sing - ing. 3Know ye that the
LORD, He is God; It is He that hath made us
and not we our-selves. We are His peo - ple, the

sheep of His pas - ture.
4 En - ter in - to His
gates with thanks-giv - ing And in - to His courts with
praise. Be thank-ful un - to Him and bless His name.
5 For the LORD is good; His mer - cy ev - er - last - ing.
His truth en - dur - eth to all gen - er - a - tions.

101 PSALM 101

AURELIA. 76.76.D.
1. [1]Of mer - cy and of jus - tice, O LORD, I'll sing to Thee.
2. [3]I will per - mit no base thing Be - fore my eyes to be.
3. [5]I'll cut him off that slan- ders His neigh - bor se - cret - ly;
4. [7]No man of works de - ceit - ful With - in my house shall dwell;
[2]In up - right - ness and wis - dom Shall my be - hav - ior be.
I hate un - faith - ful do - ing; It shall not cleave to me.
I'll not en - dure the proud heart Nor eyes that haugh - ty be.
Nor in my sight shall tar - ry A man who lies will tell.
O when in lov - ing - kind - ness Wilt Thou to me come near?
[4]The man whose heart is fro - ward Shall from my pres - ence go;
[6]My eyes are with the faith - ful That he may dwell with me;
[8]Each morn - ing with de - struc - tion The wick - ed I'll re - ward,
I'll walk with - in my dwell - ing With heart and life sin - cere.
And noth - ing that is e - vil Will I con - sent to know.
The man whose walk is up - right My min - is - ter shall be.
To free from e - vil - do - ers The cit - y of the LORD.

PSALM 102:1–12

BACA. 88.888.

1. [1]To this my prayer O lis - ten, LORD! And let my cry for help reach
2. [3]For all my days go up in smoke, And like a hearth my bones are
3. With sighs and groans my frame re - sounds.[6]I'm like a des-ert pel - i -

You. [2]In day of grief hide not Your face. Your lis - t'ning
burned.[4]Like grass my heart is crushed and dried; I dai - ly
can, Or like an owl in ru - ined wastes.[7]I lie a -

ear toward me O bend; The day I call, Your an - swer send.
food for- got - ten leave;[5]My skin and bones to - geth - er cleave.
wake, as on the roof A spar-row stands, a - lone, a - loof.

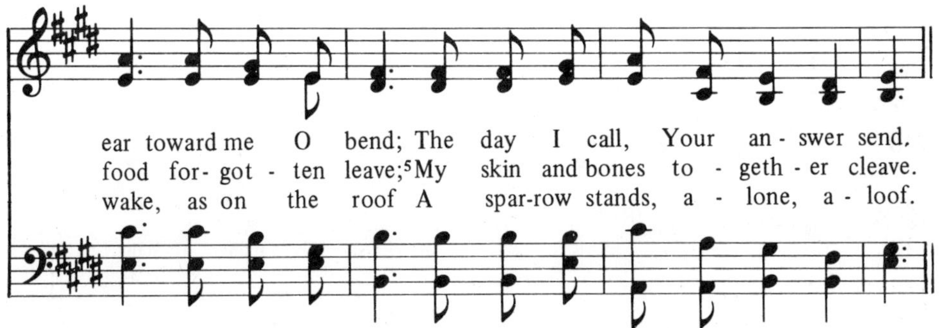

4. [8]All day my foes their taunts repeat;
   Those filled with anger curse my name.
   [9]I food with tears and ashes mix,
   [10]For You on me in anger frown;
   You raised me up to throw me down.

5. [11]An ev'ning shadow are my days;
   Like grass I wither soon away.
   [12]But You, Jeḥovah, sit enthroned
   Forever; Your memorial
   Abides through generations all.

102B

PSALM 102:12–22

PARK STREET. L.M.
6. 12 But You, Je - ho - vah, shall en - dure From age to age e - ter - nal - ly, And to all gen - er - a - tions sure Shall Your me - mo - rial ev - er be, Shall Your me - mo - rial ev - er be.
7. 13 You shall a - rise and mer - cy yet You un - to Zi - on shall ex - tend. The time has come which You have set, When You will fa - vor to her send, When You will fa - vor to her send.
8. 14 Your saints take pleas - ure in her stones; Her ver - y dust to them is dear. 15 So hea - then lands and king - ly thrones Je - ho - vah's glo - rious name shall fear, Je - ho - vah's glo - rious name shall fear.

9. [16] The LORD in glory has appeared,
Has built up Zion strong and fair,
[17] And He the destitute has heard,
Has not despised their humble prayer.

10. [18] Lest coming ages should forget,
This wondrous work shall men record,
And peoples uncreated yet
Shall praise and magnify the LORD.

11. [19]He from His holy place looked down;
The LORD viewed earth from heaven high,
[20]To hear the pris'ner's mourning groan,
And free them that are doomed to die;

12. [21]That Zion may the LORD's name tell,
Jerusalem His praise record,
[22]When gathered are the peoples all
And kingdoms join to serve the LORD.

PSALM 102:23–28 102C

ROLLAND. 88.888.

13. [23]My strength He weak - ened in the way; [24]My
14. [25]Of old You earth's foun - da - tion laid; Your
15. These shall be changed and pass a - way; [27]But

days He short-ened. Then I pled, "In mid - life take me
might - y hands the heav - ens made; [26]Yet they will die, while
You are ev - er - more the same, Be - cause Your years will

not a - way, O God, Whose years will nev - er
You en - dure. Like gar - ments they will worn out
nev - er end. [28]Your serv - ants' chil - dren dwell se -

end, But will through ag - es all ex - tend."
be; Like clothes You change them con - stant - ly.
cure Be - fore You, re - es - tab - lished sure.

103A PSALM 103:1–13

BEECHER. 87.87.D.
1. 1Bless the LORD, my soul; my whole heart Ev - er bless His ho - ly name.
2. Who with love and mer - cy crowns thee; 5Sat - is - fies thy mouth with good,
3. 7He made known His ways to Mos - es, And His acts to Is - rael's race;
4. 11For as high as is the heav - en, Far a - bove the earth be - low,
2Bless the LORD, my soul; for - get not All His mer - cies to pro - claim.
So that e - ven like the ea - gle Thou art blessed with youth re - newed.
8Ten - der, lov - ing is Je - ho - vah, Slow to an - ger, rich in grace.
Ev - er great to them that fear Him Is the mer - cy He will show.
3Who for - gives all thy trans - gres - sions, Thy dis - eas - es all Who heals;
6In His right - eous - ness Je - ho - vah Will de - liv - er those dis - tressed;
9He will not for - ev - er chide us Nor will keep His an - ger still,
12Far as east from west is dis - tant He has put a - way our sin;
4Who re - deems thee from de - struc - tion, Who with thee so kind - ly deals.
He will ex - e - cute just judg - ment In the cause of all op - pressed.
10Has not dealt as we of - fend - ed Nor re - quit - ed us our ill.
13Like the pit - y of a fa - ther Has Je - ho - vah's pit - y been.

PSALM 103:7–13 **103B**

EVENING PRAYER. 87.87.
5. [7]He made known His ways to Mos - es, And His acts to Is - rael's race.
6. [9]He will not for - ev - er chide us Nor will keep His an - ger still,
7. [11]For as high as is the heav - en, Far a - bove the earth be - low,
8. [12]Far as east from west is dis - tant He has put a - way our sin;
[8]Ten - der, lov - ing is Je - ho - vah, Slow to an - ger, rich in grace.
[10]Has not dealt as we of - fend - ed Nor re - quit - ed us our ill.
Ev - er great to them that fear Him Is the mer - cy He will show.
[13]Like the pit - y of a fa - ther Has Je - ho - vah's pit - y been.
PSALM 103:14–18
103C
COMPASSION. 87.87.
9. [14]For our frame He well re - mem - bers; That we are but dust He knows;
10. [16]O - ver it the wind now pass - es; In a mo - ment it is gone;
11. [17]But Je - ho - vah's lov - ing - kind - ness Un - to them that fear His name
12. And His right-eous - ness re - main - eth To their chil - dren and their seed,
[15]As for man, like grass he ris - es; As the flower in field he grows;
In the place where once it flour-ished It shall nev - er more be known.
From e - ter - ni - ty a - bid - eth To e - ter - ni - ty the same.
[18]Who His cov - e - nant re - mem - ber And His pre - cepts hear and heed.

103D PSALM 103:19–22

SICILIAN MARINERS. 87.87.

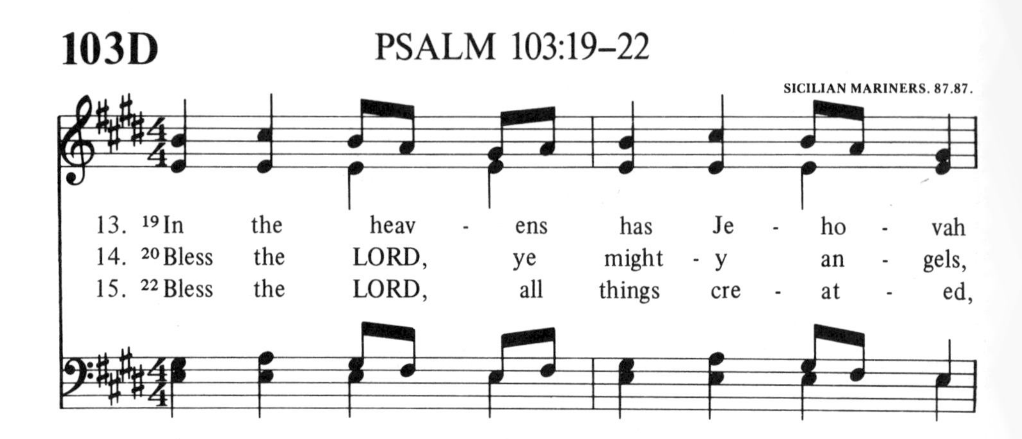
13. [19]In the heav - ens has Je - ho - vah
14. [20]Bless the LORD, ye might - y an - gels,
15. [22]Bless the LORD, all things cre - at - ed,

Found - ed His e - ter - nal throne; O - ver all is
Ye that hear and do His will; [21]Bless the LORD, all
All His hosts with one ac - cord, In all parts of

His do - min - ion; He is king and He a - lone.
ye His serv - ants Who His pleas - ure do ful - fil.
His do - min - ion. O my soul, bless thou the LORD.

PSALM 104:1–8
104A
LYONS. 10.10.11.11.
1. [1]My soul, bless the LORD! LORD God, You are great!
2. [3]The beams of Your courts in wa - ters You laid;
3. [5]You set up the earth on foun - da - tions sure,
4. [7]But at Your re - buke the high wa - ters fled;
With hon - or ar - rayed, ma - jes - tic in state,
On wings of the wind Your path - way You made.
That al - ways it should un - shak - en en - dure.
Your thun - der they heard and fast a - way sped.
[2]You cov - er Your - self with a gar - ment of light
[4]The clouds are Your char - iot; the winds do Your will;
[6]The deep like a gar - ment a - bout it You cast;
[8]The moun - tains a - rose, and the val - leys sank low;
And stretch out the sky as a cur - tain by night.
The flames and the light - nings Your pleas - ure ful - fil.
The wa - ters stood high; o - ver moun - tains they passed.
The place You ap - point - ed for them now they know.

104B PSALM 104:9–15

EMSWORTH. 10.10.11.11.
5. [9]To hold wa - ters fast You set up their bound,
6. [11]The beast of the field they fur - nish with drink;
7. [13]You wa - ter the hills with rain from Your sky,
8. So man brings forth food by work - ing the earth;
Lest turn - ing a - gain they cov - er the ground.
The wild ass - es quench their thirst on the brink.
With fruit of Your works the earth sat - is - fy.
[15]And wine that he grows his heart fills with mirth;
[10]You make springs gush forth in the val - leys be - low
[12]The birds make their nests in the trees by the spring;
[14]To nour - ish the cat - tle You cause grass to grow;
To make his face shine he ex - tracts fra - grant oil
And cause rush - ing streams be - tween moun - tains to flow.
And there in the branch - es they joy - ful - ly sing.
For crea - tures who serve man the plants You be - stow.
And finds bread that strength - ens his heart for his toil.

PSALM 104:16–23
104C
BEAUMONT. 10.10.11.11.
9. 16 The trees of the LORD are all wa - tered well;
10. 19 The moon You have set the sea - sons to show;
11. 21 The young li - ons roar, from God beg - ging meat,
Great ce - dars high up on Leb - a - non dwell.
The sun will its time for each set - ting know.
22 But at the sun - rise they quick - ly re - treat,
17 There birds build their nests; the stork makes firs its home.
20 When You make the dark - ness, the night fol - lows day,
And deep in their dens all day hide from the light,
18 On high rocks the badg - ers and goats safe - ly roam.
And beasts of the for - est creep forth seek - ing prey.
23 While man works and la - bors a - broad till the night.

104D
PSALM 104:24–30
BRADFORD. 10.10.11.11.
12. 24 How man - y works, LORD, in wis - dom You've made!
13. 26 Where ships sail the deep, Le - vi - a - thans play;
14. 29 When You hide Your face, be - wil - dered they yearn.
How full on the earth, Your rich - es dis - played!
27 These all look to You to give food each day.
When You take their breath, to dust they re - turn.
25 Out yon - der the o - cean, how great and how wide,
28 What - ev - er You give them they gath - er for food;
30 When You send Your spir - it, cre - at - ed are they.
Where small and great crea - tures un - num - bered a - bide!
When Your hand You o - pen You fill them with good.
The face of the ground You re - new eve - ry day.

PSALM 104:31–35

HOUGHTON. 10.10.11.11.
15. [31]For - ev - er O may the LORD's glo - ry stand!
16. [33]I'll sing to the LORD as long as I live,
17. [35]Con - sumed from the earth let sin - ners then be;
The LORD shall en - joy each work of His hand.
Sing praise to my God while life He will give.
The wick - ed in life no more let us see.
[32]He looks on the earth and it trem - bles in fear;
[34]My thoughts a - bout Him will sweet pleas - ure af - ford.
And now, O my soul, bless - ing give to the LORD.
When He touch - es moun - tains, the smoke will ap - pear.
For I am re - joic - ing each day in the LORD.
Let glad hal - le - lu - jahs ring; O praise the LORD!

105A PSALM 105:1–8

LOZINA. C.M.
1. [1]O thank the LORD; on His name call. His deeds tell peo - ples all. [2]O sing to Him, sing psalms to Him, His won- ders all re - call, His won - ders all re - call.
2. [3]Let hearts that seek the LORD re - joice, His ho - ly name a - dore. [4]O seek Je - ho - vah and His strength, His face seek ev - er - more, His face seek ev - er - more.
3. [5]Re - mem - ber all His won-drous deeds, The works that He has done, The right - eous judg-ments of His mouth His mir - a - cles each one, His mir - a - cles each one,

4. [6]O you, the seed of Abraham,
God's servant – you, his sons,
And all who sons of Jacob are,
His own, His chosen ones.

5. [7]He only is the LORD our God;
His judgments fill the land.
[8]He keeps in mind His covenant
That it may always stand.

PSALM 105:8–15
105B
HEBER. C.M.
6. 8A thou-sand ag-es to en-dure Com-mand-ed He His word,
7. 10A law to Ja-cob He con-firmed, A bond for Is-ra-el:
8. 12When few in num-ber, scarce-ly known,They so-journed in the land,
9. 14He let none hurt them; for their sakes To kings He gave a-larm:
9With A-brah'm made a cov-e-nant, The prom-ise I-saac heard,
11"I will to you give Ca-naan's land, Where you as heir may dwell."
13From na-tion on to na-tion went, A rest-less, wan-d'ring band,
15"Touch not My own a-noint-ed ones, Nor do My proph-ets harm."
PSALM 105:16–22
105C
SPENCER. C.M.
10. 16When He brought fam-ine on the land And broke their staff of bread,
11. 18His feet they hurt with fet-ters strong And him in irons did bind;
12. 20The king, the peo-ples' rul-er, sent To loose and set him free;
13. 22He gave him power to bind at will The princ-es of the land,
17The Jo-seph they sold as a slave He had sent on a-head.
19Till what he proph-e-sied came true, The LORD's word him re-fined.
21He made him lord of all his house, Guard of his wealth to be.
To share his wis-dom, and to make His eld-ers un-der-stand.

105D PSALM 105:23–37

CLONMEL. C.M.D.

14. [23]When Is- ra - el to E-gypt came, When Ja-cob jour - neyed west
15. [26]Then He His serv - ant Mo - ses sent And Aar- on whom He chose.
16. [30]He made their land to swarm with frogs, Kings' cham-bers filled with them.
17. [34]He spoke, and count-less lo-custs came, [35]Their fruits and leaves de - voured.

To set-tle in the land of Ham, [24]The LORD his chil - dren blessed.
[27]They mir - a - cles in E-gypt wrought, His signs a - mong their foes.
[31]He spoke, and swarms of flies and gnats Through-out their coun-try came.
[36]He killed each first - born in the land, The princ - es of their power.

He made them strong - er than their foes, [25]Whose hearts He filled with hate
[28]He dark- ness sent, the land made dark, So they His words might try.
[32]He gave them hail in - stead of rain, Flashed light-ning through their land
[37]He led His peo - ple forth en- riched With sil - ver and with gold,

That made them hunt His peo- ple out, His serv-ants chide and cheat.
[29]He turned their wa - ters in - to blood And caused their fish to die.
[33]He smote their fig trees and their vines, Slashed trees on eve - ry hand.
And there was none a - mong His tribes Who stum-bled, young or old.

PSALM 105:37–45

ST. SAVIOR. C.M.
18. 37 He led His peo - ple forth en - riched With sil - ver and with gold, And there was none a - mong His tribes Who stum - bled, young or old.
19. 38 How glad was E - gypt when they went! It shook with dread of them. 39 He spread a cloud to cov - er them; By night it shined like flame.
20. 40 At their re - quest He brought them quails; He bread from heav'n be - stowed. 41 He split the rock and wa - ter gushed; Through des - ert lands it flowed.

21. [42] His holy promise He recalled,
How Abrah'm served Him long.
[43] He led His people forth with joy,
His chosen ones with song.

22. [44] The nations' lands, the peoples' toil,
He gave them for their own,
[45] That they should keep and heed His law.
O praise the LORD alone.

106A PSALM 106:1–5

BROWN. C.M.

1. [1]O praise the LORD! O thank the LORD! For
2. [2]Who can ex - press Je - ho - vah's praise Or
3. [4]Re - gard me with the fa - vor, LORD, Which
4. [5]That I may see Thy peo - ple's good And

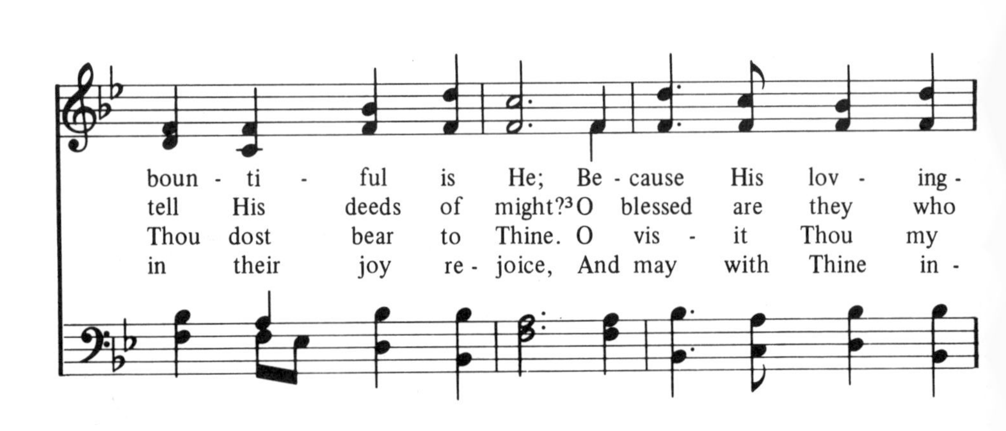
boun - ti - ful is He; Be - cause His lov - ing -
tell His deeds of might?[3]O blessed are they who
Thou dost bear to Thine. O vis - it Thou my
in their joy re - joice, And may with Thine in -

kind - ness lasts To all e - ter - ni - ty.
jus - tice keep And ev - er do the right.
soul in love; Make Thy sal - va - tion mine;
her - i - tance Ex - ult with cheer - ful voice.

PSALM 106:6–12

KNOX. C.M.
5. 6With all our fa - thers we have sinned, In- i - qui - ty have done; We have gone on in wick - ed - ness, In e - vil ways have run.
6. 7Our fa - thers did not un - der - stand Thy works in E - gypt done; Of all Thy man - y mer - cies shown, They did re - mem - ber none.
7. Though at the sea, the Sea of Reeds, They were re - bel - lious grown, 8He saved them for His own name's sake, To make His pow - er known.
8. 9And so the Red Sea He re - buked; It dried at His com - mand. And then He led them through the depths As through the des - ert land.

9. 10And from the hand that hated them,
He did His people save,
And from the hand of enemies
To them redemption gave.

10. 11The water overwhelmed their foes;
None lived of all their throng.
12His people then believed His words
And praised His name in song.

106C PSALM 106:13–23

EXETER. C.M.
11. 13 The peo - ple soon for - got His works, Nor
12. 15 And so He gave them what they asked, Though
13. 16 They en - vied Mo - ses in the camp; His
wait - ed for His will; 14 They lust - ed in the
lust - ful was their goal, But He sent lean - ness
rule they sought to shun; They en - vied Aar- on's
wil - der - ness, And God they tempt - ed still.
af - ter - ward In - to their thank - less soul.
priest - ly rank – Je - ho - vah's ho - ly one.

14. [17] The op'ning earth on Dathan closed,
Abiram's band entombed;
[18] A fire blazed in their company
And wicked ones consumed.

15. [19] Yet they at Horeb made a calf,
Before an image kneeled;
[20] They made their glory like an ox
That eats grass in the field.

16. [21] Then God their Savior they forgot,
Great things in Egypt done,
[22] In Ham's land, by the Sea of Reeds,
His awesome deeds each one.

17. [23] He said He'd cut them off, unless
Before Him in the way
He'd chosen Moses there to stand
And turn His wrath away.

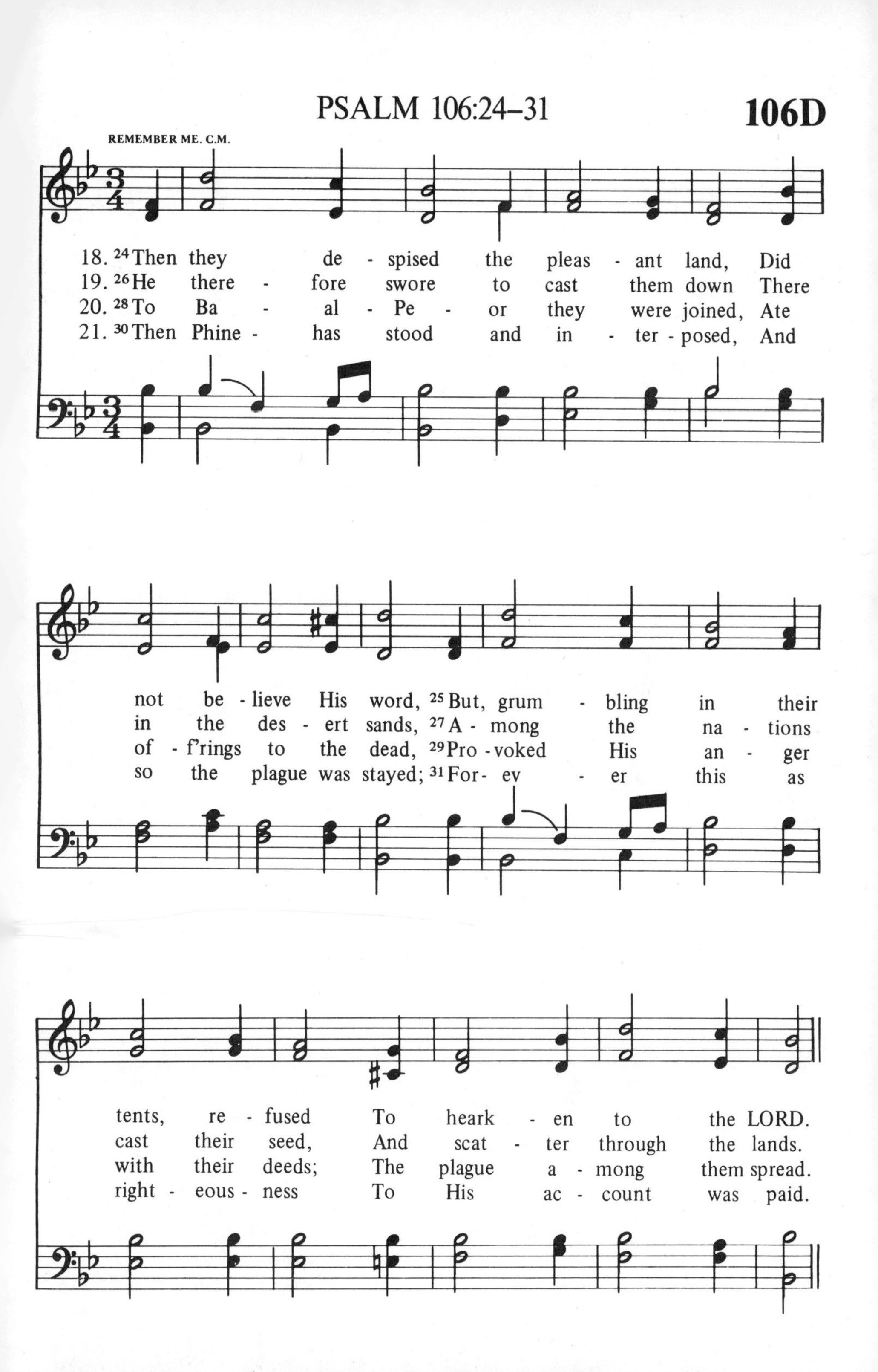
PSALM 106:24–31
106D
REMEMBER ME. C.M.
18. 24 Then they de - spised the pleas - ant land, Did
19. 26 He there - fore swore to cast them down There
20. 28 To Ba - al - Pe - or they were joined, Ate
21. 30 Then Phine - has stood and in - ter - posed, And
not be - lieve His word, 25 But, grum - bling in their
in the des - ert sands, 27 A - mong the na - tions
of - f'rings to the dead, 29 Pro - voked His an - ger
so the plague was stayed; 31 For- ev - er this as
tents, re - fused To heark - en to the LORD.
cast their seed, And scat - ter through the lands.
with their deeds; The plague a - mong them spread.
right - eous - ness To His ac - count was paid.

106E
PSALM 106:32–40
LEVEQUE. C.M.D.
22. 32At Mer - i - bah they an - gered Him, On Mo - ses e - vil brought,
23. 36When they the hea - then i - dols served, These were to them a snare,
24. Pol - lu - ted was the land with blood, 39And thus de - filed were they
33For they pro- voked his tem - per so His speech was rash and hot.
37For they to de - mons sac - ri - ficed Their sons and daugh - ters there.
In all their works; and with their acts They went the har - lot's way.
34They would not heed the LORD's com-mand The hea - then tribes to slay,
38They poured out guilt-less blood, the blood Their sons and daugh - ters shed
40A - gainst the peo - ple kin - dled was The an - ger of the LORD;
35But min - gled with the na - tions all And learned their e - vil way.
When they, to i - dols sac - ri - ficed, On Ca - naan's al - tars bled.
They so pro - voked His wrath that He His her - it - age ab - horred.

PSALM 106:41–48 106F

ALPENA. C.M.D.
25. 41 He gave them to the na - tions' power, Put ha - ters in com-mand;
26. 44 Yet their dis - tress He looked up - on When He had heard their cry,
27. 47 Save us, O LORD, our gra - cious God, From hea-then lands re- claim,
42 Their foes op-pressed them, and they were Sub-dued be - neath their hand.
45 And He re - mem - bered for their sake His cov - e - nant on high.
That we may glo - ry in Thy praise And thank Thy ho - ly name.
43 He man - y times de - liv - ered them, But reb - els still were they
Then He re - lent - ed in His grace And for His mer - cies' sake;
48 Blessed be Je - ho - vah, Is - rael's God, To all e - ter - ni - ty.
In all their plans; so down they went In sin to pine a - way.
46 He gave them pit - y from all those Who did them cap - tive take.
Let all the peo - ple say, "A - men." Praise to the LORD give ye.

106G PSALM 106:48

DELTA. Irregular
48 Bless - ed be the LORD, the God of Is - ra -
el from ev - er - last - ing ev'n to
ev - er - last - ing. Let all the
peo - ple say, "A - men!" Praise ye the LORD!

PSALM 107:1–9

107A

NEWELL. C.M.
1. [1]O praise the LORD, for He is good; His mer - cies still en - dure; [2]Thus say the ran - somed of the LORD, From all their foes se - cure, From all their foes se - cure.
2. [3]He gath - ered them from out the lands, From north, south, east, and west. [4]They wan - dered in the wil - der - ness, No cit - y found to rest, No cit - y found to rest.
3. [5]Their wea - ry soul with - in them faints When thirst and hun - ger press; [6]In trou - ble to the LORD they cried; He saved them from dis - tress, He saved them from dis - tress.
4. [7]He made the way be - fore them straight, And He be - came their guide, That they might to a cit - y go In which they would a - bide, In which they would a - bide.

5. [8]Let them give thanks unto the LORD
For all His kindness shown,
And for His works so wonderful
Which He to men makes known.

6. [9]Because the longing soul by Him
With food is satisfied;
The hungry soul that looks to Him
With goodness is supplied.

107B PSALM 107:10–16

SHADDICK. C.M.
7. [10]Some peo - ple in the dark - ness lived, In
8. [11]Be - cause a - gainst the words of God They
9. [12]He there - fore hum - bled them with toil; They
10. [14]He brought them out of dark - ness great And
death's shade did a - bide, The pris - on - ers of
in re - bel - lion turned, And coun - sel of the
fell with - out re - dress. [13]In trou - ble to the
took them from death's shade; He broke a - part the

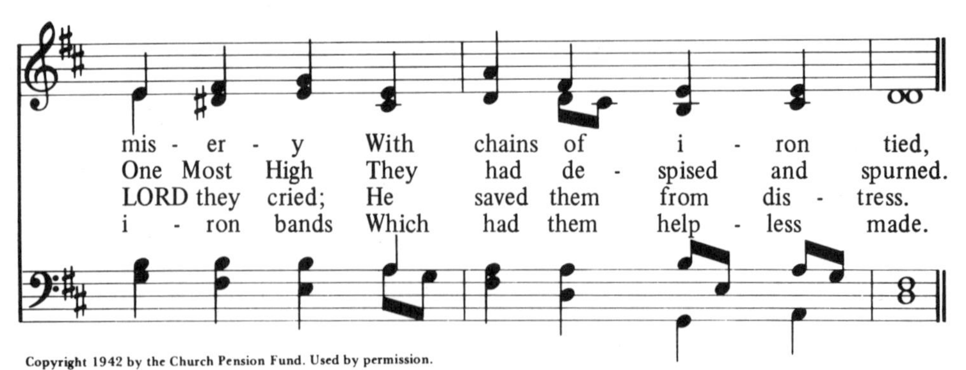
mis - er - y With chains of i - ron tied,
One Most High They had de - spised and spurned.
LORD they cried; He saved them from dis - tress.
i - ron bands Which had them help - less made.

11. [15]Let them give thanks unto the LORD
For all His kindness shown,
And for His works so wonderful
Which He to men makes known.

12. [16]For He the mighty gates of bronze
Has shattered with a stroke;
He cut the bars of iron off
And them asunder broke.

PSALM 107:17–22 **107C**

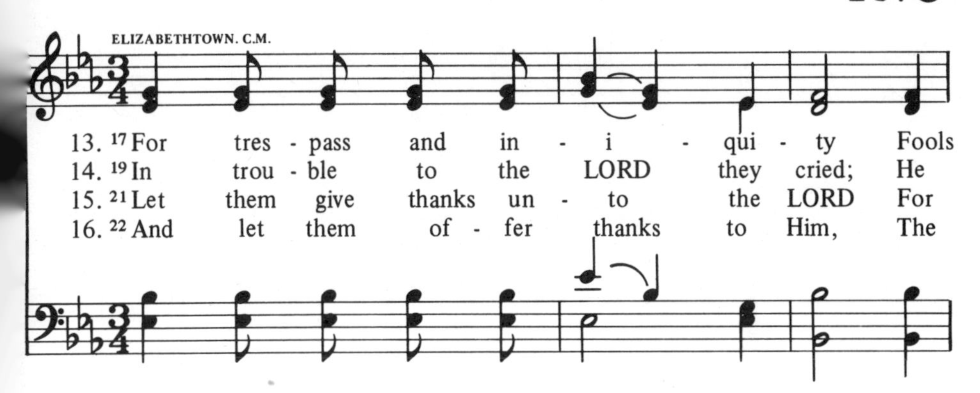
ELIZABETHTOWN. C.M.
13. 17 For tres - pass and in - i - qui - ty Fools
14. 19 In trou - ble to the LORD they cried; He
15. 21 Let them give thanks un - to the LORD For
16. 22 And let them of - fer thanks to Him, The

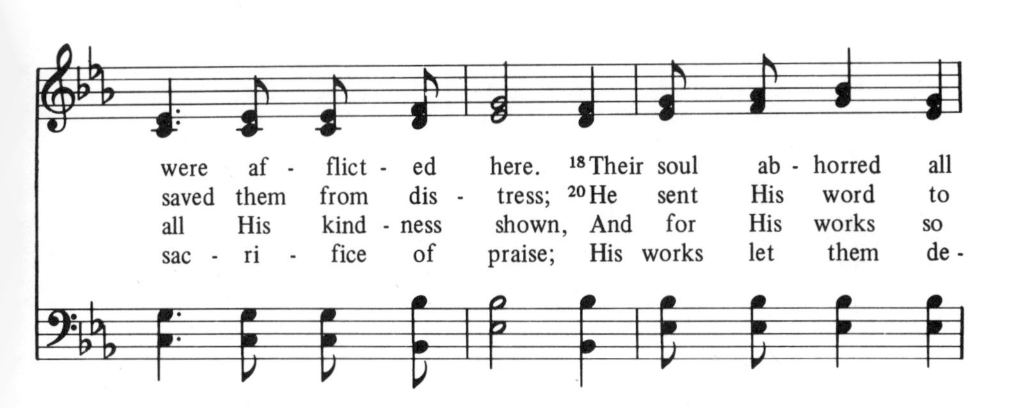
were af - flict - ed here. 18 Their soul ab - horred all
saved them from dis - tress; 20 He sent His word to
all His kind - ness shown, And for His works so
sac - ri - fice of praise; His works let them de -

food; and they To gates of death drew near.
make them whole And lift from wretch - ed - ness.
won - der - ful Which He to men makes known.
clare a - broad, In songs their voic - es raise.

107D PSALM 107:23–32

FOUNTAIN. C.M.D.
17. [23]To those who go to sea in ships And on great wa - ters trade,
18. [26]To heav - en mount-ed ships and men, Then sank to depths a - gain;
19. [29]The storm He changed in-to a calm By His com- mand and will,
20. [31]Let them give thanks un-to the LORD For all His kind - ness shown.
[24]The works and won - ders of the LORD Are in the deep dis -played.
Their souls were melt- ed and were faint With fear and trou- ble then.
And so the waves which raged be- fore Now qui- et were and still.
And for His works so won - der - ful Which He to men makes known.
[25]For His com- mand stirred up the wind That with a tem - pest blows;
[27]They stag - gered, reeled, like drunk-en men; No skill could they ex - press.
[30]Then they were glad, be - cause at rest And qui- et was the sea.
[32]A - mong the peo-ple where they meet Let them ex- alt His name.
It lift - ed wa- ters of the sea; Great roll - ing waves a- rose.
[28]In trou - ble to the LORD they cried; He saved them from dis - tress.
He led them to the ha- ven thus Where they de - sired to be.
And where the el - ders have their seat Let them His praise pro -claim.

PSALM 107:33–43
107E
CANAAN. C.M.D.
21. 33He chang-es streams to wil - der-ness, And springs to thirst - y ground,
22. 37They plant their vine-yards, sow their fields; Rich har - vests there they grow;
23. 40For He con-tempt on princ - es pours; He lets them go a - stray
24. 42When this the up - right ones ob - serve, They great-ly shall re - joice,
34A fruit - ful land to salt - y waste, When peo- ples' sins a - bound.
38His bless - ing makes them mul - ti - ply, Their herds no de - crease know.
And wan- der in the wil - der - ness Where there is not a way.
And all un-right - eous - ness, a - shamed, Shall cease to raise its voice.
35He turns the des - ert to a lake, Dry land to wa - ter springs,
39A - gain they much di - min-ished are And brought to low es - tate
41But He from trou - ble lifts the poor By set - ting them on high.
43Is an - y wise? He'll heed these things Which vers - es here re - cord,
36And that they may pre - pare a home The hun- gry there He brings.
Through sor - row and ad - ver - si - ty And through op - pres - sion great.
And like a flock in fam - i - lies He makes them mul - ti - ply.
And he'll con-sid - er well the love And kind- ness of the LORD.

108A PSALM 108:1–6

SILCHESTER. S.M.

1. [1]My heart is fixed, O God; I'll
2. [3]I will give thanks to Thee A-
3. [4]A - bove the heav - ens high Thy

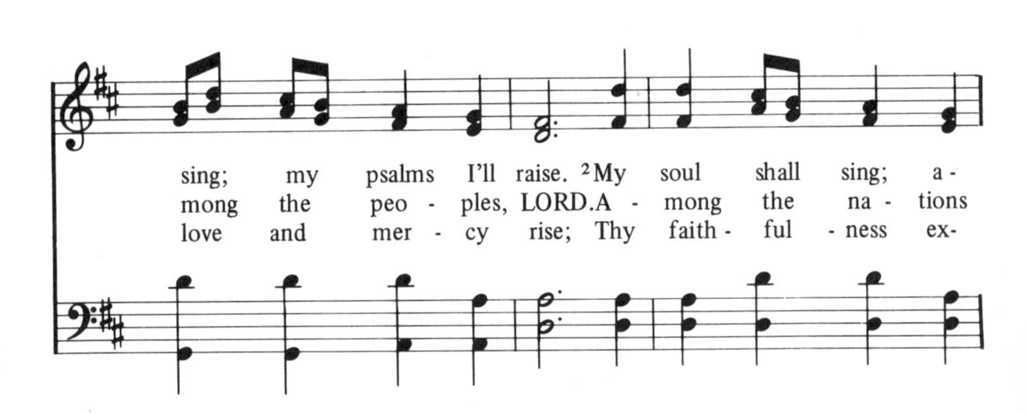
sing; my psalms I'll raise. [2]My soul shall sing; a-
mong the peo - ples, LORD. A - mong the na - tions
love and mer - cy rise; Thy faith - ful - ness ex-

wake, O harp! At dawn I'll wake to praise.
of the world To Thee I'll psalms ac - cord.
tend - eth far; It reach - es to the skies.

4. [5]Be Thou exalted far
Above the heav'ns, O God;
And let Thy glory be advanced
O'er all the earth abroad.

5. [6]That Thy beloved ones
Deliverance may see,
O save us by Thy strong right hand;
In mercy answer me.

PSALM 108:7–13 **108B**

ISHMAEL. S.M.D.
6. 7God spoke in ho - li - ness: "I will ex- ult - ant stand;
7. 9"In Mo - ab I will wash, My shoe on E - dom throw;
8. 11Hast Thou not cast us off, O God, in Whom we boast?
From She - chem un - to Suc - coth's vale I'll por- tion out the land.
And o'er the land of Pal - es - tine In tri - umph I will go."
Wilt Thou no more, O God, go forth In bat - tle with our host?
8For Gil - e - ad is Mine; Mine are Ma - nas - seh's fields;
10O who will bring me to The cit - y for - ti - fied?
12A - gainst the foe give help; In vain the help man knows.
Yes, E - phra- im de - fends My head; My scep- ter Ju - dah wields.
Or who is he that to the land Of E - dom will me guide?
13In God we shall do val - iant - ly, For He'll tread down our foes.

Music by Charles Vincent. Used by permission of Professor E. R. Vincent, Taunton, England.

108C PSALM 108

HAYDN. 11.86.D.
1. [1]My heart is read - y, O God! I'm re - joic - ing! I will
2. [4]Prais- es to You will I chant through the na - tions, For Your
3. Save by Your right hand, O God; give me an - swer! [7]In His
4. "While o - ver My land My scep - tre is Ju - dah, [9]I use
5. [11]God, have You thrown us a - way? Have You spurned us? You go
sing, yes, sing Your prais - es! My glad soul a - wak - en!
grace skies can - not meas - ure; Your truth reach - es heav - en.
tem - ple God has prom - ised, "I'll por - tion out She - chem;
Mo - ab as a wash - bowl, My shoe toss on E - dom;
not forth with our ar - mies; [12]Your help, O God, grant us!
[2]Wak - en, O harp! Let my sweet lyre a - wak - en! With my
[5]High o - ver heav - ens, O God, be ex - alt - ed! Let Your
Meas - ure in tri - umph the val - ley of Suc - coth; [8]Mine is
O - ver Phi - lis - tia I shout loud in tri - umph." [10]Who will
Fight - ing the en - e - my man's help is emp - ty, [13]But with
song I'll rouse the dawn - ing; [3]I will You praise, O LORD.
glo - ry cov - er all earth, [6]So res - cue Your be - loved.
Gil - ead, Mine Ma - nas - seh, My hel - met E - phra - im!
lead me to the for - tress And me to E - dom bring?
God we strive with val - or; He'll tram - ple down our foes.

PSALM 109:1–15

CASSELL. 87.87.D.
1. [1]God, my Praise, O be not si - lent! [2]Wick-ed and de - ceit - ful mouths
2. [5]So for good they pay me e - vil, Give me ha - tred for my love.
3. [9]With-out fa-ther be his chil-dren; May his wife a wid- ow be.
4. [13]His pos-ter - i - ty be cut off! May none live to claim his name!
Now are o -pened wide a - gainst me; Ly - ing tongues a - gainst me speak.
[6]Set a wick-ed man a - gainst him, An ac - cus -er let him face.
[10]May his chil-dren beg and wan-der, Driv- en from their ru - ined homes.
[14]May the e - vil of his fa - thers Be re - called be-fore the LORD.
[3]They with hate - ful words be - set me; They at - tack me with-out cause.
[7]When he's tried, let him be guil - ty; Let his prayer be count- ed sin.
[11]May the lend - er make him bank-rupt; Stran-gers steal his hard-earned cash.
May no wrong deed of his moth- er From the re -cord be e - rased.
[4]Spurn-ing my love, they ac - cuse me, E - ven while I pray for them.
[8]May his days be few in num-ber; May an - oth- er seize his goods.
[12]Let not one show kind - ness to him; Let none help his or - phan sons!
[15]May they all be - fore the LORD stand, Pruned from earth their mem-o - ry.

109B PSALM 109:16–21

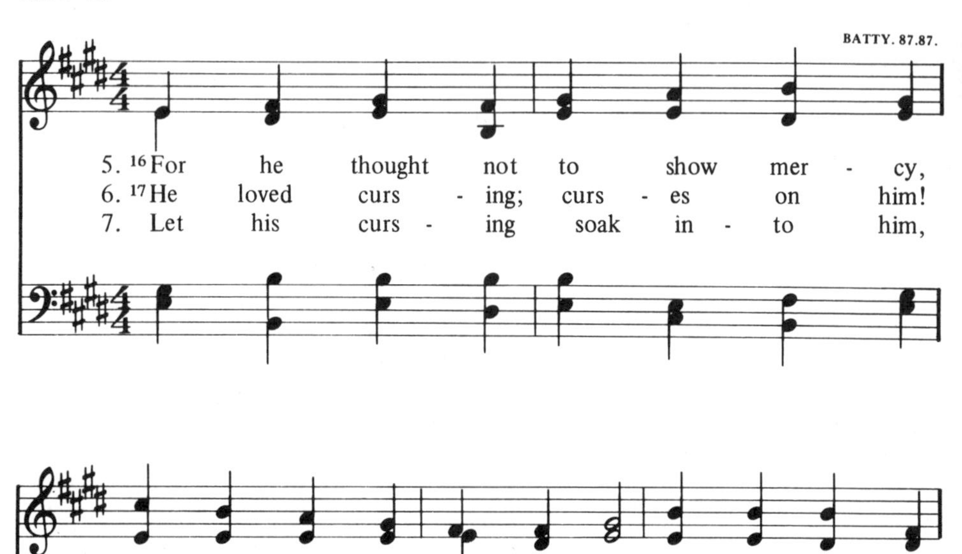
BATTY. 87.87.
5. [16]For he thought not to show mer - cy,
6. [17]He loved curs - ing; curs - es on him!
7. Let his curs - ing soak in - to him,

But he per - se - cut - ed still; And he chased the
He loathed bless - ing; give him none! [18]Like a coat he
Be like oil with - in his bones, [19]Like the garb he

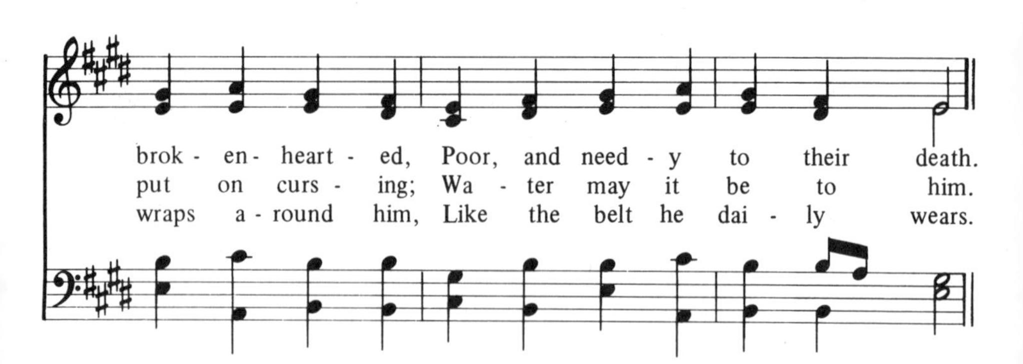
brok - en - heart - ed, Poor, and need - y to their death.
put on curs - ing; Wa - ter may it be to him.
wraps a - round him, Like the belt he dai - ly wears.

8. [20]May this be to my accusers
From the LORD their just reward;
This to those who speak but evil,
Who speak out against my life.

9. [21]But may You, my God, Jehovah,
Do for me for Your name's sake.
Great in goodness is Your mercy!
Rescue me in steadfast love.

PSALM 109:22–31 109C

ST. HILARY. 87.87.D.

10. [22]I am ver - y poor and need - y; Strick-en in me is my heart.
11. [26]Help me, O my God, Je - ho - vah; Save me in Your mer - cy great.
12. Clothed with shame be my ac - cus - ers, Wrapped up in their own dis - grace.

[23]I am gone like ev - 'ning shad - ow, Like a lo - cust shak - en off.
[27]Let them know that this is Your hand; You, O LORD, have done it all.
[30]With my mouth then will I of - fer Great thanks-giv - ing to the LORD.

[24]Both my knees are weak from fast - ing; Gaunt my bod - y has be - come.
[28]Let them curse me if You bless me. Let my foes be put to shame;
In the midst of throng - ing peo - ple, I will praise Him;[31]for He stands

[25]Scorned am I by my ac - cus - ers; See - ing me, they shake their heads.
But may glad - ness fill Your serv - ant, [29]While dis - hon - or cov - ers them.
At the right hand of the need - y, Sav - ing him from men of death.

110 PSALM 110

ALL SAINTS NEW. C.M.D.
1. [1]Je - ho-vah to my Lord has said, "Sit Thou at My right hand
2. [3]A will-ing peo-ple in Thy day Of power shall come to Thee.
3. [5]The Lord at Thy right hand shall smite Earth's ru- lers in His wrath.
Un - til I make Thy foes a stool Where-on Thy feet may stand."
Thy youth ar-rayed in ho - li - ness Like morn-ing dew shall be.
[6]A - mong the na-tions He shall judge; The slain shall fill His path.
[2]Je - ho-vah shall from Zi - on send The scep-ter of Thy power.
[4]Je - ho-vah swore, and from His oath He nev-er will de - part:
In man-y lands He'll o-ver-throw Their kings with ru-in dread;
In bat-tle with Thine en - e - mies Be Thou the con-quer-or.
"Of th'or-der of Mel-chiz - ed - ek A priest Thou ev-er art."
[7]And, march-ing, He'll drink from the brook And so lift up His head.

PSALM 111:1–5

111A

BOYNTON. C.M.
1. [1]O praise the LORD! With all my heart Thanks to the LORD I'll bring, Where up - right ones as - sem - bled are And con - gre - ga - tions sing.
2. [2]The works ac - com - plished by the LORD Are ver - y great in might. They are sought out by eve - ry - one Who finds in them de - light.
3. [3]His work dis - plays the maj - es - ty And glo - ry of His name, And His en - dur - ing right - eous - ness Is ev - er - more the same.

4. [4]His works most wondrous He has made
Remembered still to be.
Jehovah is compassionate
And merciful is He.

5. [5]Those fearing Him He fills with food
Provided by His hand.
He keeps in mind His covenant,
That it may ever stand.

111B PSALM 111:6–10

STRACATHRO. C.M.

6. [6]He has the pow - er of His works To
7. [7]His hand - i - works are truth and right; His
8. [9]He sent re - demp - tion to His folk, His
9. [10]The man who fears the LORD has learned The

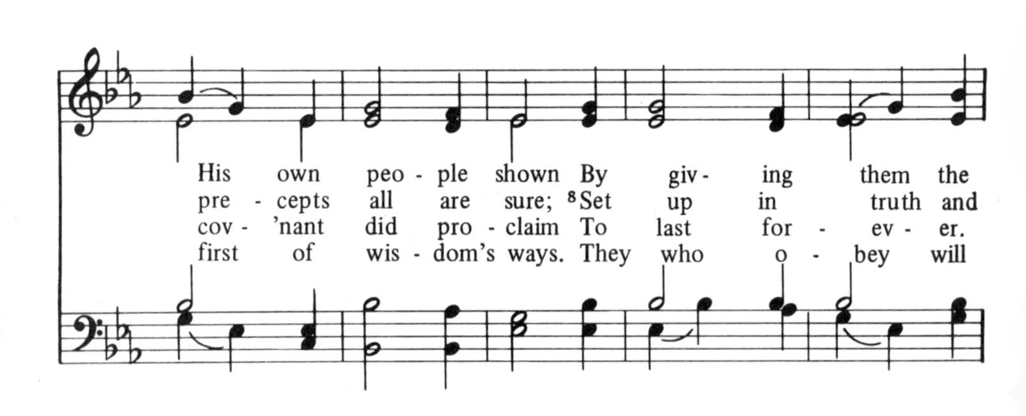
His own peo - ple shown By giv - ing them the
pre - cepts all are sure; [8]Set up in truth and
cov - 'nant did pro - claim To last for - ev - er.
first of wis - dom's ways. They who o - bey will

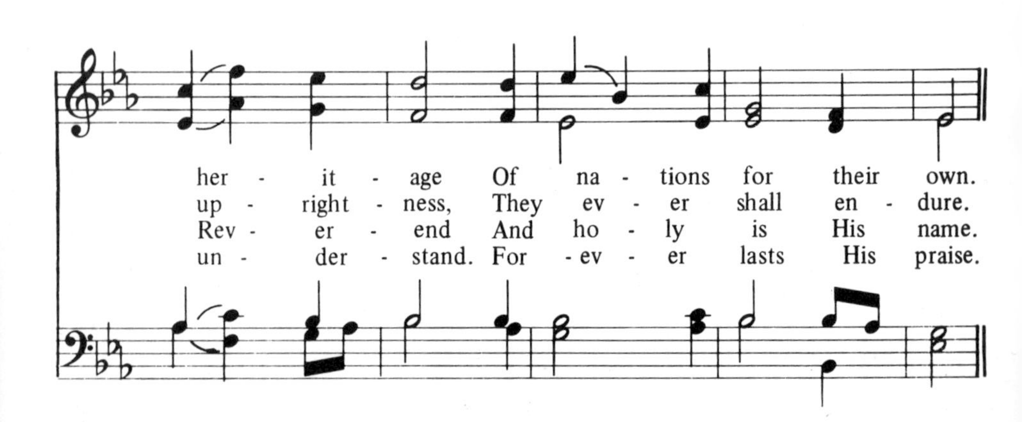
her - it - age Of na - tions for their own.
up - right - ness, They ev - er shall en - dure.
Rev - er - end And ho - ly is His name.
un - der - stand. For - ev - er lasts His praise.

PSALM 112

112A

REWARD. C.M.D.
1. 1Praise ye the LORD. The man is blessed Who fears the LORD a - right,
2. 3A - bun- dant wealth with- in his house Shall ev - er be in store;
3. 5That man is good who gra- cious- ly And free - ly gives and lends,
4. 7When he shall e - vil tid - ings hear He shall not be a - fraid;
5. 9He has dis - persed his wealth a - broad And giv - en to the poor;
The man who finds in His com - mands His pleas - ure and de - light.
And his un- spot- ted right - eous - ness En - dures for - ev - er - more.
Who just - ly gov - erns his af - fairs, Who truth and right ex - tends.
His heart is fixed; his con- fi - dence Up - on the LORD is stayed.
His horn with hon - or shall be raised, His right - eous - ness en - dure.
2His chil - dren shall be might - y men Up - on the earth re - nowned;
4Though dark - ness may sur - round the just, To him a - ris - es light;
6There sure - ly is not an - y - thing That ev - er shall him move;
8Es - tab - lished firm - ly is his heart; He shall not fear - ful be,
10The wick - ed, see - ing him, is vexed; He grits his teeth, dis - mayed,
The gen - er - a - tion of the just In bless - ing shall a - bound.
Com - pas - sion - ate and mer - ci - ful, He fol - lows what is right.
The right - eous man's me - mo - ri - al Shall ev - er - last - ing prove.
Un - til up - on his en - e - mies He his de - sire shall see.
But melts a - way, and his de - sire Will in - to noth - ing fade.

112B PSALM 112

CONFIDENCE. 10.10.10.10.
1. 1Praise to the LORD! The man is blessed in - deed
2. 3A - bun - dant rich - es are with - in his house;
3. 5That man is good who gives and free - ly lends,
4. 7At e - vil tid - ings he is not a - fraid;
5. 9With o - pen hand he of - fers to the poor;
Who makes the LORD's com - mands his great de - light.
His right - eous - ness en - dures for - ev - er - more.
And who with jus - tice gov - erns his af - fairs.
His heart is stead - fast, trust - ing in the LORD.
His good en - dures; his head is lift - ed high.
2His chil - dren will be might - y in the earth;
4The dark - ness of the just will turn to light,
6The right - eous man will nev - er be re - moved,
8His heart is stead - y; he will nev - er fear;
10The wick - ed sees and grinds his teeth in rage,
De - scend - ants of the up - right will be blessed.
For all his ways are gra - cious, kind and fair.
And ev - er will his mem - o - ry en - dure.
He comes at last to look up - on his foes.
For he de - spairs; his cher - ished hope must die.

PSALM 113

113A

HENDON. 77.77.
1. 1Praise Je - ho - vah; praise the LORD; Ye His serv - ants,
2. 3From the dawn to set - ting sun, Praise the LORD, the
3. 5Who is like the LORD our God? High in heav'n is

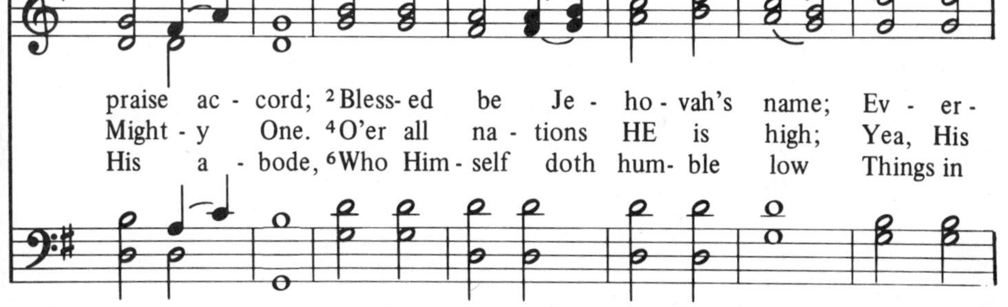
praise ac - cord; 2Bless- ed be Je - ho - vah's name; Ev - er -
Might - y One. 4O'er all na - tions HE is high; Yea, His
His a - bode, 6Who Him - self doth hum- ble low Things in

more His praise pro - claim, Ev - er - more His praise pro - claim.
glo - ry crowns the sky, Yea, His glo - ry crowns the sky.
heav'n and earth to know, Things in heav'n and earth to know.

4. [7]He the lowly makes to rise
From the dust in which he lies,
[8]That exalted he may stand
With the princes of the land.

5. [9]He the childless woman takes
And a joyful mother makes;
Keeping house she finds reward.
Praise Jehovah; praise the LORD.

113B PSALM 113

JUBILATE. 66.66.88.
1. [1]O praise the LORD! Praise ye, O serv - ants of the LORD! [2]Praise ye the LORD's name! Blessed The LORD's name ev - er - more! [3]From dawn to dusk, from east to west, Praise to the LORD's name be ex - pressed!
2. [4]LORD o - ver na - tions all, His glo - ry crowns the sky. [5]Who's like the LORD our God Who dwells in heav - en high? [6]Yet He Him - self has hum - bled low All things in heav'n and earth to know.
3. [7]From dust He lifts the poor, The help - less out - cast takes, [8]Sets him with princ - es high, Prince of His peo - ple makes. [9]The child - less wom - an, joy re - stored, Keeps home and chil - dren. Praise the LORD!

PSALM 114

KILMARNOCK. C.M.
1. [1]When Is - ra - el was go - ing forth From
2. [2]To be His ho - ly dwell - ing place His
3. [3]The sea be - held and fled a - way; The
out of E - gypt's land, And Ja - cob's house from
choice on Ju - dah fell, And He as His do -
Jor - dan stopped its flow. [4]The moun - tains skipped like
al - ien tongues They could not un - der - stand,
min - ion took His cho - sen Is - ra - el.
rams; the hills Like lambs skipped to and fro.

4. [5]O sea, why did you run away?
   O Jordan, why turn tide?
   [6]You mounts and hills, like rams and lambs
   Why leap on every side?

5. [7]O tremble, earth, before the Lord;
   The God of Jacob fear;
   [8]He made the rock a water pool,
   The flint a fountain clear.

115 A PSALM 115:1–8

SALZBURG. C.M.

1. [1]LORD, not to us, not un - to us, But
2. [2]The hea - then say, "Where is their God?" But
3. [4]Of gold and sil - ver are their gods Which

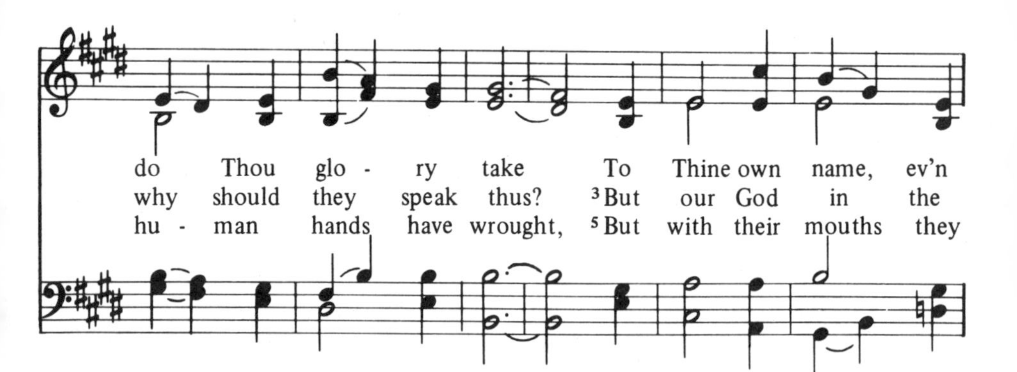

do Thou glo - ry take To Thine own name, ev'n
why should they speak thus? [3]But our God in the
hu - man hands have wrought, [5]But with their mouths they

for Thy truth And for Thy mer - cy's sake.
heav - en is; What pleas - es Him He does.
do not speak, And with their eyes see not.

4. [6]No smell their nostrils have discerned;
No sound their ears have heard;
[7]They never move their hands and feet;
Their throat emits no word.

5. [8]And like to them shall all become
By whom these gods are made;
And every one becomes like them
Whose trust on them is stayed.

PSALM 115:9–18 **115B**

SCOTT. C.M.D.
6. 9O Is - rael, trust ye in the LORD; He is their help and shield.
7. 12The LORD of us has mind- ful been, And He will bless us still;
8. 15May you be bless - ed of the LORD, Who made the heav'ns and earth.
10O house of Aar - on, trust the LORD; He is their help and shield.
He will the house of Is - rael bless; Bless Aar-on's house He will.
16The heav'ns, the heav'ns are of the LORD, Who gave to men the earth.
11O all of you that fear the LORD – He is their help and shield –
13He'll bless all those who fear the LORD, The great as well as small.
17No dead nor those to si - lence gone Give prais -es to the LORD,
Put all your trust up - on the LORD; He is their help and shield.
14O may the LORD grant you in- crease, You and your chil - dren all.
18But we for - ev - er bless the LORD. O do ye praise the LORD.

115C PSALM 115:1–11

LUX PRIMA. 77.77.77.
1. ¹Not to us, LORD, not to us, But to Your name
2. ³But our God in heav- en is; He does all that
3. ⁶They have ears but do not hear, Nos - es have but
4. ⁹Is - ra - el, trust in the LORD – He's their help and
glo - ry give, For Your stead - fast love and grace,
pleas - es Him; ⁴Their gods are of sil - ver, gold,
do not smell; ⁷They have hands but do not touch;
He's their shield! ¹⁰Aar - on's house, trust in the LORD –
For Your cov - 'nant faith - ful - ness. ²Why should hea - then
Fash - ioned by the hands of men: ⁵They have mouths but
They have feet but do not walk; In their throat they
He's their help and He's their shield! ¹¹Who the LORD fear,
na - tions say, "Where now is their might - y God?"
do not speak; They have eyes but do not see;
make no sound. ⁸Such, all who them make or trust.
trust the LORD – He's their help and He's their shield!

PSALM 115:12–18 115D

MORNING. 77.77.77.
5. 12 As the LORD has thought of us, Mind- ful still, He'll
6. 14 May the LORD so add to you That your num - bers
7. 16 Heav'ns are heav - ens of the LORD, Earth He's giv'n to
bless us now, He will bless all Is- rael's house;
will a - bound. And as gen - er - a -tions pass
sons of men. 17 Dead ones will not praise the LORD,
He will bless all Aar - on's house; 13 He'll bless all who
May your chil - dren still in - crease. 15 Bless-ed be you
Nor those bound for si - lent graves. 18 But we'll bless the
fear the LORD Wheth- er they be small or great.
of the LORD, He Who made the heav'n and earth.
LORD hence - forth, Ev - er - more. O praise the LORD!

116A
PSALM 116:1–9
OSTEND. C.M.D.
1. 1I love the LORD be - cause He heard My sup- pli- cat - ing plea;
2. 4Then called I on Je - ho - vah's name And un - to Him did say,
3. 7O thou my soul, do thou re - turn To thine own qui - et rest,
2I while I live will call on Him Who bowed His ear to me.
"De- liv - er Thou my soul, O LORD, I do Thee hum-bly pray."
Be - cause the LORD has dealt in grace; His boun -ty has thee blessed
3The cords of death on eve - ry side En - com-passed me a - round;
5The LORD is gra- cious and is just; Our God will mer- cy show;
8Thou hast re-leased my soul from death, My eyes from tears kept free;
The sor - rows of the grave took hold; I grief and trou - ble found.
6The LORD pre - serves the meek in heart; He saved me when brought low.
From fall - ing Thou hast saved my feet; 9I live and walk with THEE.

PSALM 116:10–19

116B

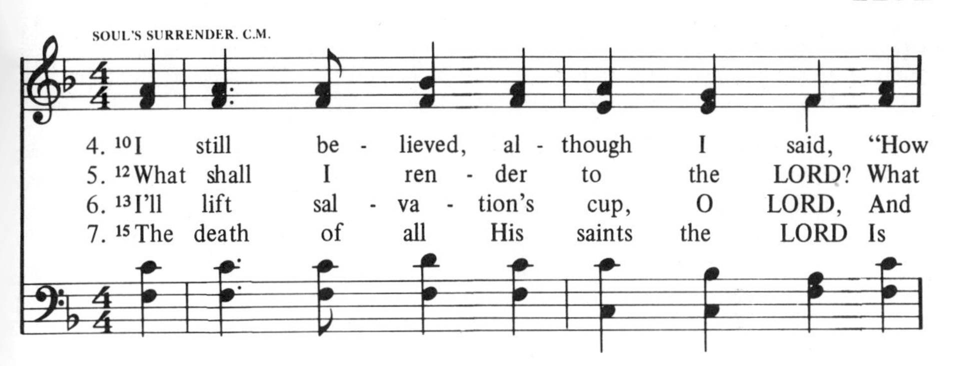
SOUL'S SURRENDER. C.M.
4. [10] I still be - lieved, al - though I said, "How
5. [12] What shall I ren - der to the LORD? What
6. [13] I'll lift sal - va - tion's cup, O LORD, And
7. [15] The death of all His saints the LORD Is

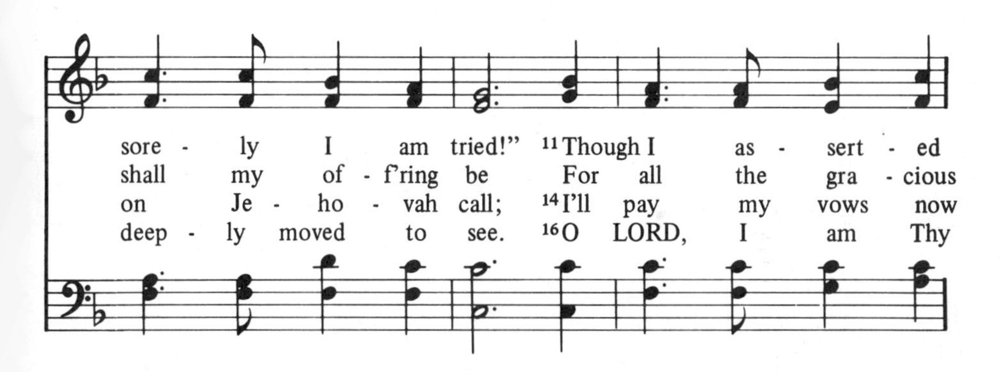
sore - ly I am tried!" [11] Though I as - sert - ed
shall my of - f'ring be For all the gra - cious
on Je - ho - vah call; [14] I'll pay my vows now
deep - ly moved to see. [16] O LORD, I am Thy

in my haste, "All liv - ing men have lied."
ben - e - fits He has be - stowed on me?
to the LORD Be - fore his peo - ple all.
hand - maid's son, Thy slave, by Thee set free.

8. [17] To Thee thankofferings I'll bring
And on Jehovah call.
[18] I'll pay my vows now to the LORD
Before His people all,

9. [19] Within His courts, Jehovah's house,
Yes, in the midst of thee,
O city of Jerusalem.
Praise to the LORD give ye.

116C PSALM 116

PILGRIMS. 11.10.11.10.9.11

1. [1] I love the LORD, be - cause He hears my plead - ing.
2. [5] The LORD our God is mer - ci - ful and right - eous;
3. You saved my eyes from tears, my feet from stum - bling.
4. [13] Sal - va - tion's cup I'll lift up in the LORD's name,
5. [17] To You I'll bring my of - f'ring of thanks - giv - ing;

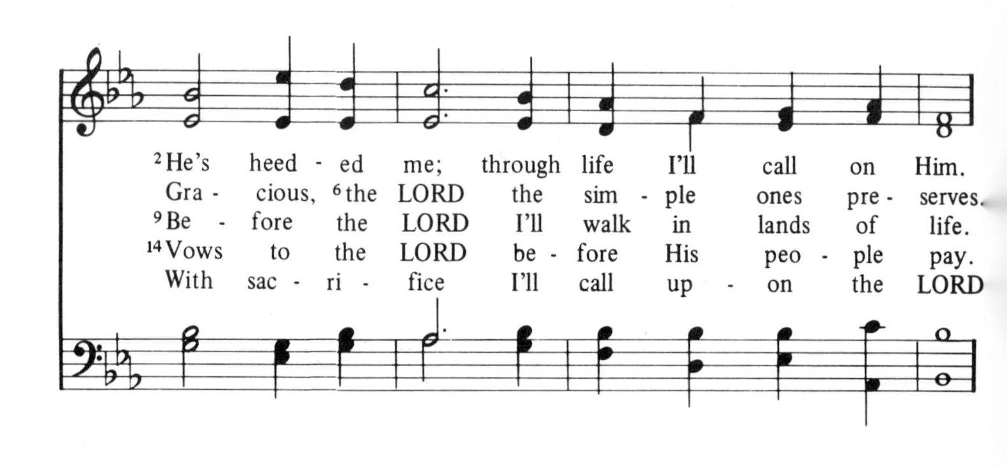
[2] He's heed - ed me; through life I'll call on Him.
Gra - cious, [6] the LORD the sim - ple ones pre - serves.
[9] Be - fore the LORD I'll walk in lands of life.
[14] Vows to the LORD be - fore His peo - ple pay.
With sac - ri - fice I'll call up - on the LORD

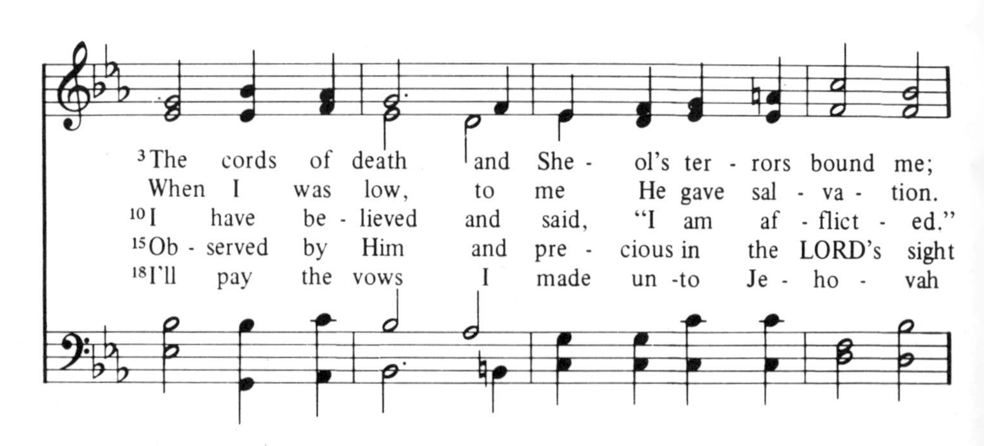
[3] The cords of death and She - ol's ter - rors bound me;
When I was low, to me He gave sal - va - tion.
[10] I have be - lieved and said, "I am af - flict - ed."
[15] Ob - served by Him and pre - cious in the LORD's sight
[18] I'll pay the vows I made un - to Je - ho - vah

In deep dis - tress I grief and trou - ble found.
7 Turn back a - gain, my soul, un - to your rest,
11 I in de - spair con - fessed, "All men are false!"
Ap - pears the death of all His saints each one.
Be - fore His peo - ple all, O may it be!

4 Then on the LORD's name in prayer I called:
Be - cause the LORD has dealt well with you,
12 What shall I ren - der now to the LORD
16 O LORD, I am Your serv - ant, Your slave.
19 With - in His courts, the house of the LORD,

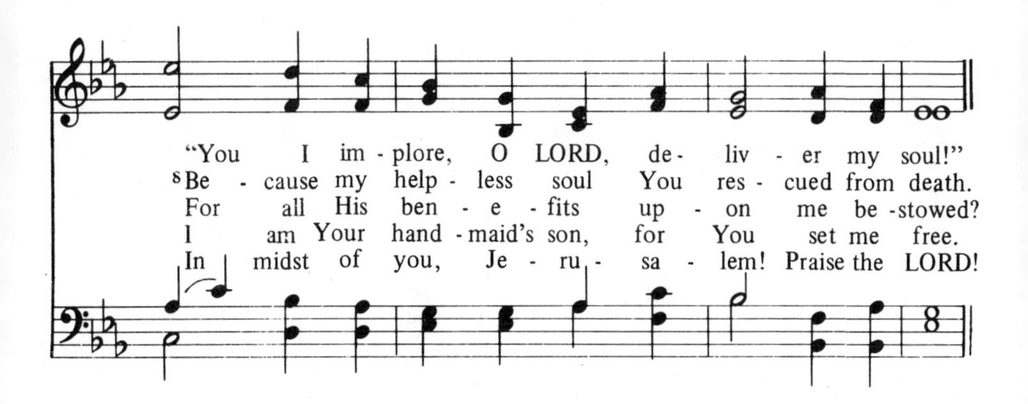
"You I im - plore, O LORD, de - liv - er my soul!"
8 Be - cause my help - less soul You res - cued from death.
For all His ben - e - fits up - on me be - stowed?
I am Your hand - maid's son, for You set me free.
In midst of you, Je - ru - sa - lem! Praise the LORD!

117A
PSALM 117
ST. MARTIN'S. C.M.
1. 1O all ye na - tions of the earth Give prais - es to the LORD;
2. 2Be - cause His lov - ing - kind - ness - es Are might - y to - ward us;
And all ye peo - ple mag - ni - fy His name with one ac - cord.
Je - ho - vah's truth en - dures for aye. The LORD O do ye bless.
117B
PSALM 117
BARNET. Irregular.
1O praise the LORD, all ye na - tions: praise Him, all ye
peo - ple. 2For His mer - ci - ful kind - ness is great toward us: and the
truth of the LORD en - dures for - ev - er. Praise ye the LORD!

PSALM 118:1–9

118A

HUDSON. C.M.D.

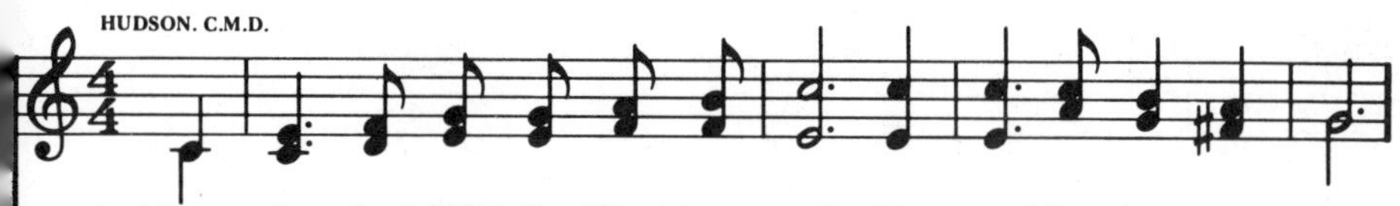

1. [1]O praise the LORD, for He is good; His stead-fast love en - dures.
2. [5]In my dis- tress I sought the LORD; Je - ho- vah an-swered me;
3. [7]The LORD is on my side with those Who ren - der help to me.

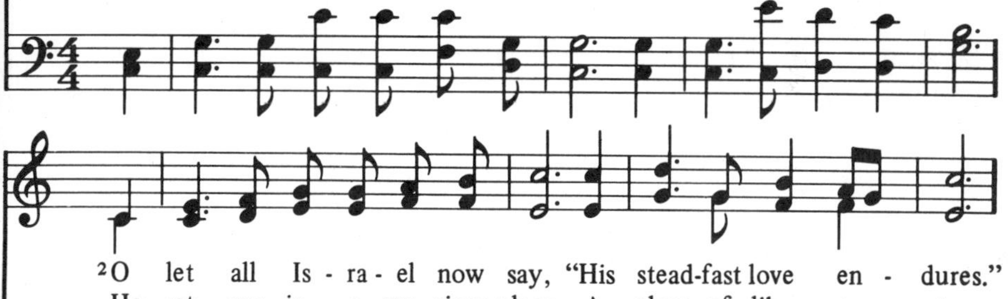

[2]O let all Is - ra - el now say, "His stead-fast love en - dures."
He set me in a spa- cious place, A place of lib - er - ty.
And so on all those hat-ing me I my de - sire shall see.

[3]O let the house of Aar - on say, "His stead-fast love en - dures."
[6]The might -y LORD is on my side; I will not be a - fraid;
[8]O bet - ter far to trust the LORD Than rest in aid of men.

[4]Let those that fear the LORD now say, "His stead-fast love en - dures."
For an - y - thing that man can do I will not be dis - mayed.
[9]Yes, bet - ter far to trust the LORD Than rest in no - ble - men.

PSALM 118:10–16

ASPURG. C.M.
4. 10 All nations have surrounded me; Their forces they deploy; But surely in Jehovah's name I will them all destroy.
5. 11 Yes, they have all surrounded me, Surrounded to annoy; But surely in Jehovah's name I will them all destroy.
6. 12 Though they surrounded me like bees, Like thorn fires soon they die, For surely in Jehovah's name Destroy them all will I.
7. 13 Hard pressed, I was about to fall; The LORD gave help to me. 14 Jehovah is my strength and song And my salvation free.

8. [15] Salvation's song and shouts of joy
Are where the righteous dwells.
The right hand of the mighty LORD
In valiant deeds excels.

9. [16] The right hand of the mighty LORD
On high exalted is.
The right hand of the mighty LORD
In valiant deeds excels.

PSALM 118:17–29

118C

JACKSON. C.M.
10. 17 I shall not die, but live and tell Je - ho - vah's power to save; 18 The LORD has sore - ly chas - tened me, But spared me from the grave.
11. 19 O set ye o - pen un - to me The gates of right - eous - ness; Then will I en - ter in - to them And I the LORD will bless.
12. 20 This is Je - ho - vah's gate; by it The just shall en - ter in. 21 I'll praise Thee Who hast heard my prayer, And hast my safe - ty been.
13. 22 That stone is made head cor - ner - stone Which build - ers did de - spise. 23 This is the do - ing of the LORD, And won - drous in our eyes.

14. [24] This is the day the LORD has made;
Let us be glad and sing.
[25] Hosanna, LORD! O give success!
O LORD, salvation bring!

15. [26] O blessed be the one who comes,
Comes in Jehovah's name;
The blessing from Jehovah's house
Upon you we proclaim.

16. [27] The LORD is God, and He to us
Has made the light arise;
O bind ye to the altar's horns
With cords the sacrifice.

17. [28] Thou art my God; I'll give Thee thanks.
My God, I'll worship Thee.
[29] O thank the LORD, for He is good;
His grace will endless be.

119A PSALM 119:1–8

CHRISTINE. 88.88.88.
1. 1How blessed the up - right in the way, They who Je-
2. 4Thy pre-cepts Thou hast giv - en us With dil - i-
3. 7Then un - to Thee I will give thanks With all sin-
ho - vah's law pur - sue. 2Blessed they who seek Him with whole
gence to be o - beyed. 5O that my ways were firm - ly
cer - i - ty of heart, When I the right-eous judg - ments
heart And keep His tes - ti - mo - nies true. 3And they do no un-
fixed To keep the stat - utes Thou hast made. 6Then shall I not be
learn, Which Thou dost un - to me im-part. 8Thy stat-utes shall be
right - eous- ness, But in His way they on- ward press.
put to shame When Thy com - mands are all my aim.
kept by me; For - sake me not then ut - ter - ly.

PSALM 119:9–16

119B

HESPERUS. L.M.
1. 9 How shall a young man cleanse his way? Let him with
2. 11 Thy word I've treas - ured in my heart, That I give
3. 13 I with my lips have oft de- clared The judg - ments
4. 15 I'll on Thy pre - cepts med - i - tate, And have re -

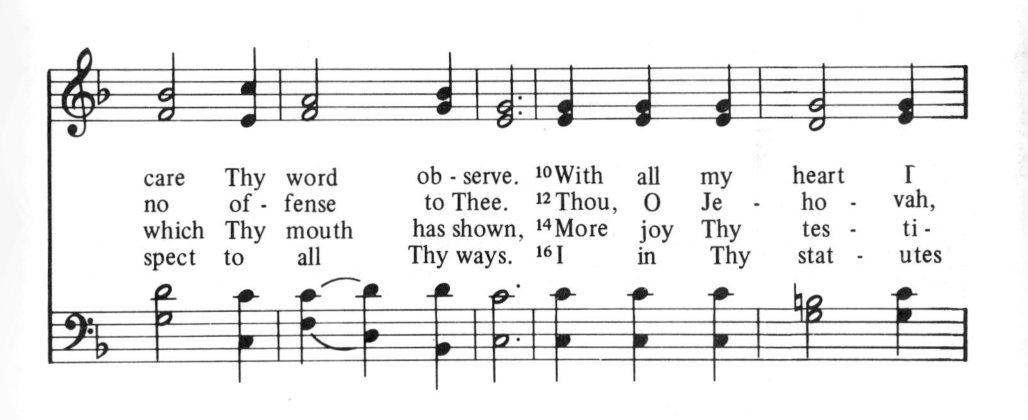
care Thy word ob - serve. 10 With all my heart I
no of - fense to Thee. 12 Thou, O Je - ho - vah,
which Thy mouth has shown, 14 More joy Thy tes - ti -
spect to all Thy ways. 16 I in Thy stat - utes

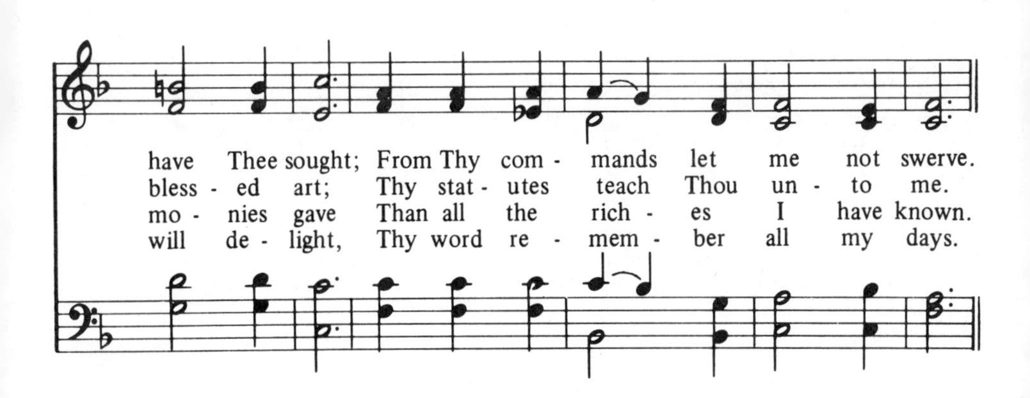
have Thee sought; From Thy com - mands let me not swerve.
bless - ed art; Thy stat - utes teach Thou un - to me.
mo - nies gave Than all the rich - es I have known.
will de - light, Thy word re - mem - ber all my days.

119C PSALM 119:17–24

ST. STEPHEN. C.M.
1. 17 Do Thou in boun - ty deal with me, Be - cause I keep Thy way, That by Thy fa - vor I may live; I will Thy word o - bey.
2. 18 Un - veil my eyes, that in Thy law The won - ders I may see. 19 I stran - ger am on earth; hide not All Thy com - mands from me.
3. 20 My soul is crushed be - cause I for Thine or - di - nanc - es yearn. 21 Thou hast re - buked the proud, ac - cursed, From Thy com - mands who turn.
4. 22 Do Thou re - move con - tempt from me; Take my re - proach a - way; For I Thy tes - ti - mo - nies still Ob - serve and will o - bey.

5. [23] The princes high against me speak
Their counsel to fulfill,
But I, Thy servant, meditate
Upon Thy statutes still.

6. [24] Thy testimonies also are
My comfort and delight;
They are as men who counsel me
And lead my steps aright.

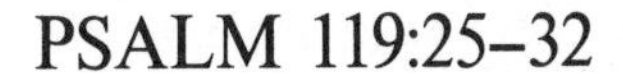
PSALM 119:25–32

119D

BOSWELL. C.M.

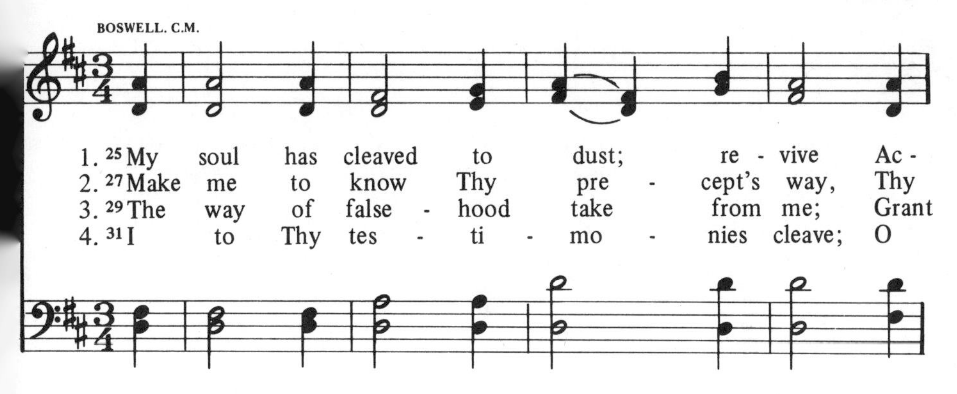
1. 25 My soul has cleaved to dust; re - vive Ac -
2. 27 Make me to know Thy pre - cept's way, Thy
3. 29 The way of false - hood take from me; Grant
4. 31 I to Thy tes - ti - mo - nies cleave; O

cord - ing to Thy word. 26 Teach me Thy stat - utes;
won - ders to re - view. 28 My soul melts down with
me Thy law in grace. 30 The faith - ful way I
LORD, no shame im - part. 32 I'll run the way of

when my ways I've told, Thou hast me heard.
grief; my strength, As Thou hast said, re - new.
choose; I'll give Thine or - di - nanc - es place.
Thy com - mands; Thou wilt en - large my heart.

119E PSALM 119:33–40

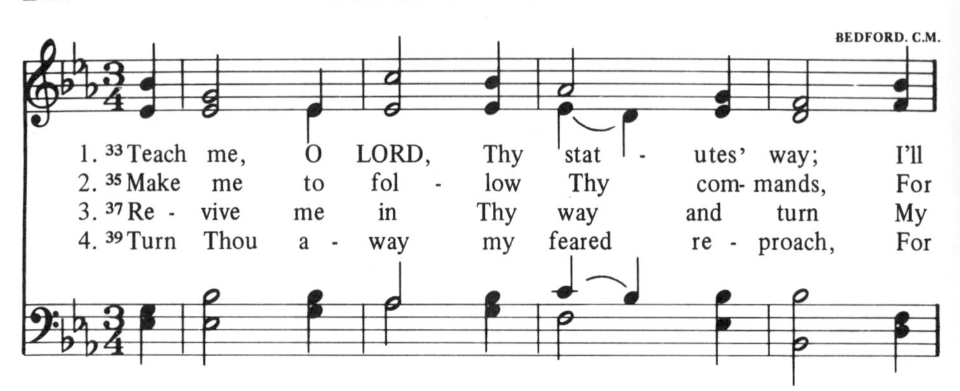
BEDFORD. C.M.
1. 33 Teach me, O LORD, Thy stat - utes' way; I'll
2. 35 Make me to fol - low Thy com- mands, For
3. 37 Re - vive me in Thy way and turn My
4. 39 Turn Thou a - way my feared re - proach, For

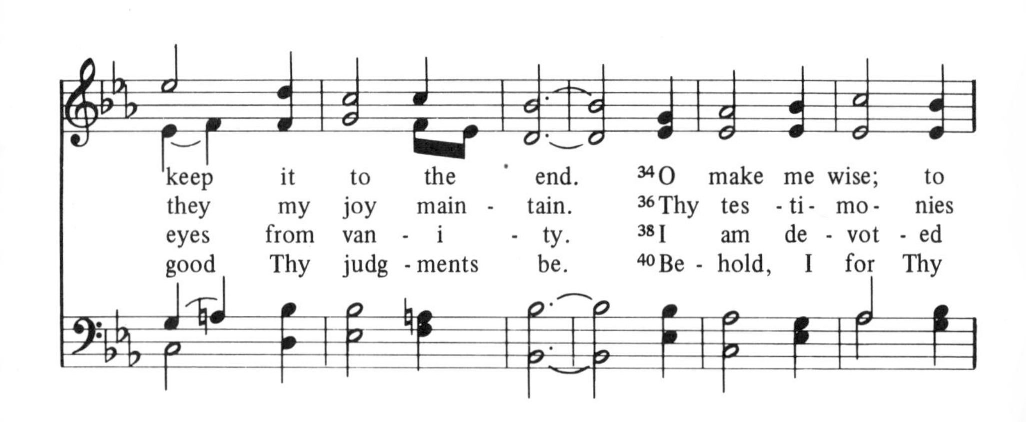
keep it to the end. 34 O make me wise; to
they my joy main - tain. 36 Thy tes - ti - mo - nies
eyes from van - i - ty. 38 I am de - vot - ed
good Thy judg - ments be. 40 Be - hold, I for Thy

keep Thy law My whole heart shall at - tend.
claim my heart; Keep me from love of gain.
to Thy fear; Con - firm Thy word to me.
pre - cepts longed; In jus - tice quick - en me.

PSALM 119:41–48

119F

CITY OF OUR GOD. C.M.
1. [41]O let Thy lov - ing - kind - ness - es Come
2. [42]Then I shall an - swer him who taunts, For
3. [44]I'll keep for - ev - er, ev - er - more, The
un - to me, O LORD. May Thy sal - va - tion
in Thy word I trust. [43]Take not from me the
law which Thou dost speak. [45]And I will walk at
al - so come Ac - cord - ing to Thy word.
word of truth; I wait Thy judg - ments just.
lib - er - ty, For I Thy pre - cepts seek.

4. [46]I'll of Thy testimonies speak
To kings and not be shamed.
[47]In Thy commandments which I love
I'll find the joy I've claimed.

5. [48]To Thy commandments which I love
My hands I'll dedicate,
And in Thy statutes evermore
I'll deeply meditate.

PSALM 119:49–56

CHARLESTOWN. 87.87.

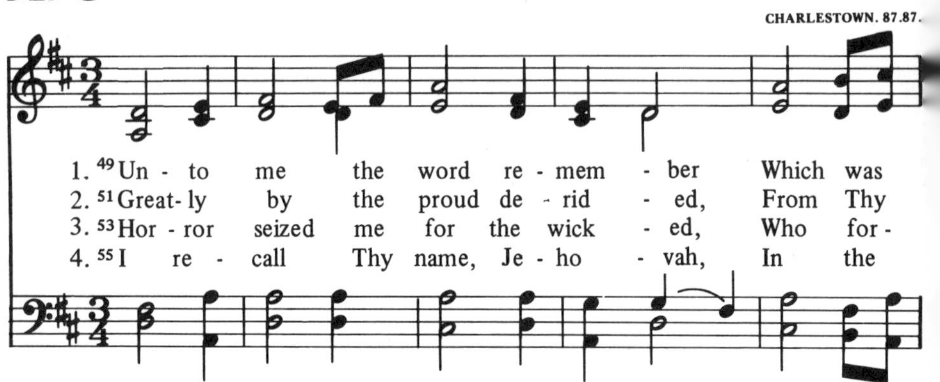
1. 49 Un - to me the word re - mem - ber Which was
2. 51 Great- ly by the proud de - rid - ed, From Thy
3. 53 Hor - ror seized me for the wick - ed, Who for -
4. 55 I re - call Thy name, Je - ho - vah, In the

made my hope by Thee. 50 This my com - fort in af -
law I've not de - clined: 52 LORD, Thy judg- ments of past
sake that law of Thine. 54 But I make my songs Thy
night, Thy law ob - serve. 56 This is mine be -cause for -

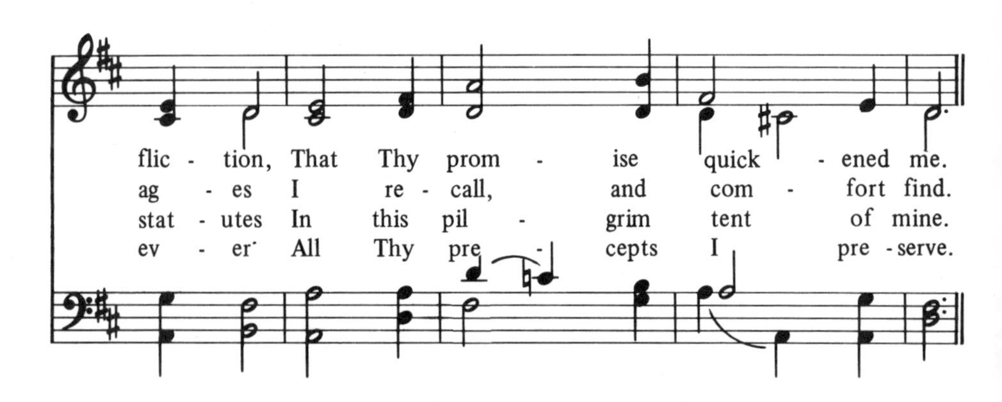
flic - tion, That Thy prom - ise quick - ened me.
ag - es I re - call, and com - fort find.
stat - utes In this pil - grim tent of mine.
ev - er All Thy pre - cepts I pre - serve.

PSALM 119:57–64

119H

HOWARD. C.M.
1. 57 The LORD my por - tion is; I've said I'll
2. 59 I viewed my ways, turned my feet toward Thy
3. 61 The wick - ed wrapped me round with cords; Thy
4. 63 I'm with those who Thy pre - cepts keep And

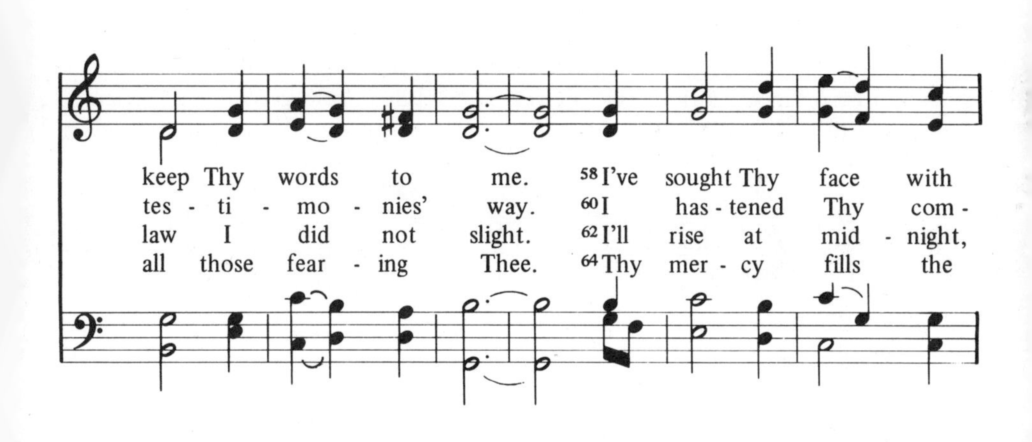
keep Thy words to me. 58 I've sought Thy face with
tes - ti - mo - nies' way. 60 I has - tened Thy com -
law I did not slight. 62 I'll rise at mid - night,
all those fear - ing Thee. 64 Thy mer - cy fills the

all my heart; As prom - ised, gra - cious be.
mands to keep; My feet made no de - lay.
thank - ing Thee For all Thy judg - ments right.
earth, O LORD; Thy stat - utes teach Thou me.

119I PSALM 119:65–72

MAITLAND. C.M.
1. 65 Ac - cord - ing to Thy word, O LORD, Thou hast Thy serv - ant blessed. 66 Teach me good judg - ment, knowl - edge give; On Thy com- mands I rest.
2. 67 Ere I af - flict - ed was I strayed; Thy word I now o - bey. 68 For good Thou art and do - est good; Teach me Thy stat - utes' way.
3. 69 The proud be - smear with lies, but I Thy pre - cepts keep a - right. 70 Their heart is bur - ied deep in fat; Thy law is my de - light.

4. 71 It has been very good for me
 That I was humbled low.
It through affliction was that I
 Thy statutes came to know.

5. 72 The law proceeding from Thy mouth
 I much more precious hold
Than countless thousands of fine coins
 Of silver and of gold.

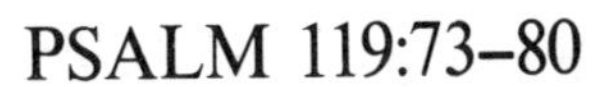
PSALM 119:73–80

119J

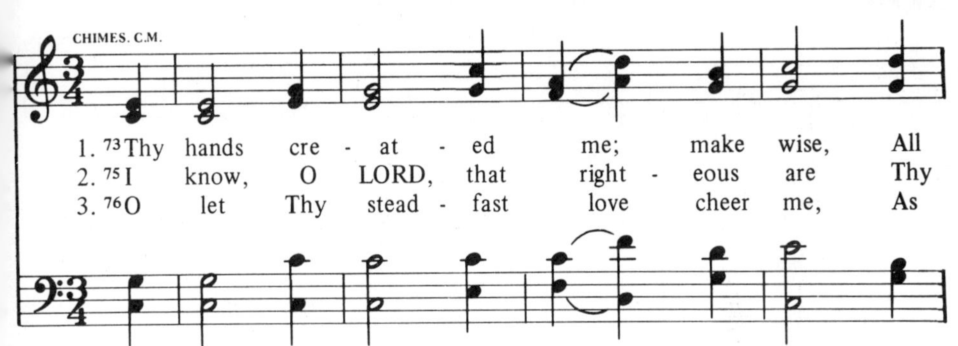
CHIMES. C.M.
1. 73 Thy hands cre - at - ed me; make wise, All
2. 75 I know, O LORD, that right - eous are Thy
3. 76 O let Thy stead - fast love cheer me, As

Thy com - mands to learn. 74 May those who fear Thee
judg - ments one and all, And that in faith - ful -
prom - ised to Thy slave. 77 May Thy com - pas - sion

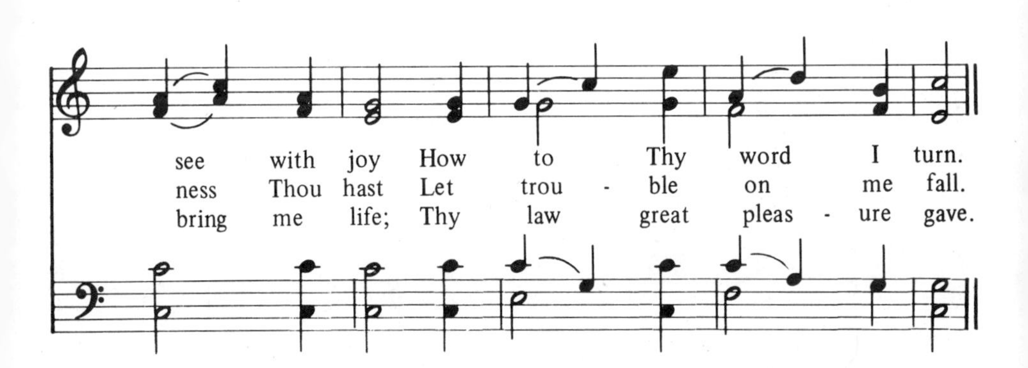
see with joy How to Thy word I turn.
ness Thou hast Let trou - ble on me fall.
bring me life; Thy law great pleas - ure gave.

4. [78] O may the arrogant be shamed
Who falsely me accuse
To overturn me; yet I shall
Upon Thy precepts muse.

5. [79] To me all turn, who, fearing Thee,
Thy testimonies claim.
[80] Let my heart in Thy statutes be
United, without shame.

119K
PSALM 119:81–88
MORNING STAR. 11.10.11.10.
1. 81 Faint-eth my soul for Thy pre-cious sal-va-tion,
2. 83 I'm like a wine-skin in smoke that is with-ered,
3. 85 Proud men have digged hid-den pits to en-snare me,
4. 87 Here on the earth they had al-most con-sumed me;
Yet do I put all my hope in Thy word.
Yet I Thy stat-utes will nev-er for-get.
Men who are not with Thy law in ac-cord.
Yet from Thy pre-cepts I nev-er will swerve.
82 Dim are my eyes for Thy word, while I'm say-ing,
84 What are the days to Thy serv-ant re-main-ing?
86 All Thy com-mand-ments are faith-ful-ness ev-er;
88 Quick-en me af-ter Thy great lov-ing-kind-ness;
"When wilt Thou give me Thy com-fort de-ferred?"
When wilt Thou judge those who me have be-set?
Wrong-ly they per-se-cute; help now af-ford.
I'll Thy de-clared tes-ti-mo-nies ob-serve.

PSALM 119:89–96

119L

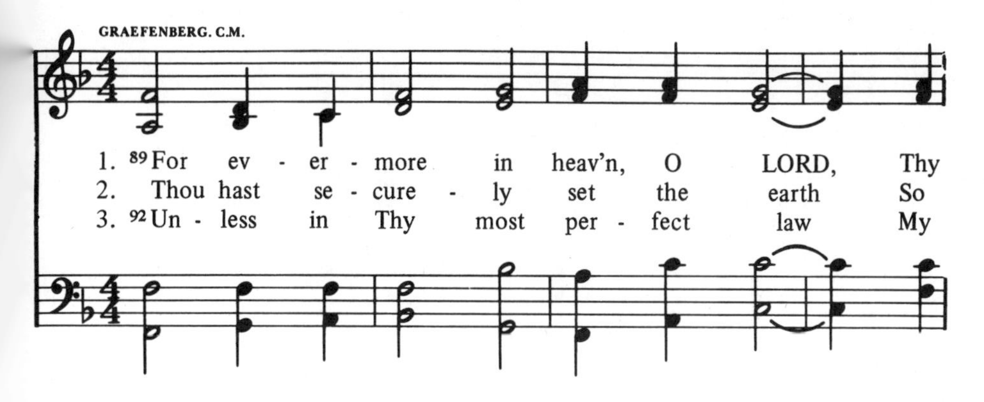
GRAEFENBERG. C.M.
1. 89 For ev - er - more in heav'n, O LORD, Thy
2. Thou hast se - cure - ly set the earth So
3. 92 Un - less in Thy most per - fect law My

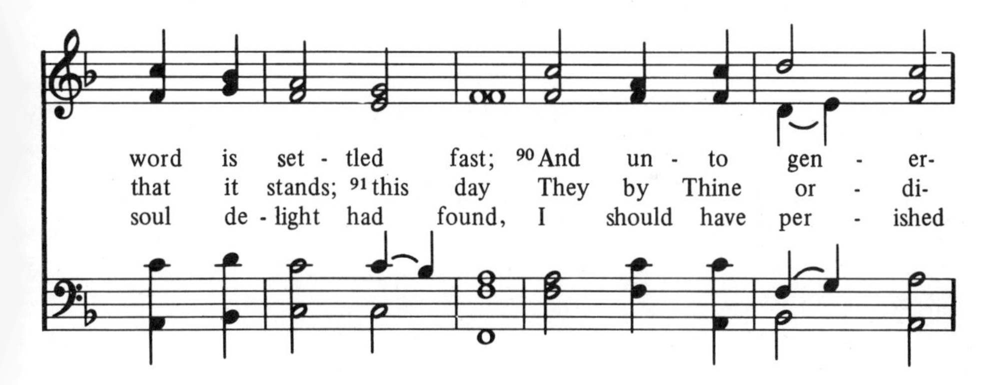
word is set - tled fast; 90 And un - to gen - er-
that it stands; 91 this day They by Thine or - di-
soul de - light had found, I should have per - ished

a - tions all Thy faith - ful - ness shall last.
nanc - es stand, For all things Thee o - bey.
at the time My trou - bles did a - bound.

4. [93] Thy precepts I will ne'er forget;
They quick'ning to me brought.
[94] For I am Thine; O save Thou me;
Thy precepts I have sought.

5. [95] The wicked seek my death, but I
Thy testimonies laud.
[96] Of all perfection bounds I've seen,
For Thy command is broad.

119M
PSALM 119:97–104
PERFECT WAY. C.M.D.
1. 97 O how I love Thy law; it is My stud- y all the day.
2. 101 I stayed my feet from e - vil ways That I Thy word ob - serve;
98 It makes me wis- er than my foes; Its pre- cepts with me stay.
102 I have been taught by Thee and from Thy judg-ments will not swerve.
99 More than my teach- ers or the old Thy serv- ant un - der - stands;
103 How sweet in taste Thy prom- is - es, Than hon- ey far more sweet!
Thy tes - ti - mo - nies I con - sult 100 And fol - low Thy com-mands.
104 Thy pre -cepts un - der -stand -ing give; I there - fore hate de - ceit.

PSALM 119:105–112

119N

HULL. C.M.
1.105 Thy word is to my feet a lamp, And
2.107 I'm hum - bled much; LORD, quick - en me Ac -
3.109 My soul is ev - er in my hand; Thy
4.111 I'm to Thy tes - ti - mo - nies heir; They

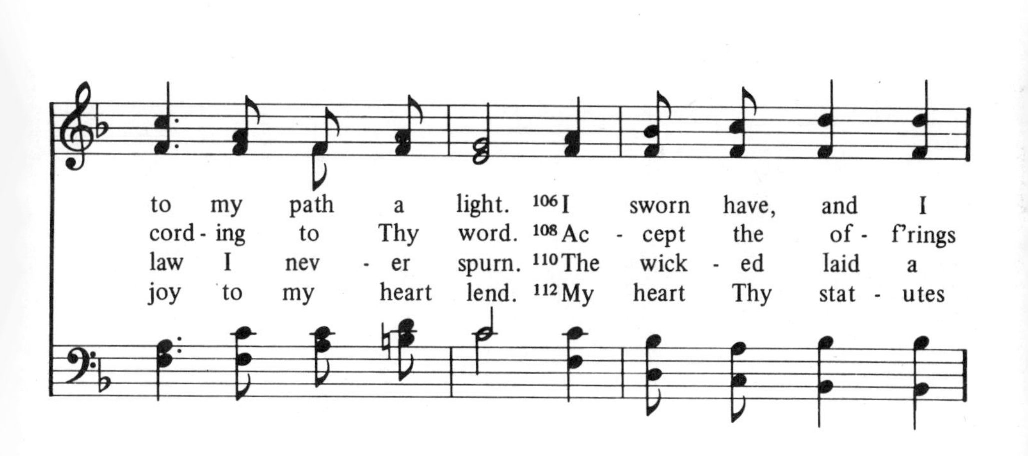
to my path a light. 106 I sworn have, and I
cord - ing to Thy word. 108 Ac - cept the of - f'rings
law I nev - er spurn. 110 The wick - ed laid a
joy to my heart lend. 112 My heart Thy stat - utes

will con - firm To keep Thy judg - ments right.
of my mouth; Teach me Thy judg - ments, LORD.
snare, yet from Thy pre - cepts I'll not turn.
longs to keep For - ev - er to the end.

119O PSALM119:105–112

LOUVAN. L.M.

1.105 Thy word a lamp is to my feet, A light to
2.107 I'm sore af - flict - ed; make me live, O LORD, ac -
3.109 My soul is ev - er in my hand, But yet Thy
4.111 Thy tes - ti - mo - nies are my joy, My cho - sen

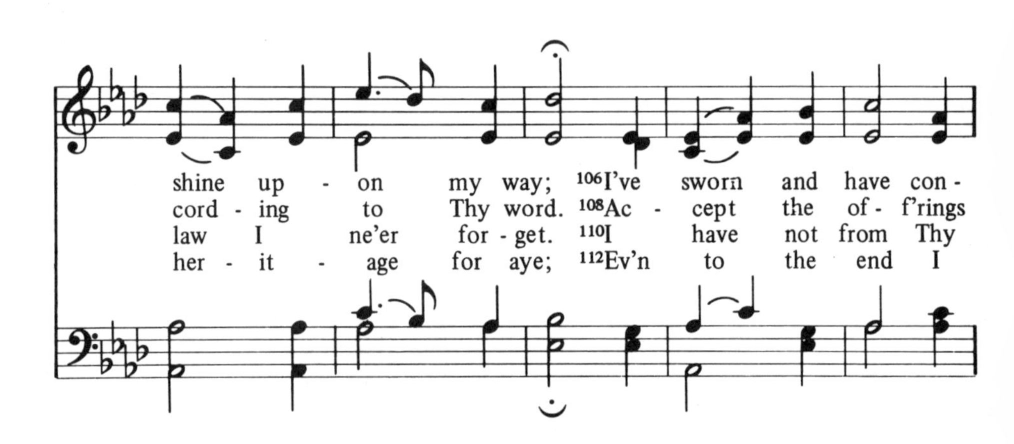
shine up - on my way; 106 I've sworn and have con -
cord - ing to Thy word. 108 Ac - cept the of - f'rings
law I ne'er for - get. 110 I have not from Thy
her - it - age for aye; 112 Ev'n to the end I

firmed the vow, Thy right - eous judg - ments to o - bey.
of my mouth, And teach Thou me Thy judg - ments, LORD.
pre - cepts strayed, Though snares for me the wick - ed set.
have in - clined My heart Thy stat - utes to o - bey.

PSALM 119:113–120 **119P**

LLOYD. C.M.
1.[113] The men of dou - ble mind I hate;
2.[115] De - part, ill - do - ers, that I may
3. Quench not my hope, [117] but hold me safe;
Thy law my love has stirred! [114] Thou art my shield and
My God's com-mand-ments heed. [116] Sus - tain as Thou hast
Thy stat - utes I'll re - spect. [118] All those who from Thy

hid - ing place; My hope is in Thy word.
prom - ised me That I may live in - deed.
stat - utes err, In scorn Thou dost re - ject.

4. How useless their deceitfulness!
   In falsehood is no gain.
   [119] Thou dost the wicked purge from earth
   Like dross, that none remain.

5. So I Thy testimonies love.
   [120] My flesh is quivering
   For fear of Thee; and deepest awe
   Thy judgments surely bring.

119Q PSALM 119:121–128

NETTLETON. 87.87.D.

1. [121] Judg-ment I have done and jus - tice; Leave me not lest foes op - press;
2. [125] I'm Thy serv-ant; give me wis - dom; I'll Thy tes - ti - mo - nies know.

[122] Be for good Thy serv-ant's sure - ty Lest the proud should me dis - tress.
[126] 'Tis Je - ho - vah's time for work-ing For Thy law they o - ver - throw.

[123] Thy just prom-ise, Thy sal - va - tion Long my fail - ing eyes to see.
[127] There-fore love I Thy com-mand-ments More than gold, the fin- est gold.

[124] With Thy serv - ant deal in mer - cy; All Thy stat - utes teach Thou me.
[128] Hence Thy pre - cepts all I hon- or, All that's false in ha - tred hold.

PSALM 119:129–136
119R
RETREAT. L.M.
1. 129 Thy tes - ti - mo - nies I ob - serve, For they are
2. 131 I o - pen wide my mouth and pant; I long for
3. 133 My steps es - tab - lish in Thy word, And let no
4. 135 Thy face make on Thy serv - ant shine; Teach me Thy
won - drous in my eyes. 130 The o - p'ning of Thy
all com - mands of Thine. 132 Turn Thou to me; the
sin o'er me have sway. 134 Re - deem me from the
stat - utes; 136 for I weep; The tears in streams flow
words gives light And makes the sim - ple - heart - ed wise.
mer - cy shown To those who love Thy name be mine.
power of man, And I Thy pre - cepts will o - bey.
from my eyes, Be - cause Thy law they do not keep.

119S PSALM 119:137–144

BISHOPTHORPE. C.M.

1. 137 Thou, LORD, art right - eous, and up - right Thine
2. 139 My zeal con - sumed me; Thy com - mands My
3. 141 I'm lit - tle and de - spised, yet I Thy
4. 143 Dis - tress and an - guish have me found; Joy
or - di - nanc - es be. 138 Thou hast Thy tes - ti-
ad - ver - sar - ies spurn. 140 Thy prom - ise is most
pre - cepts ne'er for - get. 142 E - ter - nal is Thy
Thy com - mand - ments give. 144 Thy tes - ti - mo - nies

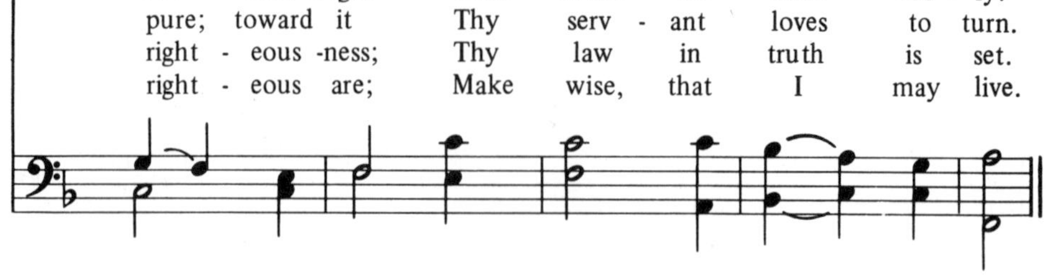
mo - nies right Com - mand - ed faith - ful - ly.
pure; toward it Thy serv - ant loves to turn.
right - eous - ness; Thy law in truth is set.
right - eous are; Make wise, that I may live.

PSALM 119:145–152

DAVIS. 11.8.11.8.

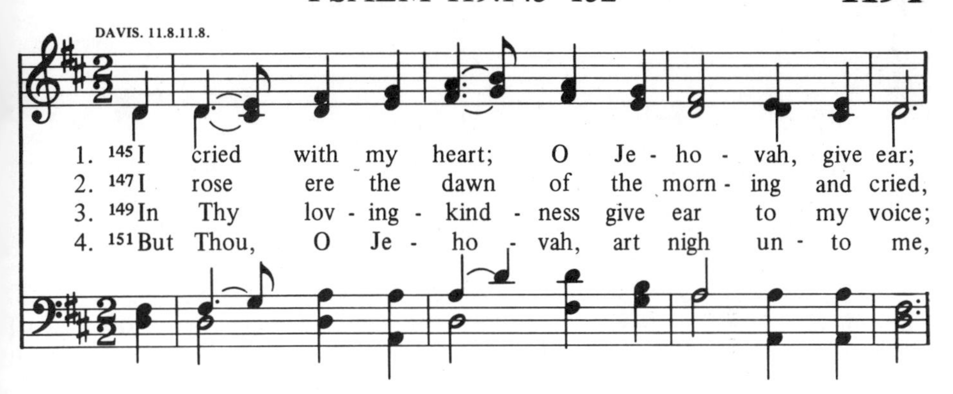
1. [145] I cried with my heart; O Je - ho - vah, give ear;
2. [147] I rose ere the dawn of the morn - ing and cried,
3. [149] In Thy lov - ing - kind - ness give ear to my voice;
4. [151] But Thou, O Je - ho - vah, art nigh un - to me,

Thy stat - utes I'll ev - er o - bey. [146] I've called Thee, and Thy tes- ti-
My hope by Thy prom - is - es stirred. [148] And ere the night watch-es were
As prom - ised, O LORD, quick-en me. [150] They come ev-er clos - er who
And true is Thine eve - ry com-mand. [152] From Thy tes-ti - mo - nies I'm

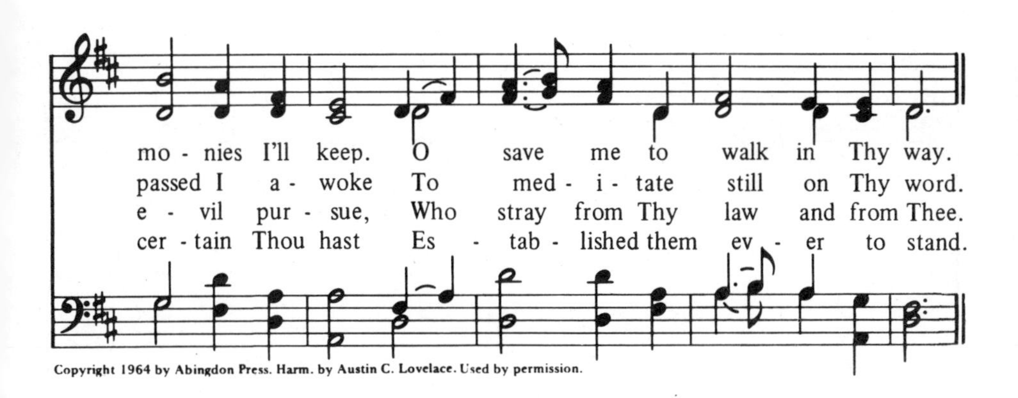
mo - nies I'll keep. O save me to walk in Thy way.
passed I a - woke To med - i - tate still on Thy word.
e - vil pur - sue, Who stray from Thy law and from Thee.
cer - tain Thou hast Es - tab - lished them ev - er to stand.

119U

PSALM 119:153–160

HAMBURG. L.M.
1. 153 Re-gard my grief and res - cue me, For I Thy
2. 155 Sal - va - tion's far from wick - ed men; Thy stat - utes
3. 157 My per - se - cu - tors man - y are, Yet from Thy
4. 159 Be-hold how I Thy pre - cepts love! O LORD, in

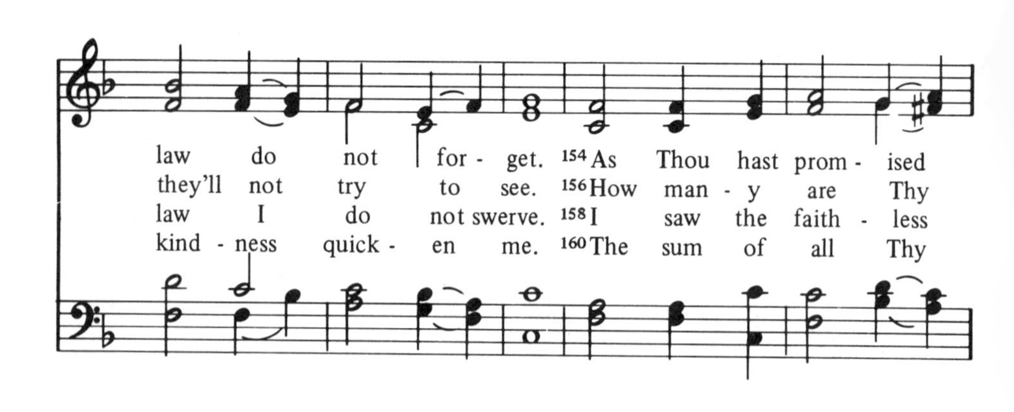
law do not for - get. 154 As Thou hast prom - ised
they'll not try to see. 156 How man - y are Thy
law I do not swerve. 158 I saw the faith - less
kind - ness quick - en me. 160 The sum of all Thy

quick - en me. Thy prom - ise keep; re - vive me yet.
mer - cies, LORD! Ful - fill Thy judg - ments; quick - en me.
and was grieved, For they Thy word do not ob - serve.
words is truth; Thy judg - ments stand e - ter - nal - ly.

PSALM 119:161–168

119V

MARLOW. C.M.
1.161 The princ - es cause - less - ly pur - sue; My
2.163 I false - hood hate and have de - spised; Thy
3.165 Great peace have those who love Thy law; They
4.167 My soul Thy tes - ti - mo - nies keeps And

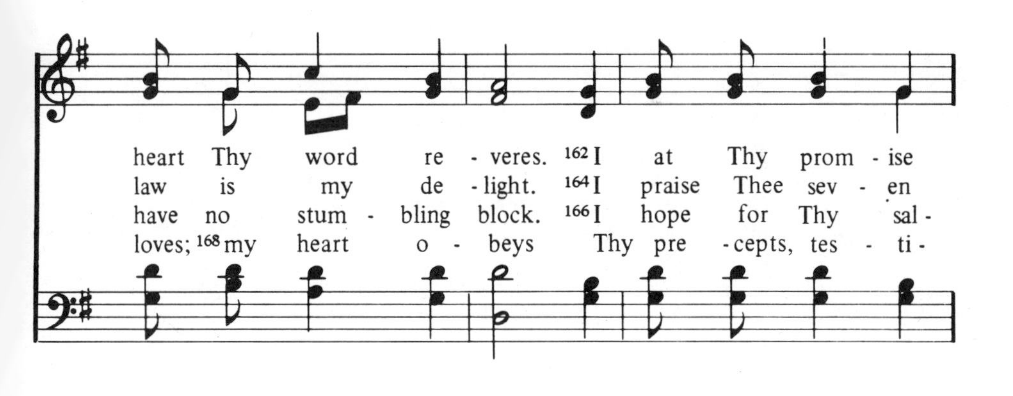
heart Thy word re - veres. 162 I at Thy prom - ise
law is my de - light. 164 I praise Thee sev - en
have no stum - bling block. 166 I hope for Thy sal -
loves; 168 my heart o - beys Thy pre - cepts, tes - ti -

joy as one For whom great spoil ap - pears.
times a day For all Thy judg - ments right.
va - tion, LORD; In Thy com - mands I walk.
mo - nies all; Be - fore Thee are my ways.

119W PSALM 119:169–176

FEDERAL STREET. L.M.

1.169 Be - fore Thee let my cry come near, O LORD; true
2.171 Since Thou Thy stat - utes teach - est me, O let my
3.173 Be read - y with Thy hand to help, Be - cause Thy
4.175 O let Thine or - di - nanc - es help; My soul shall

to Thy word, teach me. 170 Be - fore Thee let my
lips Thy praise con - fess. 172 Yea, of Thy word my
pre - cepts are my choice. 174 I've longed for Thy sal -
live and praise Thee yet. 176 A stray - ing sheep, Thy

plead - ing come; True to Thy prom - ise, res - cue me.
tongue would sing, For Thy com - mands are right - eous - ness.
va - tion, LORD, And in Thy ho - ly law re - joice.
serv - ant, seek, For Thy com - mands I ne'er for - get.

PSALM 119:169–176 119X

RUSSIA. L.M.
1. 169 Be - fore Thee let my cry come near, O LORD; true to Thy word, teach me.
2. 171 Since Thou Thy stat-utes teach-est me, O let my lips Thy praise con- fess.
(Melody)
(Soprano) 170 Be- fore Thee let my plead-ing come; True to Thy prom - ise, res - cue me.
172 Yea, of Thy word my tongue would sing, For Thy com - mands are right-eous - ness.
(Alto) 170 Be - fore Thee let my plead - ing come; True to Thy prom-ise, res - cue me.
172 Yea, of Thy word my tongue would sing, For Thy com-mands are right-eous- ness.
(Melody) 170 Be - fore Thee let my plead-ing come; True to Thy prom-ise, res-cue me, True to Thy prom-ise res - cue me.
172 Yea, of Thy word my tongue would sing, For Thy com-mands are right-eous-ness, For Thy com-mands are right-eous - ness.
(Bass) 170 Be - fore Thee let my plead-ing come; True to Thy prom - ise, res - cue me, True to Thy prom-ise, res - cue me.
172 Yea, of Thy word my tongue would sing, For Thy com-mands are right - eous - ness, For Thy com-mands are right- eous- ness.

3. 173 Be ready with Thy hand to help,
   Because Thy precepts are my choice.
   174 I've longed for Thy salvation, LORD,
   And in Thy holy law rejoice.

4. 175 O let Thine ordinances help;
   My soul shall live and praise Thee yet.
   176 A straying sheep, Thy servant, seek,
   For Thy commands I ne'er forget.

120 PSALM 120

AYRSHIRE. C.M.
1. [1]I cried in trou - ble to the LORD, And
2. [3]What shall be giv - en you, false tongue? What
3. [5]A - las for me, that I so - journ So
4. [6]Too long my soul has made its home With

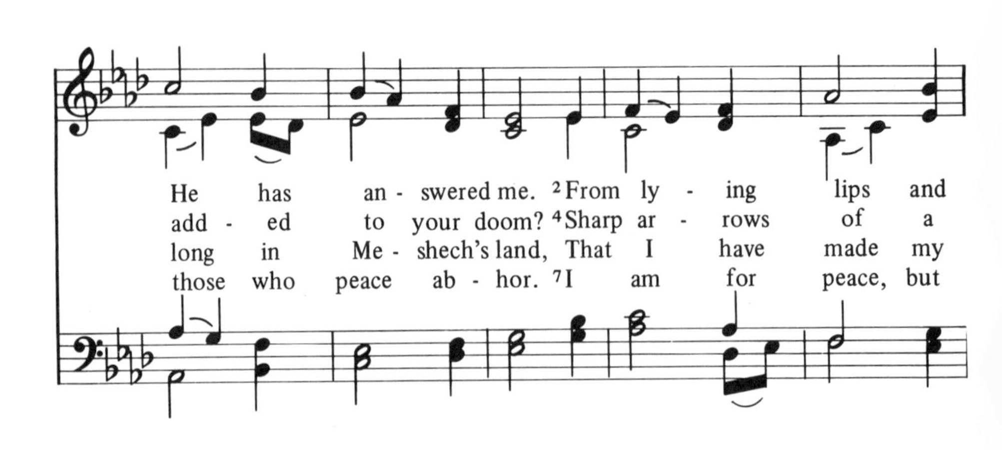
He has an - swered me. [2]From ly - ing lips and
add - ed to your doom? [4]Sharp ar - rows of a
long in Me - shech's land, That I have made my
those who peace ab - hor. [7]I am for peace, but

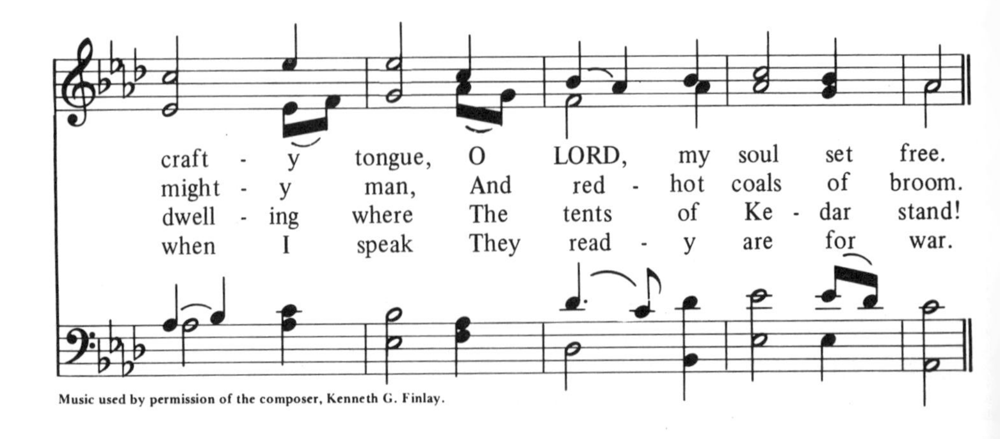
craft - y tongue, O LORD, my soul set free.
might - y man, And red - hot coals of broom.
dwell - ing where The tents of Ke - dar stand!
when I speak They read - y are for war.

Music used by permission of the composer, Kenneth G. Finlay.

PSALM 121
121A
HOPE. C.M.
1. 1I to the hills will lift my eyes. From
2. 3Thy foot He'll not let slide, nor will He
3. 5The LORD thee keeps; the LORD thy shade On
4. 7The LORD shall keep thee from all ill; He
whence shall come my aid? 2My safe - ty com - eth
slum - ber that thee keeps. 4Lo, He that keep - eth
thy right hand doth stay; 6The moon by night thee
shall pre - serve thy soul. 8The LORD as thou shalt
from the LORD Who heav'n and earth has made.
Is - ra - el, He slum - bers not nor sleeps.
shall not smite, Nor yet the sun by day.
go and come For - ev - er keeps thee whole.

PSALM 121

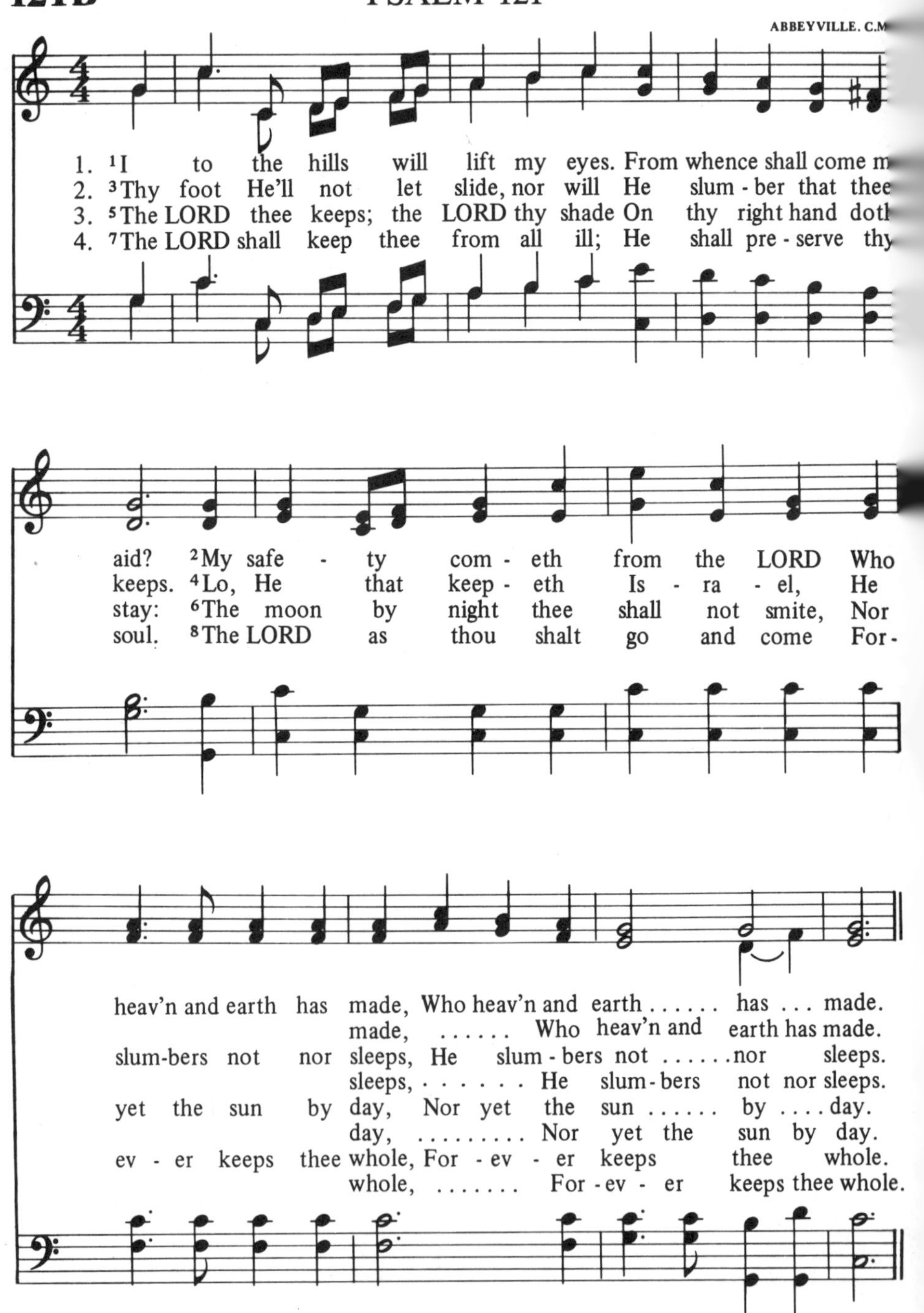
ABBEYVILLE. C.M
1. [1]I to the hills will lift my eyes. From whence shall come m
2. [3]Thy foot He'll not let slide, nor will He slum - ber that thee
3. [5]The LORD thee keeps; the LORD thy shade On thy right hand dot
4. [7]The LORD shall keep thee from all ill; He shall pre - serve thy
aid? [2]My safe - ty com - eth from the LORD Who
keeps. [4]Lo, He that keep - eth Is - ra - el, He
stay: [6]The moon by night thee shall not smite, Nor
soul. [8]The LORD as thou shalt go and come For -
heav'n and earth has made, Who heav'n and earth ...... has ... made.
made, ... Who heav'n and earth has made.
slum-bers not nor sleeps, He slum - bers not ......nor sleeps.
sleeps, ... He slum - bers not nor sleeps.
yet the sun by day, Nor yet the sun ...... by .... day.
day, ... Nor yet the sun by day.
ev - er keeps thee whole, For - ev - er keeps thee whole.
whole, ... For - ev - er keeps thee whole.

PSALM 121

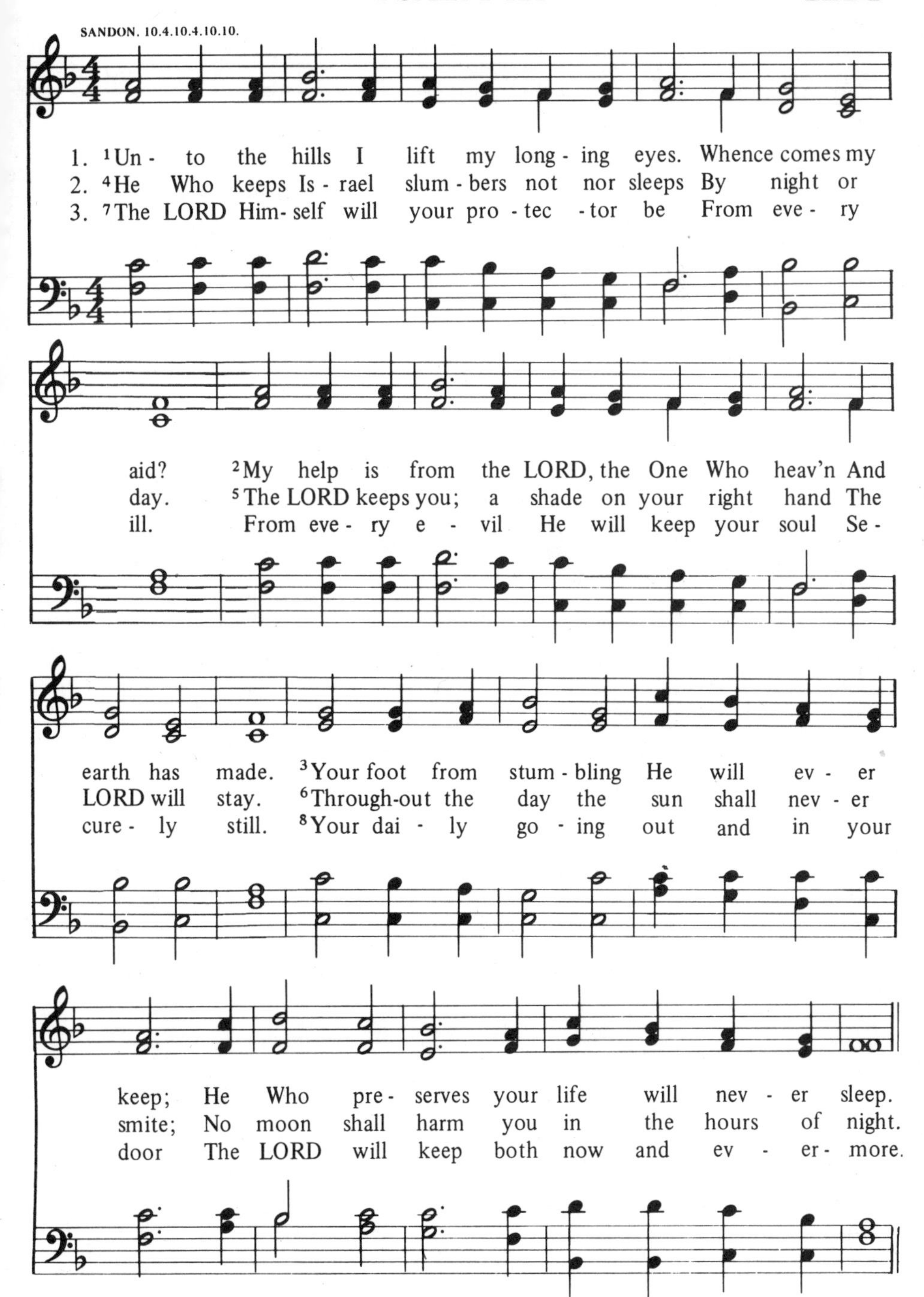
SANDON. 10.4.10.4.10.10.
1. [1]Un - to the hills I lift my long - ing eyes. Whence comes my
2. [4]He Who keeps Is - rael slum - bers not nor sleeps By night or
3. [7]The LORD Him- self will your pro - tec - tor be From eve - ry
aid? [2]My help is from the LORD, the One Who heav'n And
day. [5]The LORD keeps you; a shade on your right hand The
ill. From eve - ry e - vil He will keep your soul Se -
earth has made. [3]Your foot from stum - bling He will ev - er
LORD will stay. [6]Through-out the day the sun shall nev - er
cure - ly still. [8]Your dai - ly go - ing out and in your
keep; He Who pre - serves your life will nev - er sleep.
smite; No moon shall harm you in the hours of night.
door The LORD will keep both now and ev - er - more.

122A

PSALM 122

ST. ASAPH. C.M.D.
1. [1]I joyed when to Je - ho - vah's house, "Go up," they said to me.
2. An or - di - nance for Is - ra - el, To thank the LORD a - lone.
3. [7]I there-fore wish that peace may still With-in thy walls re - main,
[2]"Je - ru - sa - lem, with- in thy gates Our feet shall stand-ing be."
[5]For thrones of judg -ment there are set, Ev'n Da- vid's roy- al throne.
And ev - er may thy pal - ac - es Pros - per- i - ty re - tain.
[3]Je - ru - sa - lem a cit - y is, Com-pact - ly built and strong,
[6]O pray ye that Je - ru - sa - lem May have a - bun - dant peace;
[8]For broth-ers' and com - pan-ions' sake Let me now wish thee peace;
[4]Where - to the tribes go up, the tribes That to the LORD be - long.
For eve - ry one that lov - eth thee Shall pros-per and in- crease.
[9]And for the house of God the LORD My care shall nev- er cease.

PSALM 122

122B

CWM RHONDDA. 87.87.877.
1. [1]I was glad to hear them say-ing, "To the LORD's house let us go." [2]For our feet will soon be stand-ing In your gates, Je-ru-sa-lem, [3]Sa-lem, well con-struct-ed cit-y; [4]There as-sem-ble all the tribes, (the tribes) Tribes that are Je-ho-vah's own.
2. This the or-di-nance for Is-rael, Here to thank Je-ho-vah's name. [5]There are set the thrones of judg-ment; There is Da-vid's house en-throned. [6]Pray then for the peace of Sa-lem; May they pros-per who love you. (love you) [7]Be there peace with-in your walls.
3. In your pal-ac-es be safe-ty. [8]For the sake of broth-ers all, For the sake of my com-pan-ions, I am say-ing, "Peace to you!" [9]For Je-ho-vah's house with-in you, Tem-ple of the LORD our God, (our God) I will ev-er seek your good.

PSALM 123

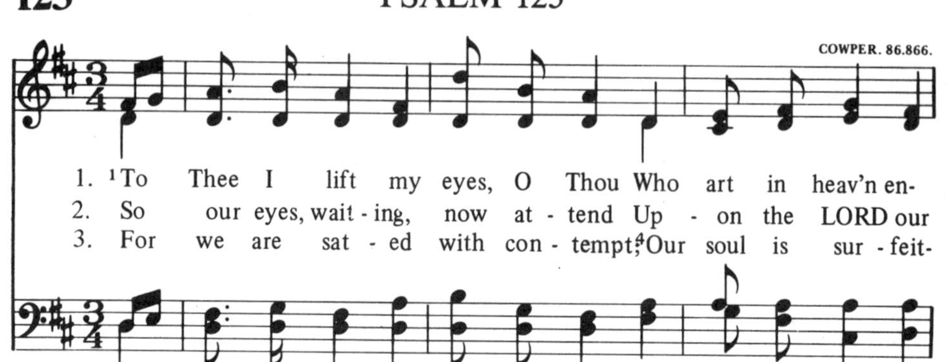
COWPER. 86.866.
1. [1]To Thee I lift my eyes, O Thou Who art in heav'n en-
2. So our eyes, wait - ing, now at - tend Up - on the LORD our
3. For we are sat - ed with con - tempt;[4]Our soul is sur - feit-

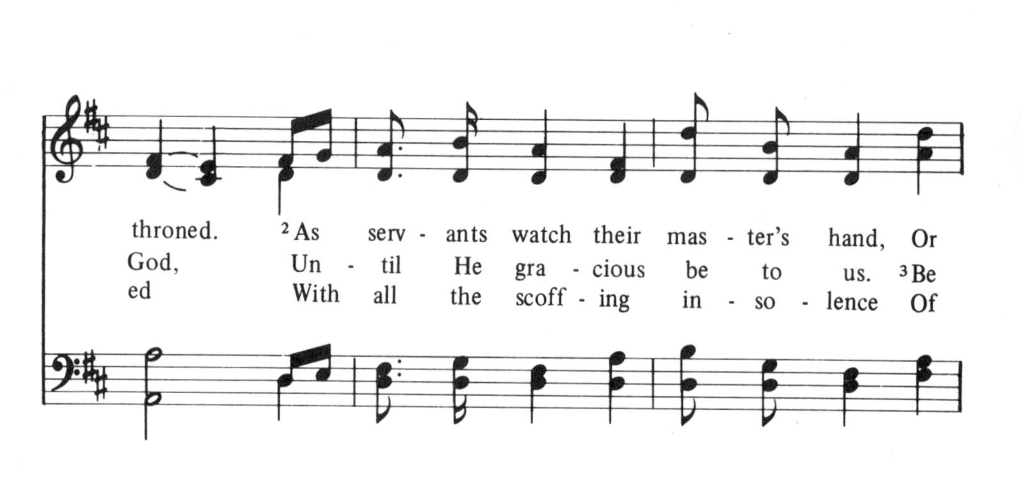
throned. [2]As serv - ants watch their mas - ter's hand, Or
God, Un - til He gra - cious be to us. [3]Be
ed With all the scoff - ing in - so - lence Of

as a maid's eyes wait Her mis - tress' hand to see,
gra - cious to us, LORD. Be gra - cious un - to us.
those who live at ease, And with the proud's con - tempt.

PSALM 124

BELGRAVE. C.M.
1. 1"Un - less the LORD had been for us," Let
2. 3"They would have swal - lowed us a - live In
3. 5"The wa - ters would in swell - ing might Our
4. 7Like birds freed from a fowl - er's trap, From

Is - ra - el now say, 2"Un - less the LORD had
rage be - yond con - trol; 4The wa - ters would have
soul have o - ver - borne." 6Blessed be the LORD, Who
out their net we're freed. 8Our help is in Je-

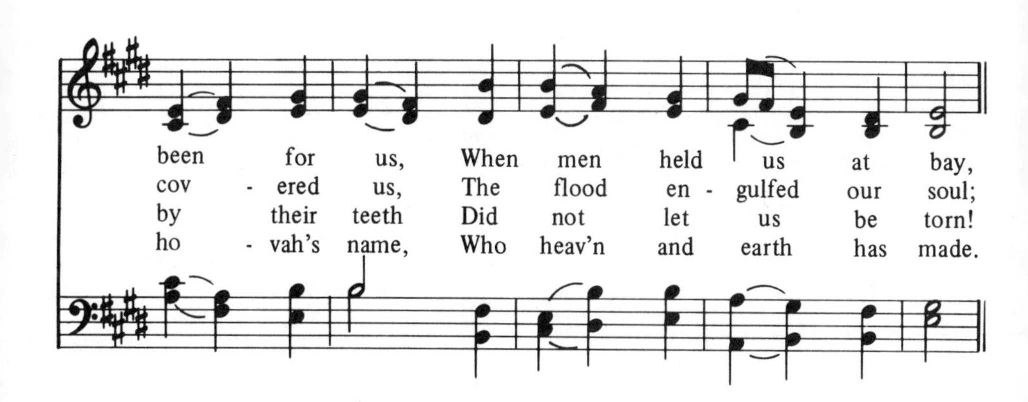
been for us, When men held us at bay,
cov - ered us, The flood en - gulfed our soul;
by their teeth Did not let us be torn!
ho - vah's name, Who heav'n and earth has made.

PSALM 124

OLD 124TH. 10.10.10.10.10.

1. [1]Now Is - ra - el may say and that in truth, "If that the
2. "Yea, when their wrath a - gainst us fierce- ly rose, [4]Then as fierce
3. [6]Blessed be the LORD Who made us not their prey; [7]As from the

LORD had not our right main-tained, [2]If that the LORD had
floods be - fore them all things drown, So had they brought our
snare a bird es - cap - eth free, Their net is rent and

not with us re - mained, When cru-el men a - gainst us rose to
soul to death quite down; [5]The rag - ing streams, with their proud swell - ing
so es - caped are we. [8]Our on - ly help is in Je - ho - vah's

strive, [3]We sure - ly had been swal - lowed up a - live.
waves, Had then our soul o'er - whelmed as in the grave."
name, Who made the earth and all the heav'n - ly frame.

PSALM 125

ABBEYVILLE. C.M.
1. [1]Like Zi - on's moun - tain shall they be Who in the LORD con-
fide, A mount which nev - er can be moved But
ev - er shall a - bide, But ev - er shall a - bide.
ev - er shall a - bide, . . . But ev - er shall a - bide.

2. [2]As all around Jerusalem
The mountains firmly stand,
The LORD for evermore surrounds
The people of His hand.

3. [3]Upon the land of righteous ones
No evil rule shall press,
Lest righteous men put forth their hands
To work unrighteousness.

4. [4]O LORD, to those men who are good
Show Yourself good and kind,
And likewise show Your goodness to
All them of upright mind.

5. [5]Yet shall the LORD drive out all those
In crooked ways who dwell,
Along with all who practice sin;
But peace on Israel!

126A PSALM 126

GENEVA. C.M.
1. [1]The LORD brought Zi - on's ex - iles back.
The LORD brought Zi - on's ex - iles back.
The LORD brought Zi-on's ex-iles back.
2. "The LORD has done great things for them,"
"The LORD has done great things for them,"
"The LORD has done great things for them,"
We were as men that dreamed. [2]Our tongue was filled with
Our tongue was filled with
The heath- en were a - greed. [3]The LORD has done great
The LORD has done great
mel - o - dy; Our mouth with laugh - ter teemed.
things for us, And we re - joice in - deed!

3. [4]O LORD, as streams revive the south,
Our exile band restore.
[5]Then those that sow their seed in tears
Shall reap with joy once more.

4. [6]Though bearing forth the precious seed
The reaper sowing grieves,
He doubtless shall return again
And bring with joy his sheaves.

PSALM 126

RUTHERFORD. 664.66.64.
1. ¹When Zi - on's ex - ile bands The LORD brought back, we were As those who dream. ²For then our mouth was filled With laugh - ter and de - light; Our tongue then o - ver - flowed With shouts of joy.
2. A - mong the na - tions all They said, "The LORD has done Great things for them!" ³The LORD has done for us Great things, and we are glad. ⁴Re - store our for - tunes, LORD, Like des - ert streams.
3. ⁵For those who sow in tears Shall reap at har - vest time With shouts of joy. ⁶The one who weep - ing goes, Bear - ing his pre - cious seed, Shall sing - ing come a - gain, Bear - ing his sheaves.

127A PSALM 127

SYRACUSE. C.M.
1. [1]Ex - cept the LORD shall build the house The build - ers lose their pain;
2. [2]'Tis vain for you to rise be - times, Or late from rest to keep,
3. [3]Lo, chil - dren are the LORD's good gift; Rich pay - ment are men's sons.
4. [5]Who has his quiv - er filled with these, O hap - py shall he be;
Ex - cept the LORD the cit - y keep The watch - men watch in vain.
To eat the bread of toil; for so He gives His loved ones sleep.
[4]The sons of youth as ar - rows are In hands of might - y ones.
When foes they greet with - in the gate They shall from shame be free.

127B PSALM 127

CHANT G.

1. [1]Except the LORD / build the / house, //
   They / labor in / vain that / build it:

2. Except the LORD / keep the / city, //
   The watchman / waketh / but in / vain.

3. [2]It is vain for you to rise up early, to / sit up / late, //
   To eat the bread of sorrows: for so He giveth /
   His be/lov·ed / sleep.

4. [3]Lo, children are an / heritage · of the / LORD: //
   And the fruit of the / womb is / His re/ward.

5. [4]As arrows are in the hand of a / mighty / man; //
   So are / children / of the / youth.

6. [5]Happy is the man that / hath his · quiver / full of them: //
   They shall not be ashamed, but they shall speak
   with the / ene·mies / in the / gate.

For "AN INTRODUCTION TO CHANTING" please turn to page 440.

PSALM 128

128A

MCKEE. C.M.
1. [1]How bless - ed all who fear the LORD, And
2. [3]Your wife will as a fruit - ful vine With -
3. [4]Be - hold, thus shall the man be blessed Who
4. And may you see Je - ru - s'lem's good All
walk with- in His ways! [2]You'll eat your la - bor's
in your house be found; Your chil - dren will as
tru - ly fears the LORD! [5]The LORD from Zi - on
days on earth you dwell. [6]May you your chil - dren's

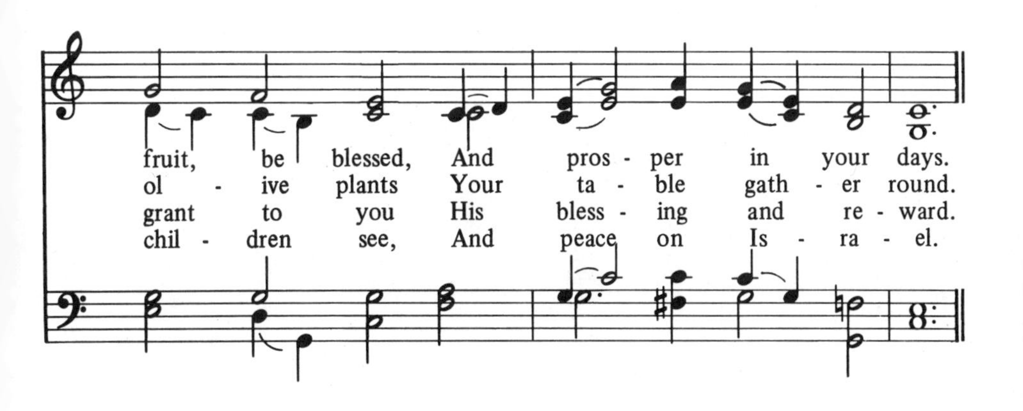
fruit, be blessed, And pros - per in your days.
ol - ive plants Your ta - ble gath - er round.
grant to you His bless - ing and re - ward.
chil - dren see, And peace on Is - ra - el.

128B PSALM 128

ULSTER. 87.87.
1. [1]Blessed the man that fears Je - ho - vah And that walk - eth in His ways;
2. [4]Lo, on him that fears Je - ho - vah Shall this bless - ed - ness at - tend;
[2]Thou shalt eat of thy hands' la - bor And be pros - pered all thy days.
[5]For Je - ho - vah out of Zi - on Shall to thee His bless - ing send.
[3]Like a vine with fruit a - bound - ing In thy house thy wife is found,
Thou shalt see Je - ru - s'lem pros - per All thy days till life shall cease;
And like ol - ive plants thy chil - dren, Com - pass - ing thy ta - ble round,
[6]Thou shalt see thy chil - dren's chil - dren, Un - to Is - ra - el be peace,
And like ol - ive plants thy chil - dren, Com - pass - ing thy ta - ble round.
Thou shalt see thy chil - dren's chil - dren, Un - to Is - ra - el be peace.

PSALM 129

OLD 110TH. 11.10.11.10.
1. [1]"Time and a - gain they great - ly did op - press me
2. [3]Up - on my back, like plow - men plow - ing fur - rows,
3. [5]Let them be shamed and fall back in con - fu - sion,
4. [7]From such the reap - er can - not get one hand full,
From my youth up," let Is - ra - el de - clare;
So did they make their goug - es deep and long.
All those who bear for Zi - on bit - ter hate.
Nor can the one who binds fill up his arms.
[2]"Time and a - gain they great - ly did op - press me
[4] Yet is Je - ho - vah right - eous in His deal - ings;
[6] Let them be - come like grass up - on the house - tops
[8] None pass - ing say, "Je - ho - vah's bless - ing on you!
From my youth up, yet they did not pre - vail."
The ropes of law - less men He cuts a - part.
Which with - ers up be - fore it can be pulled.
We give you bless - ing in Je - ho - vah's name!"

130A
PSALM 130
EVADNA. C.M.
1. [1]LORD, from the depths to Thee I cried. [2]My Lord, give ear to
2. [3]LORD, who shall stand if Thou, my Lord, Shouldst mark in - i - qui -
3. [5]I wait, my soul a - waits the LORD; My hope is in His
4. [7]O Is - ra - el, hope in the LORD; The LORD saves gra- cious -
me. O hear my voice and heark - en to My
ty? [4]But yet with Thee for - give - ness is, That
word. [6]More than the watch - men wait for morn My
ly. [8]And He shall Is - ra - el re - deem From
sup - pli - cat - ing plea, My sup - pli - cat - ing plea.
men may rev - 'rence Thee, That men may rev - 'rence Thee.
soul waits for my Lord, My soul waits for my Lord.
all in - i - qui - ty, From all in - i - qui - ty.

PSALM 130

130B

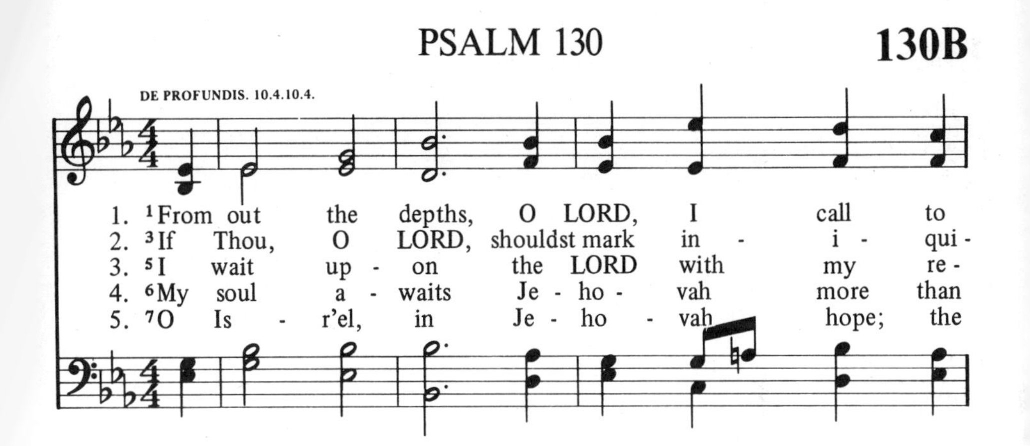
DE PROFUNDIS. 10.4.10.4.
1. [1]From out the depths, O LORD, I call to
2. [3]If Thou, O LORD, shouldst mark in - i - qui -
3. [5]I wait up - on the LORD with my re -
4. [6]My soul a - waits Je - ho - vah more than
5. [7]O Is - r'el, in Je - ho - vah hope; the

Thee; [2]Lord, hear my cry. And be Thine ear at -
ty, Lord, who would live? [4]But Thou for - giv - est
quest; My soul doth wait. And in His word my
light Of com - ing day, Yea, more than ea - ger
LORD Will mer - cy show. [8]Re- demp - tion full from

ten - tive to the plea I lift on high.
sin, that men to Thee May rev - 'rence give.
hope doth sure - ly rest With heart e - late.
watch - men in the night The morn - ing ray.
all in - i - qui - ty Shall Is - r'el know.

PSALM 131

HUMILITY. C.M.
1. [1]My heart not haugh - ty is, O LORD,
2. [2]My soul I stilled and qui - et - ed.
3. [3]Up - on Je - ho - vah let the hope

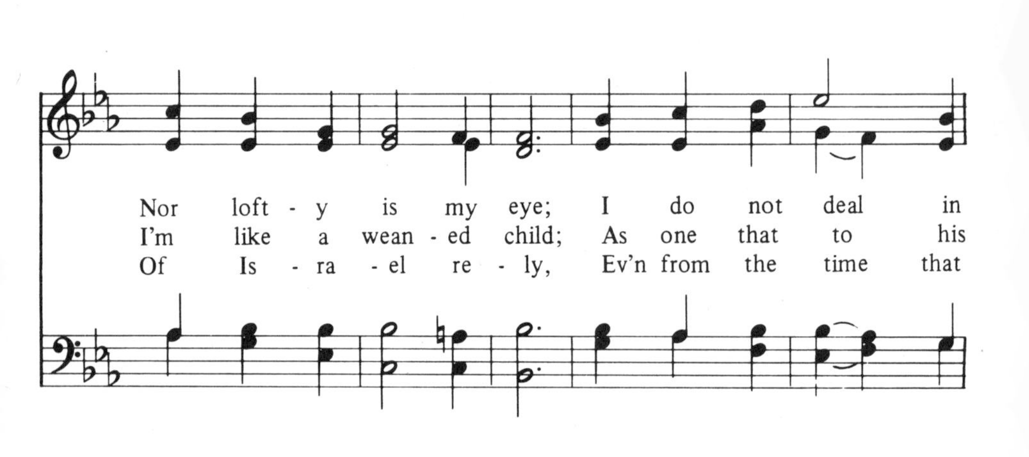
Nor loft - y is my eye; I do not deal in
I'm like a wean - ed child; As one that to his
Of Is - ra - el re - ly, Ev'n from the time that

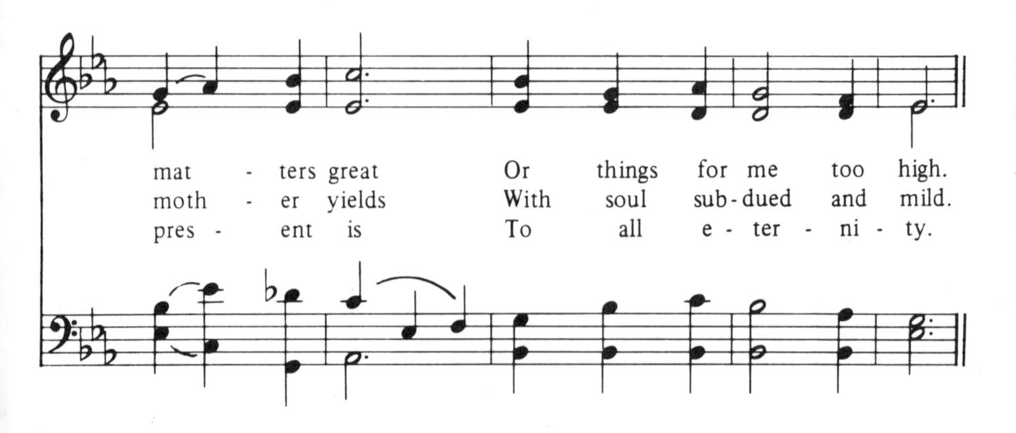
mat - ters great Or things for me too high.
moth - er yields With soul sub - dued and mild.
pres - ent is To all e - ter - ni - ty.

PSALM 132:1–10

RATHBUN. 87.87.
1. [1] LORD, re - mem - ber Thou for Da - vid, How he
2. [3]"I my dwell - ing will not en - ter, On my
3. [5]"Till I find a place of dwell - ing Where Je-
4. [6] Lo, we heard of it in Eph - rath, Found the
deep af - flic - tion bore; [2]To the Might - y
bed will not re - pose, [4]Will not give my
ho - vah may a - bide, For the Might - y
ark in Ja - ar's field. [7]Let us now His
One of Ja - cob, Vow - ing, to the LORD he swore:
eye - lids slum - ber, Nor my eyes in sleep will close,
One of Ja - cob Hab - i - ta - tion to pro - vide."
dwell - ing en - ter, At His foot - stool wor - ship yield.

5. [8]Rise, O LORD, Thy rest to enter,
Thou, and Thine own ark of might;
[9]Let Thy priests be clothed with justice;
Let Thy saints shout with delight.

6. [10]For the sake of Thine own servant,
Yes, for David's sake I pray,
Let the face of Thine anointed
Not be turned by Thee away.

132B PSALM 132:11–18

DORRNANCE. 87.87.

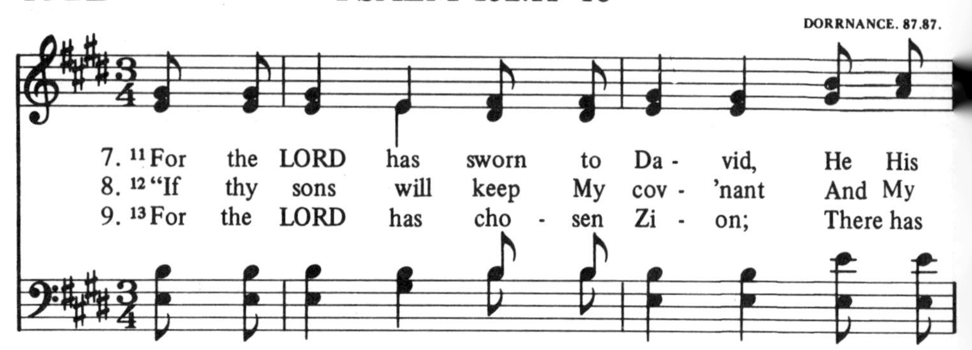
7. 11 For the LORD has sworn to Da - vid, He His
8. 12 "If thy sons will keep My cov - 'nant And My
9. 13 For the LORD has cho - sen Zi - on; There has

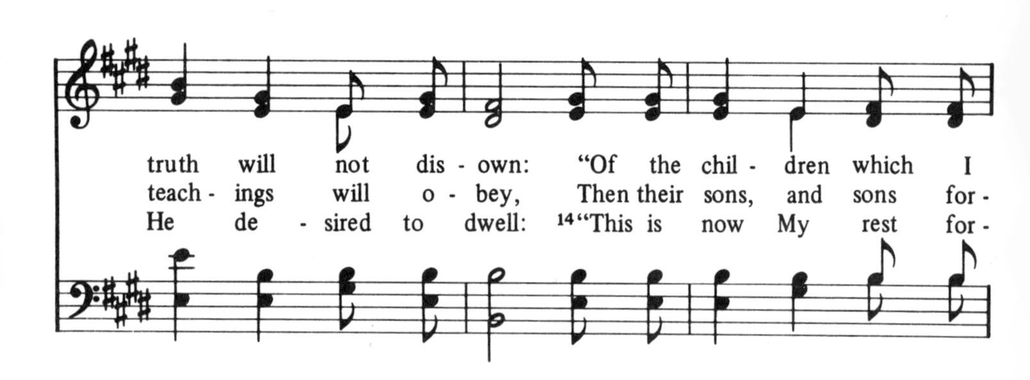
truth will not dis - own: "Of the chil - dren which I
teach - ings will o - bey, Then their sons, and sons for -
He de - sired to dwell: 14 "This is now My rest for -

give thee I will place up - on thy throne.
ev - er, Shall up - on thy throne hold sway."
ev - er; Here I'll stay; I love it well.

10. 15 "I will bless her rich provision;
To her poor their bread I'll bring,
16 Clothe her priests with My salvation,
And her saints for joy shall sing.

11. 17 "I'll make David's power to flourish,
Mine anointed's lamp prepare;
18 I with shame his foes will cover;
He a glorious crown shall wear."

PSALM 133 — 133A

AZMON. C.M.

1. [1]Be - hold how good a thing it is, And how be - com - ing well,
2. [2]For it is like the pre - cious oil Poured out on Aar - on's head,
3. [3]Like Her - mon's dew up-on the hills Of Zi - on that de - scends,

When those that breth-ren are de - light In u - ni - ty to dwell.
That, go - ing down up - on his beard, Up - on his gar -ments spread.
The LORD com-mands His bless - ing there, Ev'n life that nev - er ends.

PSALM 133 — 133B

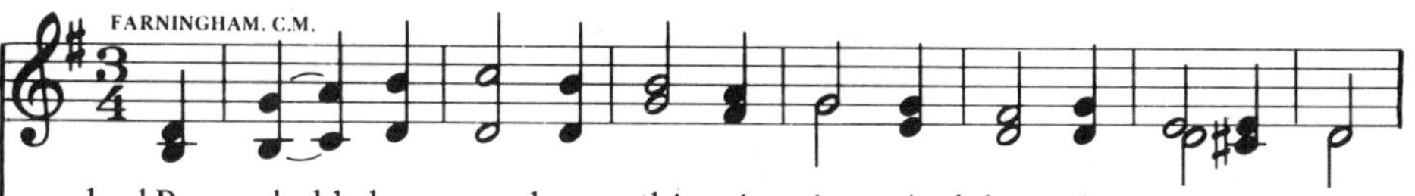
FARNINGHAM. C.M.

1. [1]Be - hold how good a thing it is, And how be - com- ing well,
2. [2]For it is like the pre - cious oil Poured out on Aar - on's head,
3. [3]Like Her - mon's dew up - on the hills Of Zi - on that de -scends,

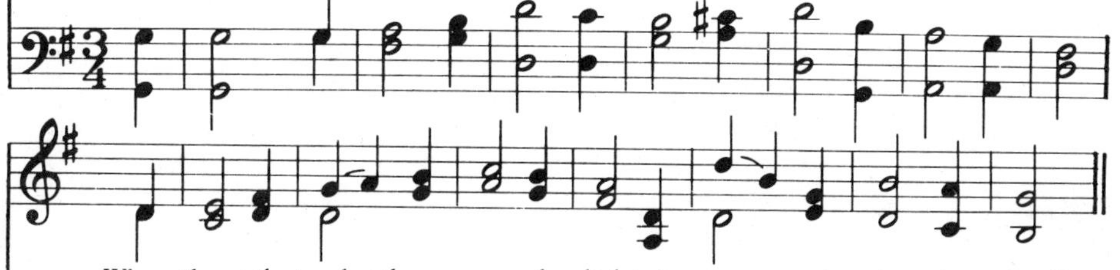

When those that breth-ren are de - light In un - ni - ty to dwell.
That, go- ing down up - on his beard, Up - on his gar- ments spread.
The LORD com - mands His bless-ing there, Ev'n life that nev - er ends.

134A PSALM 134

ZION. 87.87.47

1. [1]Lo, with prais - es to Je - ho - vah, Bless - ing
2. [2]Toward His ho - ly sanc - tu - ar - y Let you

give with one ac - cord, All of you who faith - ful
hands be lift - ed high To give bless - ing to Je -

serv - ice To Je - ho - vah do af - ford, Stand - ing
ho - vah. [3]And from Zi - on in re - ply The LORD

night - ly In the dwell - ing of the LORD, Stand - ing
bless you, He Who made the earth and sky, The LORD

night - ly In the dwell - ing of the LORD.
bless you, He Who made the earth and sky.

PSALM 134
134B
WATCH. Irregular.
1 Bless the LORD, all serv - ants of the LORD,
Ye who night - ly guard the house of the LORD.
2 Lift up your hands in the ho - ly place, and
pray, and bless the LORD a - lone. 3 The LORD Who made the heav - en
and the earth Bless you from out of Zi - on.

135A PSALM 135:1–12

HOW GOOD THE LORD IS. 87.87.

1. 1Hal - le - lu - jah! Praise the LORD's name! Praise Him,
2. 5Well I know how great the LORD is; Our Lord
3. 8Who slew all of E - gypt's first born, 9On you,

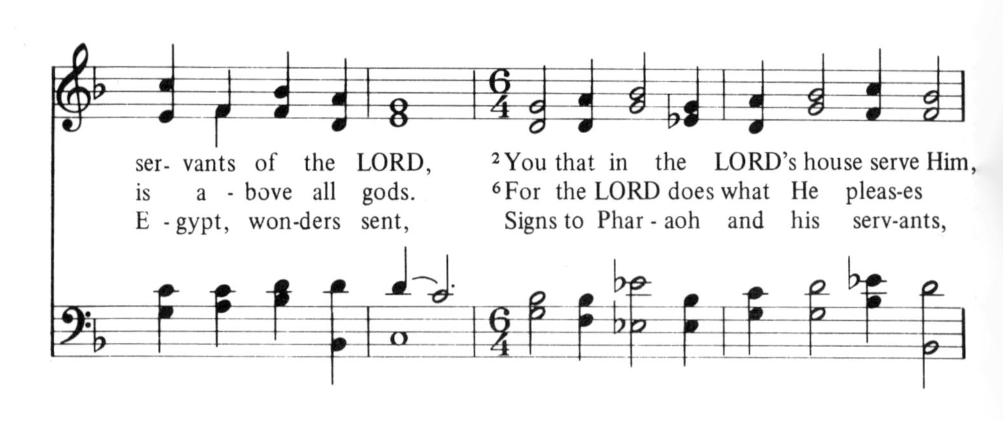
ser- vants of the LORD, 2You that in the LORD's house serve Him,
is a - bove all gods. 6For the LORD does what He pleas-es
E - gypt, won-ders sent, Signs to Phar - aoh and his serv-ants,

In God's court - yard stand - ing guard.
In all heav'n, earth, deeps, and floods.
10Who killed kings, their king - doms rent —

3 Praise the LORD! How good the LORD is! Sing His name — how
7 He it is Who lifts the va - pors From the ends of
11 Might- y Si - hon, Og of Ba - shan — Then the kings of
sweet its tone! 4 For the LORD has cho - sen Ja - cob,
earth and sea, Who with light - nings brings the rain down,
Ca - naan fell! 12 God their land gave to His peo - ple,
Is - ra - el to be His own.
From His store the wind sets free,
Willed it all to Is - ra - el.

135B PSALM 135:1–12

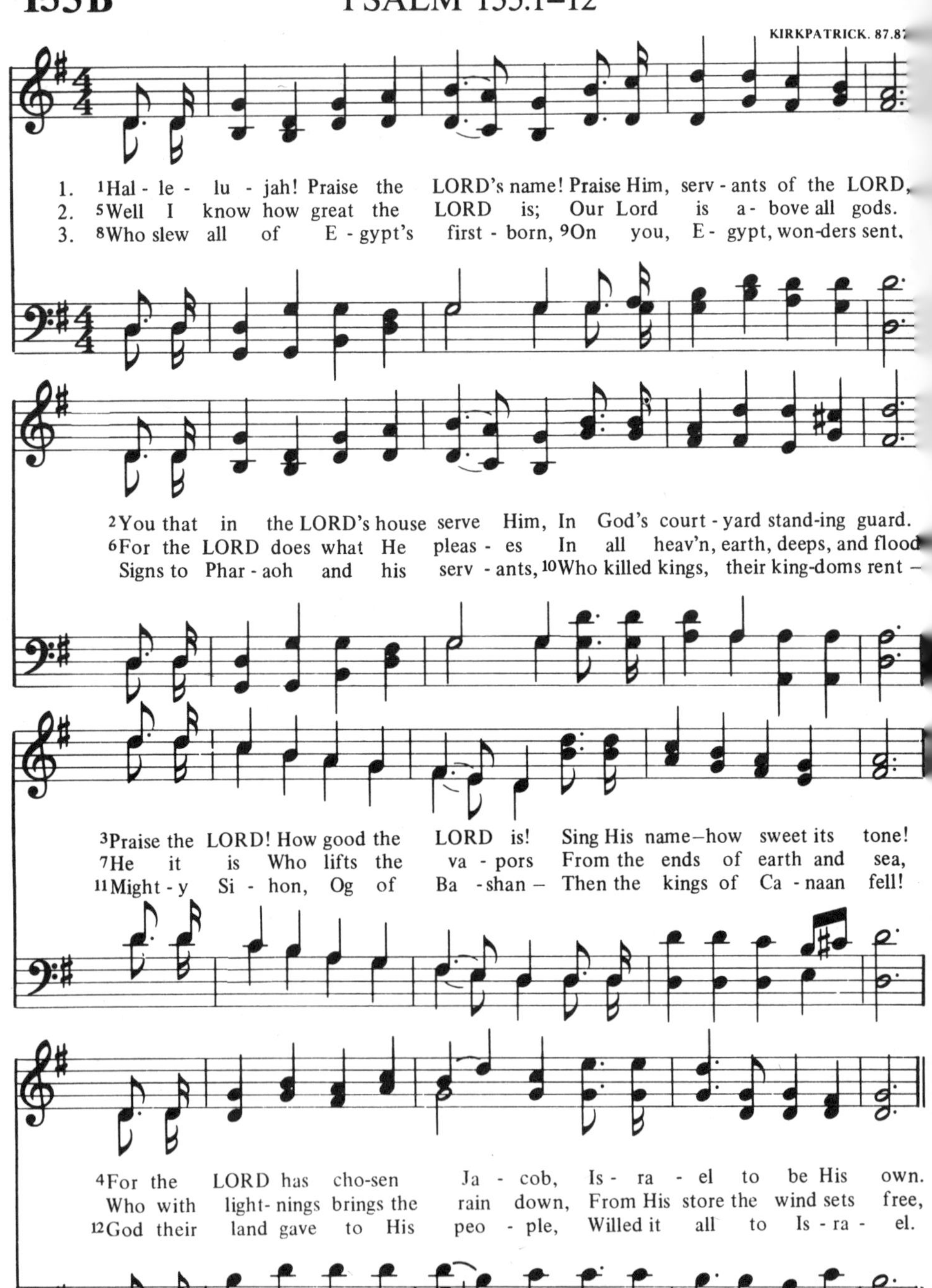

KIRKPATRICK. 87.87
1. 1Hal - le - lu - jah! Praise the LORD's name! Praise Him, serv - ants of the LORD,
2. 5Well I know how great the LORD is; Our Lord is a- bove all gods.
3. 8Who slew all of E - gypt's first - born, 9On you, E- gypt, won-ders sent,
2You that in the LORD's house serve Him, In God's court - yard stand-ing guard.
6For the LORD does what He pleas - es In all heav'n, earth, deeps, and flood
Signs to Phar - aoh and his serv - ants, 10Who killed kings, their king-doms rent –
3Praise the LORD! How good the LORD is! Sing His name–how sweet its tone!
7He it is Who lifts the va - pors From the ends of earth and sea,
11Might - y Si - hon, Og of Ba - shan – Then the kings of Ca - naan fell!
4For the LORD has cho-sen Ja - cob, Is - ra - el to be His own.
Who with light- nings brings the rain down, From His store the wind sets free,
12God their land gave to His peo - ple, Willed it all to Is - ra - el.

PSALM 135:13–21

TRIUMPH. 87.87.

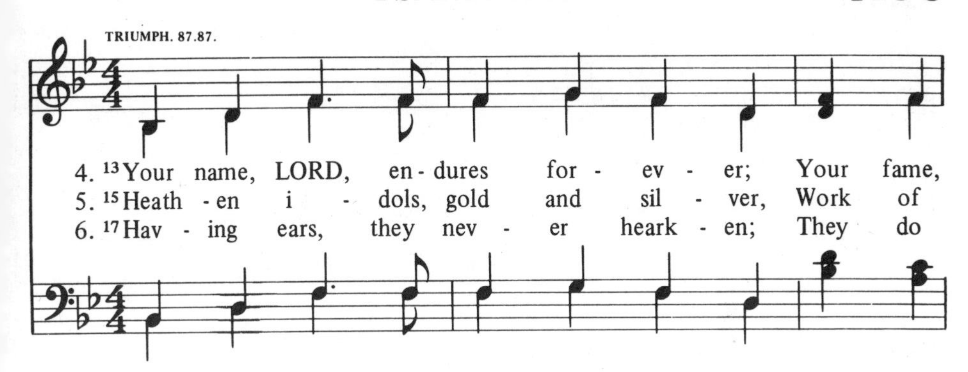
4. 13 Your name, LORD, en - dures for - ev - er; Your fame,
5. 15 Heath - en i - dols, gold and sil - ver, Work of
6. 17 Hav - ing ears, they nev - er heark - en; They do

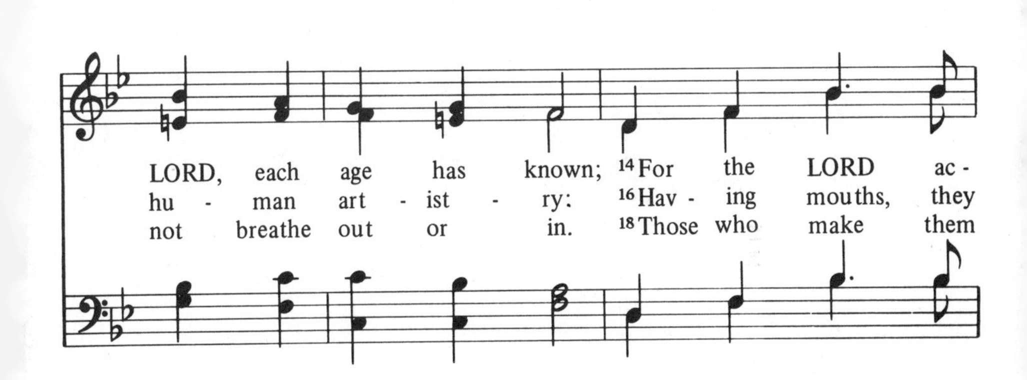
LORD, each age has known; 14 For the LORD ac -
hu - man art - ist - ry: 16 Hav - ing mouths, they
not breathe out or in. 18 Those who make them

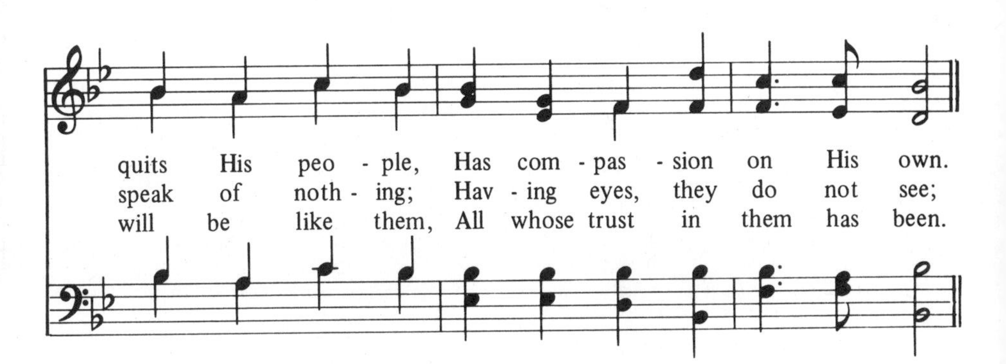
quits His peo - ple, Has com - pas - sion on His own.
speak of noth - ing; Hav - ing eyes, they do not see;
will be like them, All whose trust in them has been.

7. [19] Bless the LORD, O house of Isr'el!
House of Aaron, bless the LORD!
[20] Bless the LORD, O house of Levi!
All who fear Him, bless the LORD!

8. Blessings to the LORD you worship!
[21] Blessed from Zion be the LORD,
He whose dwelling is in Salem!
Hallelujah! Praise the LORD!

136A PSALM 136

SHINING SHORE. 87.87.D. (Iambic)
1. 1O thank the LORD, for good is He; His mer - cy lasts for - ev - er.
2Thanks to the God of gods give ye; His mer - cy lasts for - ev - er.
2. 3O prais - es give the King of kings; His mer - cy lasts for - ev- er;
4For He a - lone does won-drous things; His mer - cy lasts for - ev - er;

3. 5Who in His wisdom framed the skies;
His mercy lasts forever;
6Who made the earth from waters rise;
His mercy lasts forever;

4. 7Who placed the great lights on display;
His mercy lasts forever;
8The sun to rule the sky by day;
His mercy lasts forever;

5. 9The moon and stars to rule the night;
His mercy lasts forever;
10Who Egypt's firstborn all did smite;
His mercy lasts forever;

6. 11Who freed all Isr'el from their charm;
His mercy lasts forever;
12With mighty hand and outstretched arm;
His mercy lasts forever;

7. 13Who by His wind the Red Sea clave;
His mercy lasts forever;
14Led Isr'el through the parted wave;
His mercy lasts forever;

8. 15O'er Pharaoh He the Red Sea spread;
His mercy lasts forever;
16Through desert wastes His people led;
His mercy lasts forever;

9. [17] To Him Who great kings overthrew;
His mercy lasts forever;
[18] Who famous kings in battle slew;
His mercy lasts forever;

10. [19] King Sihon, of the Amorites;
His mercy lasts forever;
[20] And Og, the king of Bashanites;
His mercy lasts forever;

11. [21] Their land He gave to Israel;
His mercy lasts forever;
[22] His servant gave a place to dwell;
His mercy lasts forever.

12. [23] He thought on us when we were low;
His mercy lasts forever;
[24] And made us free from every foe;
His mercy lasts forever.

13. [25] He food bestows on all that live;
His mercy lasts forever.
[26] Thanks to the God of heaven give;
His mercy lasts forever.

PSALM 136 — 136B

CONSTANCE. 87.87.D. (Iambic)
1. [1] O thank the LORD, for good is He; His mer - cy lasts for - ev - er.
[2] Thanks to the God of gods give ye; His mer-cy lasts for - ev - er.
2. [3] O prais - es give the King of Kings; His mer- cy lasts for - ev - er;
[4] For He a - lone does won - drous things; His mer-cy lasts for - ev - er;

137 PSALM 137

DUNLAPS CREEK. C.M.
1. [1]By Ba - bel's streams we sat and wept; Our thoughts to Zi - on turned.[2]There on its wil - low trees we hung Our harps which now we spurned.
2. [3]For there a song de - mand - ed they Who did us cap - tive bring, And our tor - men - tors called for mirth: "A song of Zi - on sing!"
3. [4]O how the LORD's song shall we sing With - in a for - eign land? [5]If you, Je - ru - s'lem, I for - get, Let with - er my right hand.

4. [6]Let my tongue cleave to my mouth's roof
If you I should forget,
And if above my chiefest joy
I Salem do not set.

5. [7]Remember Edom's sons, O LORD,
How in Jerus'lem's day
They cried, "Tear down! Tear down its walls!
Its base in ruins lay!"

6. [8]O Babel's daughter, near your doom,
O happy count that one
Who shall deal back to you again
As you to us have done!

7. [9]Yes, happy count that one who adds
To your destruction's shock,
Who takes and breaks your little ones
Against the mighty rock.

PSALM 138

138A

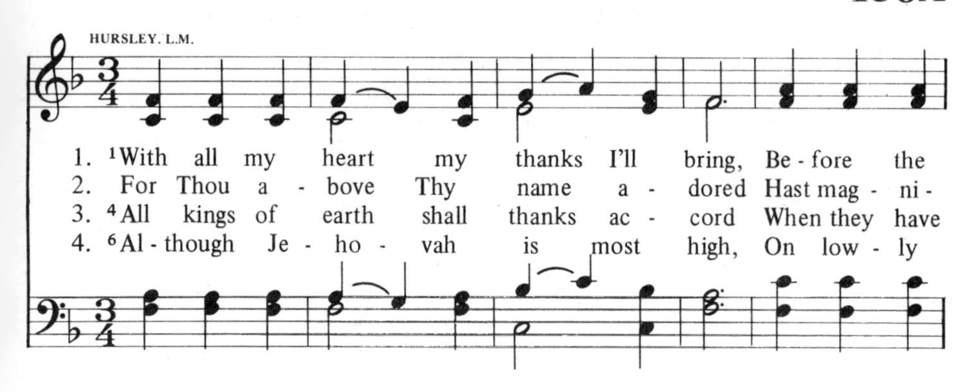
HURSLEY. L.M.
1. [1]With all my heart my thanks I'll bring, Be - fore the
2. For Thou a - bove Thy name a - dored Hast mag - ni -
3. [4]All kings of earth shall thanks ac - cord When they have
4. [6]Al - though Je - ho - vah is most high, On low - ly

gods Thy prais - es sing; [2]I'll wor- ship in Thy
fied Thy faith - ful word. [3]The day I called Thy
heard Thy words, O LORD;[5]Je - ho - vah's ways they'll
ones He bends His eye; But those that proud and

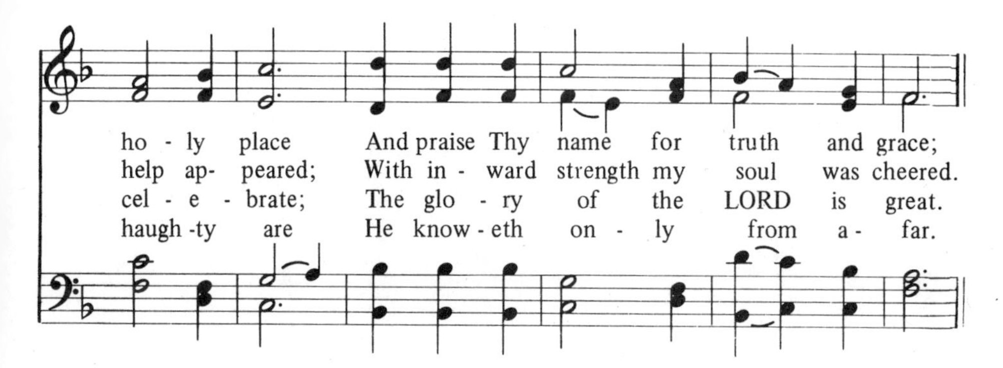
ho - ly place And praise Thy name for truth and grace;
help ap- peared; With in - ward strength my soul was cheered.
cel - e - brate; The glo - ry of the LORD is great.
haugh -ty are He know - eth on - ly from a - far.

5. [7]Through trouble though my pathway be,
Thou wilt revive and comfort me.
Thine outstretched hand Thou wilt oppose
Against the wrath of all my foes.

6. Thy hand, O LORD, shall set me free
[8]And perfect what concerneth me;
Thy mercy, LORD, forever stands;
Leave not the work of Thine own hands.

138B PSALM 138

WESLEY. L.M.
1. [1]With all my heart my thanks I'll bring, Be - fore the
2. For Thou a - bove Thy name a - dored Hast mag - ni -
3. [4]All kings of earth shall thanks ac - cord When they have
4 [6]Al-though Je - ho - vah is most high, On low - ly
gods Thy prais - es sing; [2]I'll wor - ship in Thy
fied Thy faith - ful word. [3]The day I called Thy
heard Thy words, O LORD; [5]Je - ho - vah's ways they'll
ones He bends His eye; But those that proud and
ho - ly place And praise Thy name for truth and grace;
help ap - peared; With in - ward strength my soul was cheered.
cel - e - brate; The glo - ry of the LORD is great.
haugh - ty are He know - eth on - ly from a - far.

5. [7]Through trouble though my pathway be,
Thou wilt revive and comfort me.
Thine outstretched hand Thou wilt oppose
Against the wrath of all my foes.

6. Thy hand, O LORD, shall set me free
[8]And perfect what concerneth me;
Thy mercy, LORD, forever stands;
Leave not the work of Thine own hands.

PSALM 139:1–8

139A

HOLLEY. L.M.
1. [1]LORD, Thou hast searched me; [2]Thou hast known My ris - ing
2. [3]Thou know - est all the ways I plan, My path and
3. [5]Be - hind, be - fore me, Thou dost stand And lay on
4. [7]Where shall I from Thy Spir - it flee, Or from Thy

and my sit - ting down; And from a - far Thou
ly - ing down dost scan; [4]For in my tongue no
me Thy might - y hand; [6]Such knowl-edge is for
pres - ence hid - den be? [8]In heav'n Thou art, if

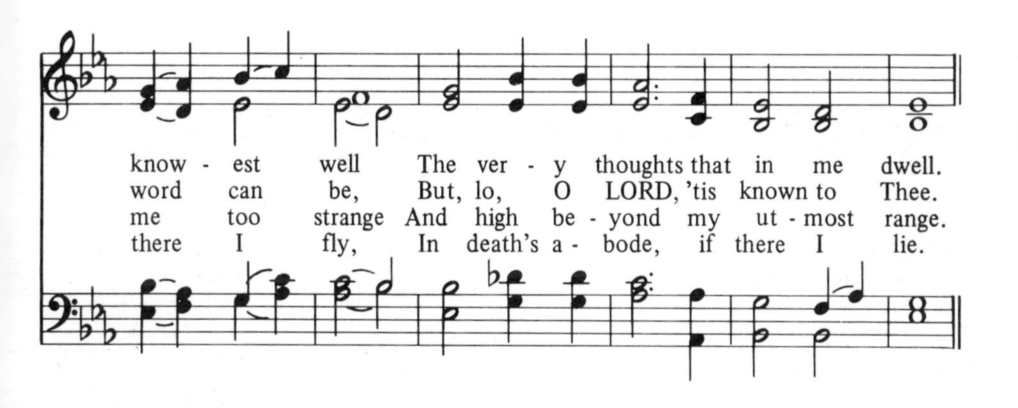
know - est well The ver - y thoughts that in me dwell.
word can be, But, lo, O LORD, 'tis known to Thee.
me too strange And high be - yond my ut - most range.
there I fly, In death's a - bode, if there I lie.

139B PSALM 139:9–16

MARYTON. L.M.
5. [9]If I the wings of morn - ing take And ut - most
6. [11]If I say, "Dark - ness cov - ers me," [12]The dark - ness
7. [13]My in - ward parts were formed by Thee; Thou, e'er my
sea my dwell - ing make,[10]Ev'n there Thy hand shall
hid - eth not from Thee. To Thee both night and
birth, didst cov - er me; [14]And I Thy prais - es

guide my way, And Thy right hand shall be my stay.
day are bright; The dark - ness shin - eth as the light.
will pro - claim, For strange and won - drous is my frame.

8. Thy wondrous works I surely know;
[15]When as in depths of earth below
My frame in secret first was made,
'Twas all before Thine eyes displayed.

9. [16]Mine unformed substance Thou didst see;
The days that were ordained to me
Were written in Thy book, each one,
When as of them there yet was none.

HOLLEY. L.M.
10. [17]Thy thoughts, O God, to me are dear; How great their
11. [19]The wick - ed Thou wilt slay, O God; De - part from
12. [21]Do not I hate Thy foes, O LORD? And Thine as -
13. [23]Search me, O God; my heart dis - cern; And try me,
sum! [18]they more ap - pear In num - ber than the
me, ye men of blood, [20]They speak of Thee in
sail - ants hold ab - horred? [22]I tru - ly hate all
eve - ry thought to learn, [24]And see if an - y
sand to me. When I a - wake, I'm still with Thee.
words pro - fane, The foes who take Thy name in vain.
foes of Thine; I count them en - e - mies of mine.
sin holds sway. Lead in the ev - er - last - ing way.

140A PSALM 140:1–7

ST. PAUL. C.M.
1. ¹From men of greed and vi - o - lence, O
2. ³As keen as an - y ser - pent's fangs So
3. ⁴Guard me from men of vi - o - lence, O
4. ⁵The proud hid traps and cords for me; They
LORD, my soul re - lease; ²They e - vil in their
sharp their tongues they make, And un - der - neath their
LORD, from law - less force; Their pur - pose is to
have a se - cret net A - long the way - side
hearts de - vise, And wars they would in - crease.
lips there hides The ven - om of a snake.
bring me down, To o - ver - throw my course.
spread for me, And snares for me they set.

5. ⁶But I have said unto the LORD,
"In truth my God art Thou."
Jehovah, hear my voice when I
In supplication bow.

6. ⁷My Lord Jehovah is for me
Salvation's strength and stay;
He is the cover for my head
When comes the battle-day.

PSALM 140:8–13

140B

DETROY. C.M.
7. 8 Grant not, O LORD, that wick - ed men See
8. 9 As for the head of all those men Who
9. 10 Let burn - ing coals up - on them fall; To
10. 11 Let not the slan - der - er on earth En-

their de - sire draw nigh. And do not help them
have sur - round - ed me, By all the mis - chief
flames let them be cast, And in - to deep - est
joy se - cu - ri - ty; Let e - vil hunt the

in their plots To lift them - selves on high.
of their lips Let them now cov - ered be.
pits from which They can - not rise at last.
vi - o - lent And smite re - lent - less - ly.

11. [12] I know Jehovah will maintain
The cause of those oppressed;
He will defend the right of those
By poverty distressed.

12. [13] And then the righteous to Thy name
Their thanks will surely give;
And they that upright are in heart
Shall in Thy presence live.

141A

PSALM 141:1–4

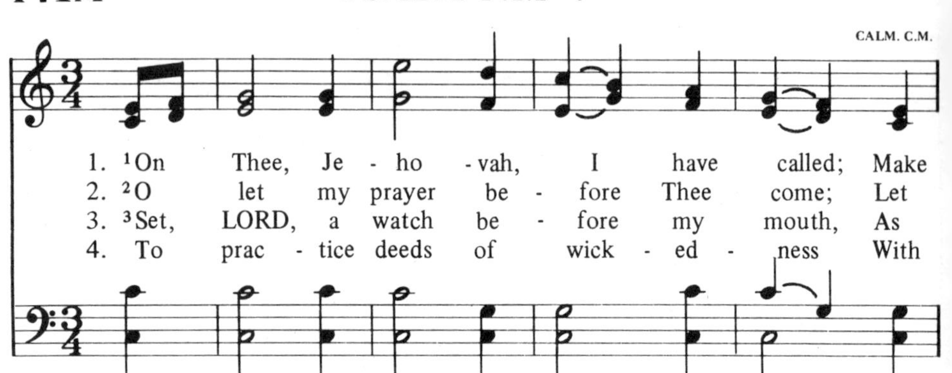
CALM. C.M.
1. [1]On Thee, Je - ho - vah, I have called; Make
2. [2]O let my prayer be - fore Thee come; Let
3. [3]Set, LORD, a watch be - fore my mouth, As
4. To prac - tice deeds of wick - ed - ness With

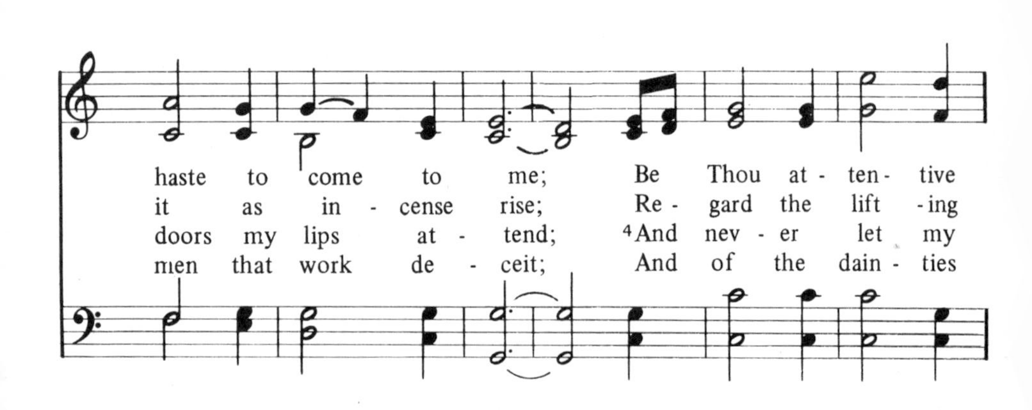
haste to come to me; Be Thou at - ten - tive
it as in - cense rise; Re - gard the lift - ing
doors my lips at - tend; [4]And nev - er let my
men that work de - ceit; And of the dain - ties

to my voice When- e'er I cry to Thee.
of my hands As th'eve - ning sac - ri - fice.
heart in - cline To an - y e - vil end,
they se - cure O let me nev - er eat.

PSALM 141:5–10

141B

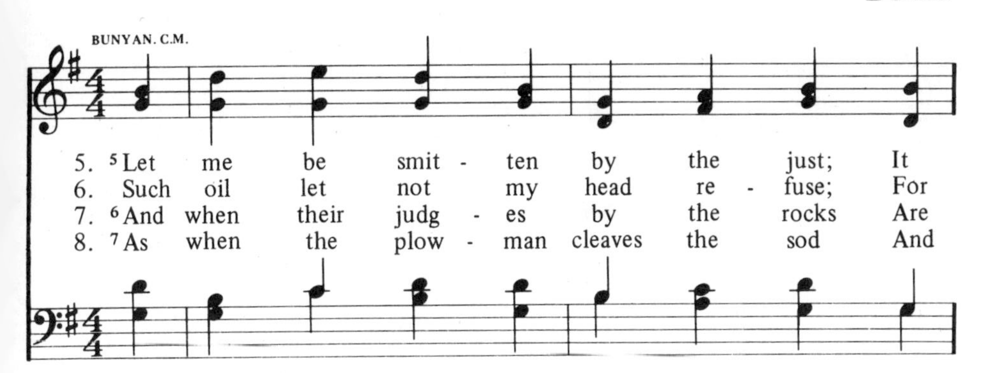
BUNYAN. C.M.
5. [5]Let me be smit - ten by the just; It
6. Such oil let not my head re - fuse; For
7. [6]And when their judg - es by the rocks Are
8. [7]As when the plow - man cleaves the sod And

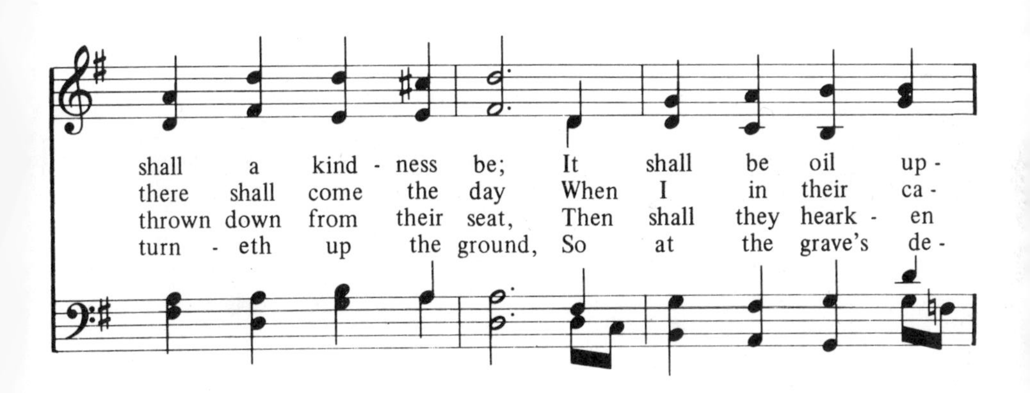
shall a kind - ness be; It shall be oil up -
there shall come the day When I in their ca -
thrown down from their seat, Then shall they heark - en
turn - eth up the ground, So at the grave's de -

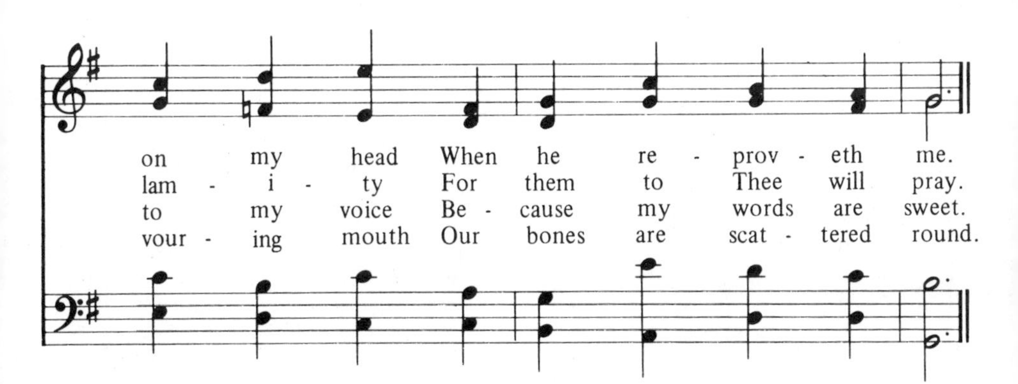
on my head When he re - prov - eth me.
lam - i - ty For them to Thee will pray.
to my voice Be - cause my words are sweet.
vour - ing mouth Our bones are scat - tered round.

9. [8]For unto Thee, Jehovah Lord,
I look with longing eyes;
My soul do not leave destitute;
My hope on Thee relies.

10. [9]O keep me from the traps and snares
Which wicked men have set.
[10]While I pass safely by, let them
Be caught in their own net.

PSALM 142

PATMOS. C.M.
1. [1]To Thee, O LORD, I lift my voice;
2. [3]Ev'n when my soul is o - ver - whelmed,
3. [4]Up - on my right hand look and see;
4. [5]To Thee I cried, O LORD, and said,
I sup - pli - ca - tion make, [2]Pour out my plaint be -
Thou know - est well my way. With - in the way in
There's none to know me there. All ref - uge fail - eth
Thou my sure ref - uge art, And in the land of
fore the LORD, To Him my trou - ble take.
which I walk A snare for me they lay.
me, and none Has for my soul a care.
those that live, The por - tion of my heart.

5. [6]Since I am brought exceeding low,
Attend upon my cry;
Save me from persecuting foes
Who stronger are than I.

6. [7]From prison bring my soul, that I
With thanks Thy name may bless;
When Thou art bountiful to me
The just shall round me press.

PSALM 143:1–6

INVITATION. 66.66.D.
1. [1]My prayer, Je - ho - vah, hear, And to my sup - pliant cry
2. [3]The foe my soul has sought, My life to earth doth tread;
3. [5]Yet I re - call to mind What an - cient days re - cord,
In faith - ful - ness give ear; In right -eous - ness re - ply.
To dark - ness I am brought, As those that long are dead.
Thy works of eve - ry kind, Which thought to me af - ford.
[2]In judg - ment call not me, Thy serv - ant, to be tried;
[4]My spir - it, there - fore, vexed, Is o - ver-whelmed with - in;
[6]And I spread forth my hands To Thee be - seech - ing - ly;
No liv - ing man can be In Thy sight jus - ti - fied.
My heart in me per-plexed And des- o - late has been.
My soul as wea - ry lands Is thirst - ing af - ter Thee.

143B PSALM 143:7–12

I NEED THEE EVERY HOUR. 66.66.D.
4. 7 LORD, let my prayer pre-vail; To an - swer it make speed.
5. 8 Be - cause I trust in Thee, O cause Thou me to hear
6. 9 O LORD, de - liv - er me From all who me op - pose.
7. 11 O LORD, for Thy name's sake Be pleased to quick - en me;
My spir - it quite doth fail; Hide not Thy face in need,
Thy lov - ing - kind - ness free, When morn - ing doth ap - pear.
To Thee a - lone I flee To hide me from my foes.
In right - eous - ness, O take My soul from mis - er - y.
Lest I be like to those That do in dark - ness sit,
Make me to know the way Where-in my path should be,
10 No God have I but Thee; Teach me to do Thy will;
12 In mer - cy cut off those That en' - mies are to me;
Or him that down-ward goes To share the dread - ful pit.
Be - cause my soul each day Do I lift up to Thee.
Thy Spir - it's good; lead me On e - ven path- way still.
Slay of my soul the foes; I serv - ant am to Thee.

PSALM 143

143C

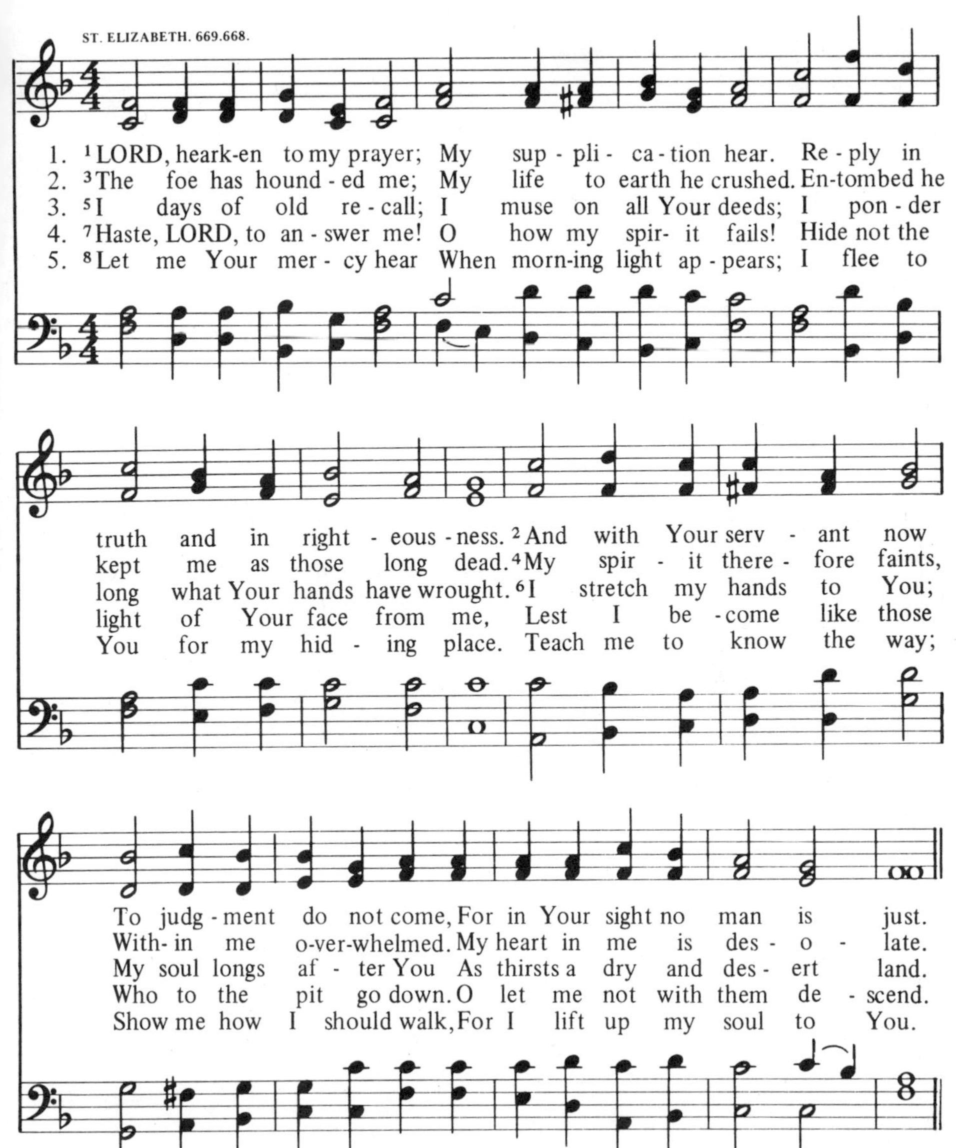
ST. ELIZABETH. 669.668.
1. [1]LORD, heark-en to my prayer; My sup - pli - ca - tion hear. Re - ply in
2. [3]The foe has hound - ed me; My life to earth he crushed. En-tombed he
3. [5]I days of old re - call; I muse on all Your deeds; I pon - der
4. [7]Haste, LORD, to an - swer me! O how my spir- it fails! Hide not the
5. [8]Let me Your mer - cy hear When morn-ing light ap - pears; I flee to
truth and in right - eous - ness. [2]And with Your serv - ant now
kept me as those long dead. [4]My spir - it there - fore faints,
long what Your hands have wrought. [6]I stretch my hands to You;
light of Your face from me, Lest I be - come like those
You for my hid - ing place. Teach me to know the way;
To judg - ment do not come, For in Your sight no man is just.
With- in me o-ver-whelmed. My heart in me is des - o - late.
My soul longs af - ter You As thirsts a dry and des - ert land.
Who to the pit go down. O let me not with them de - scend.
Show me how I should walk, For I lift up my soul to You.

6. [9]Deliver me, O LORD,
From all my enemies;
That You may hide me I flee to You.
[10]Teach me to do Your will;
My God of Spirit good,
O make me dwell in upright lands.

7. [11]For Your name's sake, O LORD,
Deal graciously with me;
Relieve my soul in Your righteousness.
[12]My foes slay in Your grace;
Destroy my enemies,
Because I am Your servant true.

144A PSALM 144:1–8

CAPEL. C.M.

1. [1]O blessed for - ev - er be the LORD Who
2. [2]My good - ness, for - tress, my high tower, De -
3. [3]LORD, what is man to have Thy care? His
4. [5]O Thou Je - ho - vah, bow the heav'ns; De -

is my rock of might; Who doth in - struct my
liv - er - er, and shield, In Whom I trust, Who
son to have Thy thought? [4]For man is like a
scend Thou from the skies; Touch Thou the ev - er -

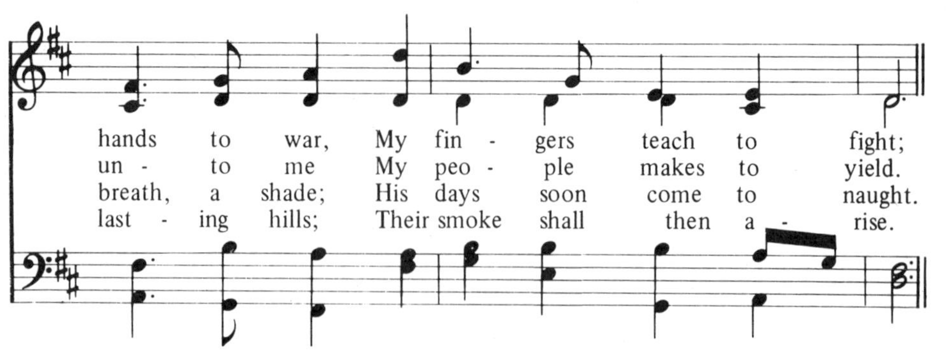
hands to war, My fin - gers teach to fight;
un - to me My peo - ple makes to yield.
breath, a shade; His days soon come to naught.
last - ing hills; Their smoke shall then a - rise.

From THE ENGLISH HYMNAL by permission of the Oxford University Press

5. [6]Cast forth Thy lightning; scatter them;
Thine arrows shoot; them rout.
[7]Stretch forth Thy hand and rescue me;
From waters draw me out.

6. And from the hand of aliens save,
[8]Whose mouth speaks vanity;
And whose right hand a right hand is
That works deceitfully.

PSALM 144:9–15 144B

MARSELLA. C.M.
7. 9 O God, a new song I will sing In praises unto Thee; And on a ten-stringed instrument To Thee make melody.
8. 10 For Thou art He that unto kings Salvation will afford; Who rescues David from all hurt, His servant from the sword.
9. 11 O from the hand of aliens save Whose mouth speaks vanity; And their right hand a right hand is That works deceitfully.

10. 12 When all our sons in sturdy growth
Like plants in vigor spring,
Our daughters corner-stones that grace
The palace of a king;

11. 13 When to afford all kind of store
Our garners shall be filled;
When our sheep, thousands in our fields,
Ten thousands more shall yield;

12. 14 When strong our oxen are for work;
When not a foe is nigh,
Nor is there going forth to war,
Within our streets no cry;

13. 15 The people dwell in happiness
Who are in such a case;
Who take the LORD to be their God,
They are a blessèd race.

144C PSALM 144:1–8

PISGAH. 66.66.888.
1. [1]Blessed be the LORD, my Rock, Who trains my hands for war,
2. [3]O LORD, what then is man That You take note of him?
3. [5]O LORD, bow low Your heav'ns; May You Your - self come down.
4. [7]Your hand send from on high To res - cue me and save
My fin - gers for the fight. [2]My Stead - fast Love, my Fort,
What is the son of man That You con - sid - er him?
Yes, touch the moun- tain - tops And cause them thus to smoke.
From wa - ters great and deep, From hands of al - ien folk,
My Strong -hold, my De - liv - er - er, My Shield in Whom I
[4]A breath, a noth - ing - ness, is man. As for the days of
[6]Make light - ning flash and scat - ter them. O may Your ar - rows
[8]Whose mouth speaks al - ways what is false, And ev - en the right
ref - uge take, He brings my peo - ple un - der me.
man, they all Are like a shad - ow pass - ing by.
be sent forth To trou - ble and dis - qui - et them!
hand of whom Is a right hand of cun - ning lies.

PSALM 144:9–15
144D
LISCHER. 66.66.888.
5. 9O God, in praise to You, A new song I will sing.
6. 11O res - cue me and save, Grant me de - liv - er - ance,
7. 12So be our sons like plants Grown stur - dy in their youth,
8. 14Yes, may our cat - tle bear. May there be no at - tacks,
Up - on a ten - stringed harp Your prais - es I will play.
From hands of al - ien folk, From power of for - eign - ers,
And may our daugh - ters be Like pal - ace cor - ner - stones;
No go - ing forth to war, No out - cry in our streets.
10For He sal - va - tion gives to kings; His serv-ant Da - vid
Whose mouth speaks al-ways what is false, And ev- en the right
13All kinds of goods fill up our barns; Our flocks of sheep be
15O hap-py peo - ple who are thus! O hap- py peo - ple
He will help And keep him from the wast- ing sword.
hand of whom Is a right hand of cun-ning lies.
mul - ti-plied By thou - sands and ten thou- sands more;
who can say They have the LORD to be their God!

145A PSALM 145:1–7

DUKE STREET. L.M.

1. 1 I will Thee praise, my God, O King, And I will
2. 3 The LORD is great; He praise ex - ceeds; His great - ness
3. 5 Up - on Thy glo - rious maj - es - ty And won - drous
4. 7 They ut - ter shall a - bun - dant - ly The mem - 'ry

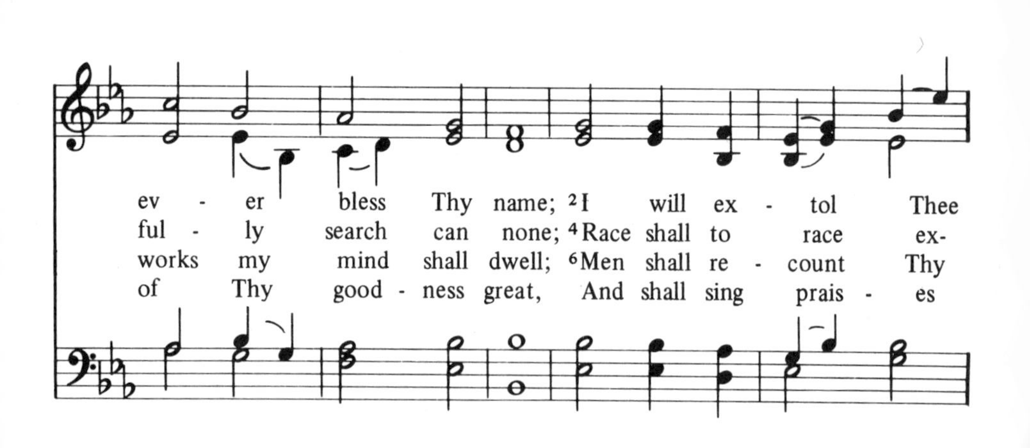
ev - er bless Thy name; 2 I will ex - tol Thee
ful - ly search can none; 4 Race shall to race ex-
works my mind shall dwell; 6 Men shall re - count Thy
of Thy good - ness great, And shall sing prais - es

eve - ry - day And ev - er - more Thy praise pro - claim.
tol Thy deeds And tell Thy might - y acts each one.
dread - ful acts, And of Thy great - ness I will tell.
cheer - ful - ly While they Thy right - eous - ness re - late.

PSALM 145:8–14

145B

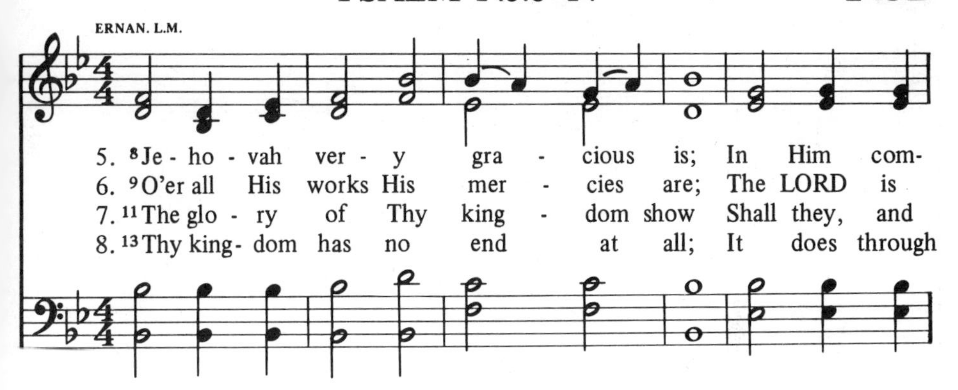
ERNAN. L.M.
5. 8 Je - ho - vah ver - y gra - cious is; In Him com-
6. 9 O'er all His works His mer - cies are; The LORD is
7. 11 The glo - ry of Thy king - dom show Shall they, and
8. 13 Thy king - dom has no end at all; It does through

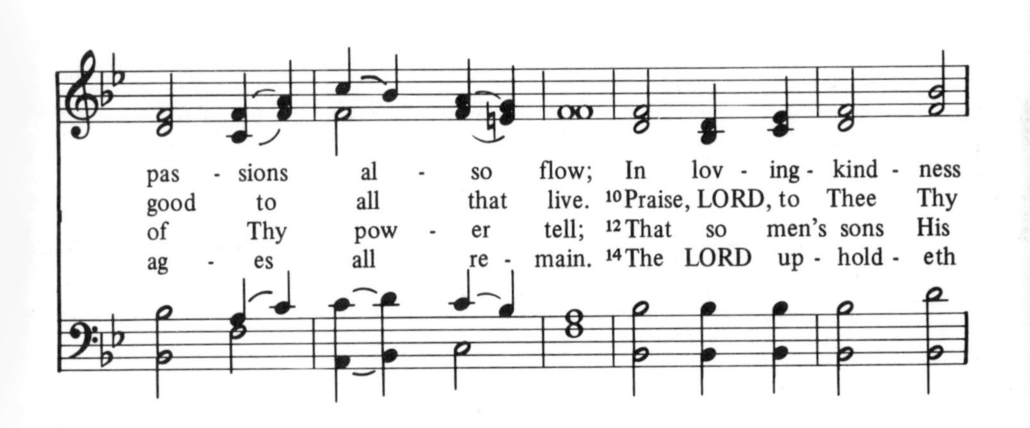
pas - sions al - so flow; In lov - ing - kind - ness
good to all that live. 10 Praise, LORD, to Thee Thy
of Thy pow - er tell; 12 That so men's sons His
ag - es all re - main. 14 The LORD up - hold - eth

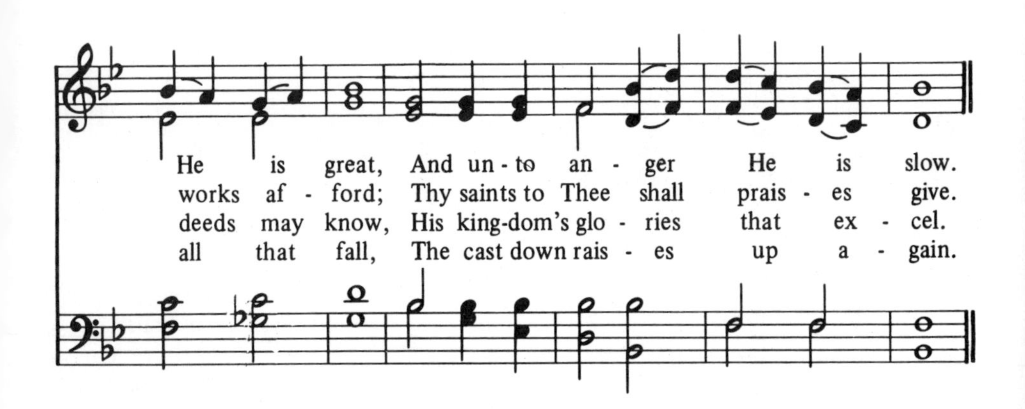
He is great, And un - to an - ger He is slow.
works af - ford; Thy saints to Thee shall prais - es give.
deeds may know, His king-dom's glo - ries that ex - cel.
all that fall, The cast down rais - es up a - gain.

145C PSALM 145:15–21

ROCKINGHAM. L.M.

9. [15]The eyes of all upon Thee wait; Their food in season Thou dost give; [16]Thine opened hand doth satisfy The wants of all on earth that live.
10. [17]The LORD is just in His ways all; In all His works His grace is shown; [18]The LORD is nigh to all that call, Who call in truth on Him alone.
11. [19]He will the just desire fulfill Of such as do Him fear indeed; Their cry regard and hear He will, And save them in the time of need.

12. [20]The LORD doth safely keep all those
Who bear to Him a loving heart,
But workers all of wickedness
Destroy will He and clean subvert.

13. [21]Then with my mouth and lips I will
Jehovah's name with praise adore.
And let all bless His holy name
Forever and for evermore.

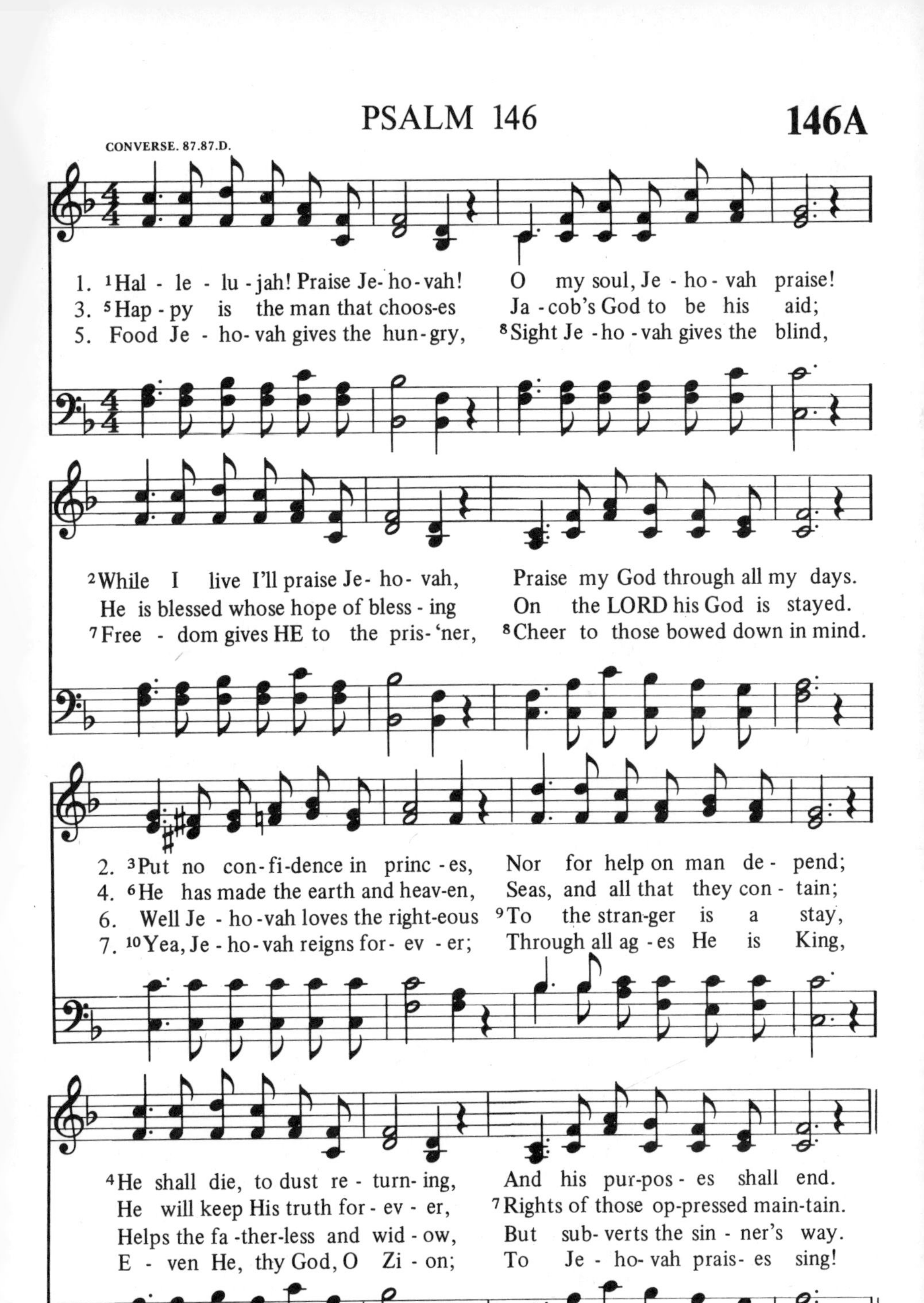
PSALM 146
146A
CONVERSE. 87.87.D.
1. [1]Hal - le - lu - jah! Praise Je- ho- vah! O my soul, Je - ho - vah praise!
3. [5]Hap - py is the man that choos-es Ja - cob's God to be his aid;
5. Food Je - ho- vah gives the hun- gry, [8]Sight Je - ho - vah gives the blind,
[2]While I live I'll praise Je- ho- vah, Praise my God through all my days.
He is blessed whose hope of bless - ing On the LORD his God is stayed.
[7]Free - dom gives HE to the pris- 'ner, [8]Cheer to those bowed down in mind.
2. [3]Put no con- fi- dence in princ - es, Nor for help on man de - pend;
4. [6]He has made the earth and heav-en, Seas, and all that they con - tain;
6. Well Je - ho - vah loves the right-eous [9]To the stran-ger is a stay,
7. [10]Yea, Je - ho - vah reigns for- ev - er; Through all ag - es He is King,
[4]He shall die, to dust re - turn- ing, And his pur-pos - es shall end.
He will keep His truth for - ev - er, [7]Rights of those op-pressed main-tain.
Helps the fa -ther-less and wid - ow, But sub- verts the sin - ner's way.
E - ven He, thy God, O Zi - on; To Je - ho- vah prais- es sing!

146B PSALM 146

HALLELUJAH. 87.87.
1. [1]Hal - le - -lu - jah! Praise Je - ho - vah!
2. [3]Put no con - fi - dence in princ - es,
3. [5]Hap - py is the man that choos - es
O my soul, Je - ho - vah praise! [2]While I live I'll
Nor for help on man de - pend; [4]He shall die, to
Ja - cob's God to be his aid; He is blessed whose
praise Je - ho - vah, Praise my God through all my days.
dust re - turn - ing, And his pur - pos - es shall end.
hope of bless - ing On the LORD his God is stayed.

4. [6]He has made the earth and heaven,
Seas, and all that they contain;
He will keep His truth forever,
[7]Rights of those oppressed maintain.

5. Food Jehovah gives the hungry,
[8]Sight Jehovah gives the blind,
[7]Freedom gives HE to the pris'ner,
[8]Cheer to those bowed down in mind.

6. Well Jehovah loves the righteous,
[9]To the stranger is a stay,
Helps the fatherless and widow,
But subverts the sinner's way.

7. [10]Yea, Jehovah reigns forever;
Through all ages He is King,
Even He, thy God, O Zion;
To Jehovah praises sing!

PSALM 147:1–11 147A

ONWARD. C.M.
1. [1]Praise ye the LORD, for it is good Praise to our God to sing; For it is pleas - ant, and to praise It is a come - ly thing.
2. [2]The LORD builds up Je - ru - sa - lem, Brings back her cap - tive sons. [3]He binds up all their wounds and heals The brok - en - heart - ed ones.
3. [4]He counts the num - ber of the stars; He names them eve - ry one. [5]Our Lord is great and great in power; His wis - dom search can none.

4. [6]The LORD upholds the meek and brings
   The wicked to the ground.
   [7]With thanks, O praise the LORD our God;
   With harps His praises sound;

5. [8]Who covereth the heav'ns with clouds,
   Who for the earth below
   Prepareth rain, Who maketh grass
   Upon the mountains grow.

6. [9]He cares for beasts that roam the field
   And doth their food supply;
   He watches o'er the ravens young
   And feeds them when they cry.

7. [10]In strength of horse or speed of man
   The LORD takes no delight;
   [11]But those that fear and trust His love
   Are pleasing in His sight.

147B PSALM 147:12–20

APHEKA. C.M.D.
8. 12 O Sa - lem, praise the LORD! To God, O Zi - on, praise ex - press!
9. 16 Like ash - es scat - ters He the frost, Like wool spreads snow on land.
10. 19 And yet this ver - y word of His To Ja - cob He makes known,
13 For thy gates' bars He has made strong, Thy sons in thee has blessed.
17 Like mor - sels casts He forth His ice. Who in His cold can stand?
His judg - ments and His code of laws To Is - ra - el has shown.
14 He made thy bor - der peace, on thee The fin - est wheat con - ferred.
18 Then He sends forth His might - y word; He makes His wind to blow;
20 Not so to an - y na - tion round Did He His grace ac - cord,
15 He sends forth His com - mand to earth And swift - ly speeds His word.
The snow and ice are melt - ed then; A - gain the wa - ters flow.
In that His judg - ments they've not known. O do ye praise the LORD!

PSALM 148

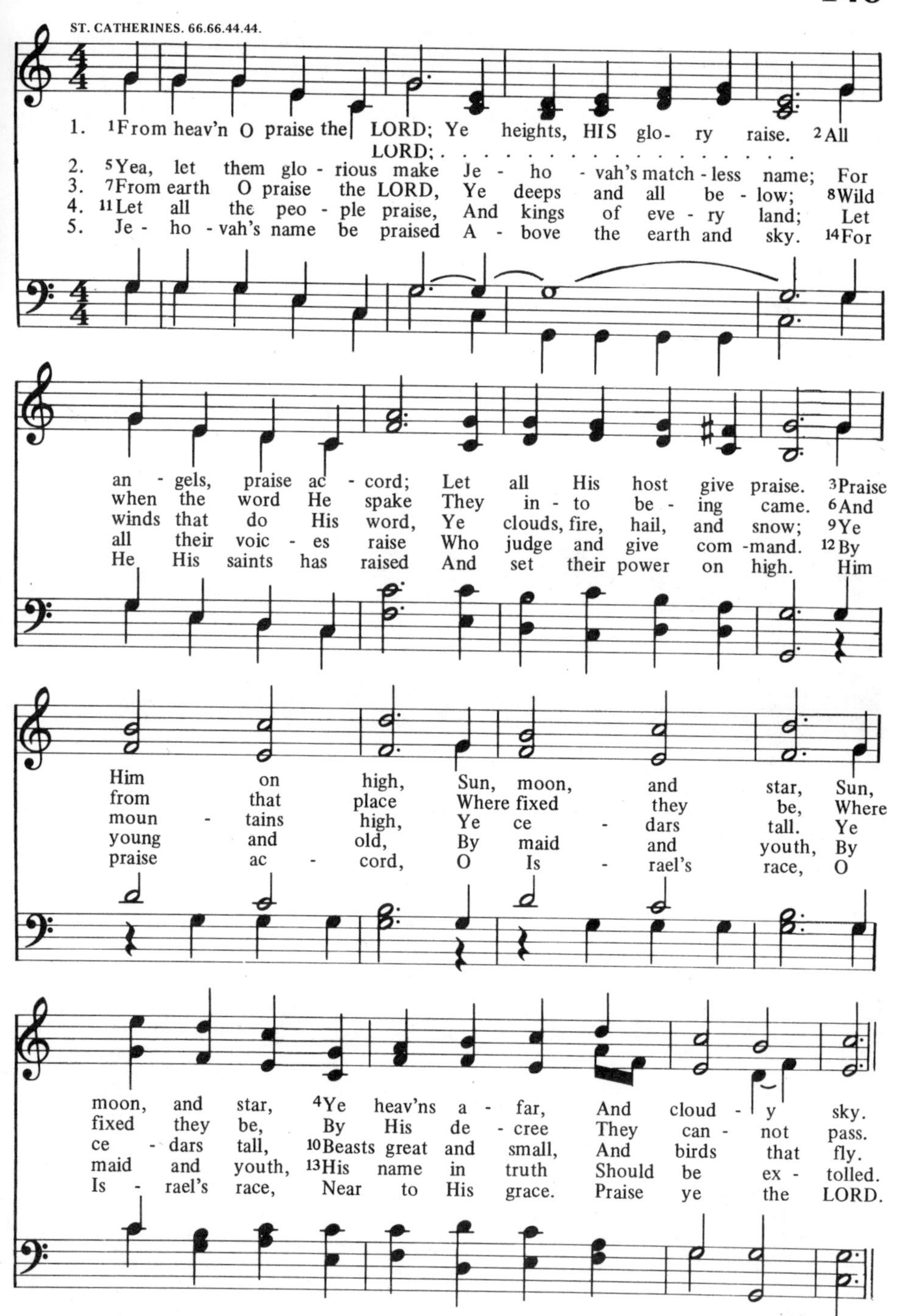

ST. CATHERINES. 66.66.44.44.
1. 1From heav'n O praise the LORD; Ye heights, HIS glo- ry raise. 2All
LORD; . . . .
2. 5Yea, let them glo - rious make Je - ho - vah's match - less name; For
3. 7From earth O praise the LORD, Ye deeps and all be - low; 8Wild
4. 11Let all the peo - ple praise, And kings of eve - ry land; Let
5. Je - ho - vah's name be praised A - bove the earth and sky. 14For
an - gels, praise ac - cord; Let all His host give praise. 3Praise
when the word He spake They in - to be - ing came. 6And
winds that do His word, Ye clouds, fire, hail, and snow; 9Ye
all their voic - es raise Who judge and give com -mand. 12By
He His saints has raised And set their power on high. Him
Him on high, Sun, moon, and star, Sun,
from that place Where fixed they be, Where
moun - tains high, Ye ce - dars tall. Ye
young and old, By maid and youth, By
praise ac - cord, O Is - rael's race, O
moon, and star, 4Ye heav'ns a - far, And cloud - y sky.
fixed they be, By His de - cree They can - not pass.
ce - dars tall, 10Beasts great and small, And birds that fly.
maid and youth, 13His name in truth Should be ex - tolled.
Is - rael's race, Near to His grace. Praise ye the LORD.

PSALM 149

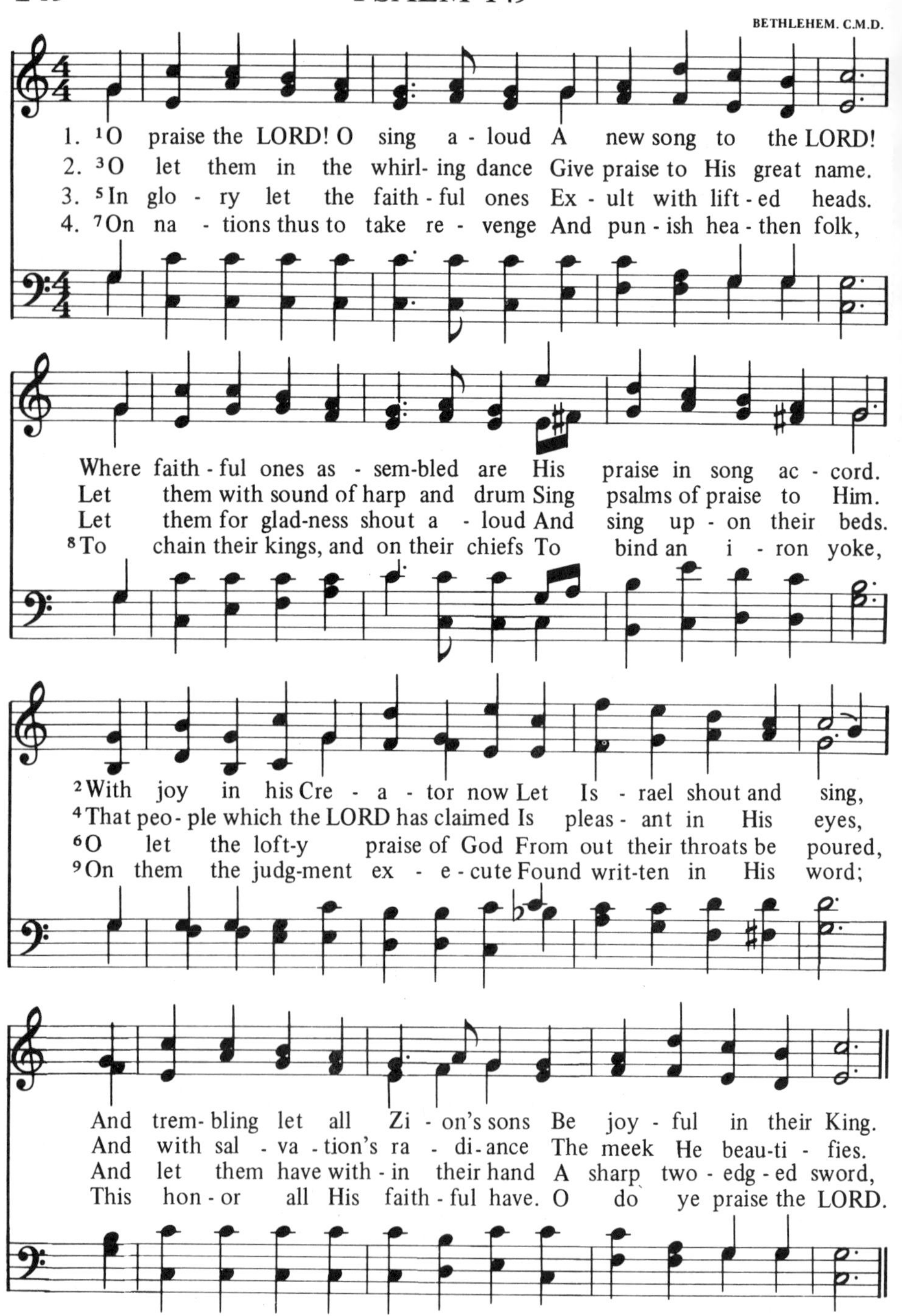
BETHLEHEM. C.M.D.
1. 1O praise the LORD! O sing a - loud A new song to the LORD!
2. 3O let them in the whirl- ing dance Give praise to His great name.
3. 5In glo - ry let the faith - ful ones Ex - ult with lift - ed heads.
4. 7On na - tions thus to take re - venge And pun - ish hea - then folk,
Where faith - ful ones as - sem-bled are His praise in song ac - cord.
Let them with sound of harp and drum Sing psalms of praise to Him.
Let them for glad-ness shout a - loud And sing up - on their beds.
8To chain their kings, and on their chiefs To bind an i - ron yoke,
2With joy in his Cre - a - tor now Let Is - rael shout and sing,
4That peo- ple which the LORD has claimed Is pleas - ant in His eyes,
6O let the loft-y praise of God From out their throats be poured,
9On them the judg-ment ex - e - cute Found writ-ten in His word;
And trem- bling let all Zi - on's sons Be joy - ful in their King.
And with sal - va - tion's ra - di- ance The meek He beau-ti - fies.
And let them have with - in their hand A sharp two - edg - ed sword,
This hon - or all His faith - ful have. O do ye praise the LORD.

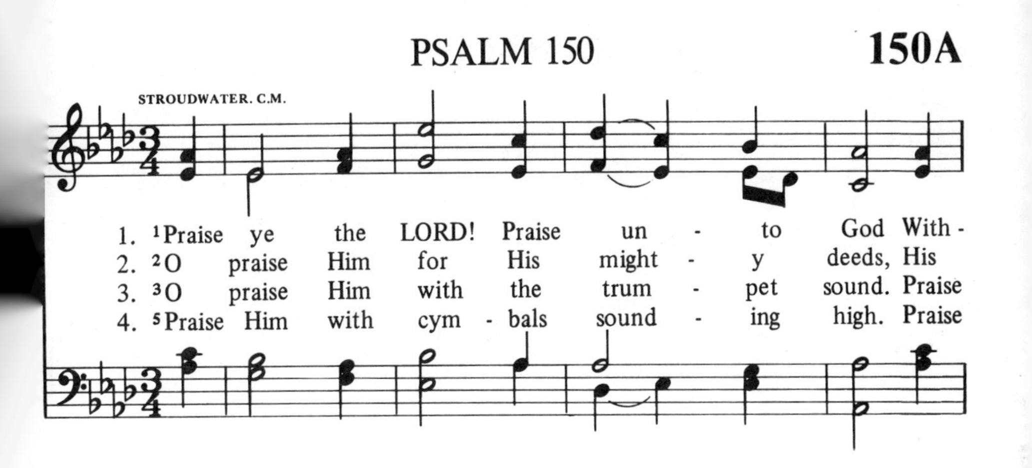
PSALM 150
150A
STROUDWATER. C.M.
1. 1Praise ye the LORD! Praise un - to God With -
2. 2O praise Him for His might - y deeds, His
3. 3O praise Him with the trum - pet sound. Praise
4. 5Praise Him with cym - bals sound - ing high. Praise

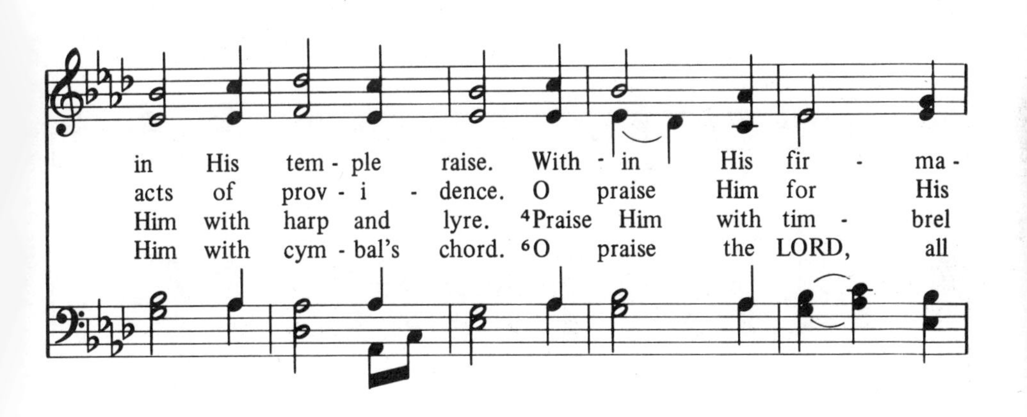
in His tem - ple raise. With - in His fir - ma -
acts of prov - i - dence. O praise Him for His
Him with harp and lyre. 4Praise Him with tim - brel
Him with cym - bal's chord. 6O praise the LORD, all

ment of power To Him O give ye praise.
glo - ry great, His match - less ex - cel - lence.
in the dance. Praise Him with strings and choir.
things that breathe! O do ye praise the LORD!

150B PSALM 150

OMEGA. Irregular.
[1]Praise the LORD! Praise God in His sanct - u - a - ry.
Praise Him in His might- y ex -panse. [2]Praise Him for His
might- y deeds. Praise Him ac - cord - ing to His ex- cel - lent great-ness.
[3]Praise Him with the trum-pet sound. Praise Him with the harp and lyre.

[4]Praise Him with tim - brel and danc - ing. Praise
Him with stringed in - stru - ments and pipe. [5]Praise Him with loud
cym - bals. Praise Him with re - sound - ing cym - bals. [6]Let
eve - ry - thing that has breath praise the LORD! Praise the LORD!

AN INTRODUCTION TO CHANTING

WHAT IS IT?

Chanting is the singing of a prose text to a simple, repeated melody. Good chanting is essentially good reading aloud; it uses the rhythms and stresses of natural speech.

The ancient Hebrews never used metrical "tunes" in the modern sense. In the synagogue, the Law, the Prophets, and the Writings (including the Psalms), were read in a sing-song recitation which was half speech, half song. Originally chanting involved only a single line (that is. no part-singing), and only two or three pitches. The early Christian church retained this practice, adapting it to the recitation of the Psalms in Latin translation. Our present system of chanting in four parts is called Anglican Chant, and dates from sixteenth-century England.

WHY DO IT?

Chanting has several advantages over metrical Psalmody, stemming from the fact that in chanting, the music completely serves the text. The music is not difficult or interesting in itself, but has character and meaning only in conjunction with words. The meaning of the text is thus more immediate, and the parallel structure of the Hebrew poetry is more apparent. The difficulties of translating ancient non-metrical poems into sensible English rhyme are rendered unnecessary. Chanting encourages the use of entire Psalms rather than selections.

HOW TO DO IT?

A single chant consists of two halves. Each half contains a Reciting-tone and an Inflection. The Inflection of the first half normally contains three notes; that of the second half, five.

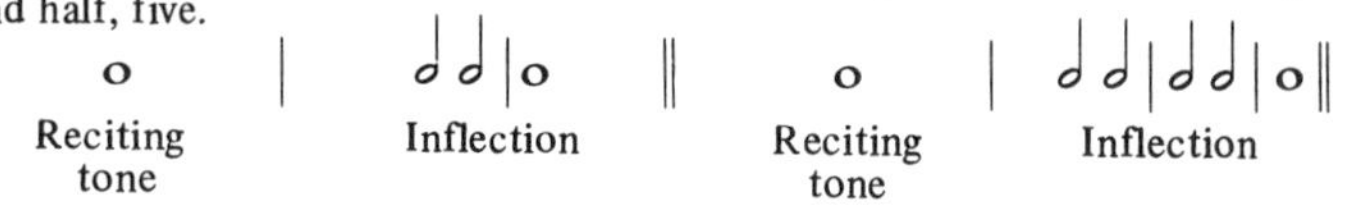

Reciting tone	Inflection	Reciting tone	Inflection

The text of a Psalm which is "pointed" for chanting contains marks which correspond to the features of the chant. A vertical line / corresponds to the bar-lines of the Inflections, and a double line // to the double bar at the midpoint of the chant. If more than two syllables fall between bar-lines, the division of the syllables among the notes may be obvious (i.e., change notes for a new word, as in Psalm 19:1, "glory of"); or a dot · may indicate the point of change (Ps. 19:1, "firma·ment"). Be sure to give the syllables equal duration – ♫ or ♫♪ ,and NOT ♫♪ or ♪♫ .

Learning to chant a Psalm begins with reading the first verse aloud, with sensitivity and correct articulation. When the group reads this verse well, monotone it. Sing it through on a single pitch, one that is comfortable for all, with the same stress and meaning used in reading it. Breathe only at the end of each half-verse.

Third, sing the notes of the chant on a neutral syllable (such as LA or LOO), giving the notes equal duration.

Finally, when the notes are learned, sing the verse to the music of the chant. After the first verse is mastered, follow the same procedure with each succeeding verse: read, monotone, chant.

Some important details of chanting include:

1. The pace is the same throughout the chant. Do not rush through the Recitation and then slow the Inflection.

2. The bar-lines and note-values do not have their usual metric significance; their use is simply a matter of convenience and custom. Do not sing the Inflection as if it were in $\frac{2}{2}$ meter.

3. Feminine line endings (those in which the final syllable is unaccented) must be observed in singing. The temptation to accent such syllables must be resisted, as it produces a disagreeable "thump" and violates the principle of natural speech rhythm.

4. Each syllable must receive the same emphasis it has in reading, not more. Some chanters unnaturally prolong the last syllable before each Inflection and the last syllable of each half-verse, thus interrupting the textual rhythm of the Psalm.

ALPHABETICAL INDEX OF TUNES

Name of Tune	Number	Meter	Composer, Arranger or Source
ABBEYVILLE	121B,125	C.M.	William B. Bradbury
ABERYSTWYTH	5B	77.77.D.	Joseph Parry, 1879
ABRIDGE	99A	C.M.	Isaac Smith, c.1770
ACH GOTT UND HERR (See GOELDEL)			
ADORO TE (See ST. CHRYSOSTOM)			
AGAWAM	69B	C.M.	William B. Bradbury
AJALON	51E	77.77.77	Richard Redhead, 1853
ALEXANDRIA	95A	C.M	William Arnold
ALL THE WAY (See ULSTER)			
ALL SAINTS NEW	110	C.M.D.	Henry S. Cutler, 1872
ALPENA	106F	C.M.D.	George F. Root, 1871
ALPHA	41C	Irregular	Eleanor Hutcheson, 1972
AMAZING GRACE (See NEW BRITAIN)			
AMSTERDAM	8B	76.76.77.76	Freylinghausen, *Gesangbuch*, 1704; Arr. John Wesley, 1742
ANCYRA	31D	C.M.D..	B.C. Unseld
ANDRE	72C	L.M.	William B. Bradbury
ANGEL'S STORY	30A	76.76.D	Arthur H. Mann
APHEKA	147B	C.M.D.	Lowell Mason, 1841
ARLINGTON	1A,40A	C.M.	Thomas A. Arne, 1762; Arr. Ralph Harrison, 1784
ARTAXERXES (See ARLINGTON)			
ASPURG	118B	C.M.	Johann G. Frech, 1825
AURELIA	101	76.76.D	Samuel S. Wesley, 1825
AUSTRIA	94A	87.87.D	Franz J. Haydn
AYRSHIRE	120	C.M.	Kenneth G. Finlay, 1936
AZMON	43,133A	C.M.	Carl G. Glaser, 1839
BACA	102A	88.888.	William B. Bradbury
BALERMA	17B	C.M.	Mel. by Francois H. Barthelemon, Arr. Robert Simpson
BARNABAS	28B	76.76.77.76	Adapted from *French Psalter*, 1561
BARNET	117B	Irregular	Eleanor Hutcheson, 1972
BARROW (See PRINCE)			
BATTY	109B	87.87	Thommen, *Erbaulicher, Musicalischer Christenschatz, 1745*
BEATITUDO	90B	C.M.	John B. Dykes, 1875
BEAUMONT	104C	10.10.11.11	Alt. from John Beaumont, 1801
BEECHER	103A	87.87.D	John Zundel
BEDFORD	119E	C.M.	William Wheall
BELGRAVE	124A	C.M.	William Horsley
BELIEVE	68B	C.M.	English Melody
BELMONT	12A	C.M.	William Gardiner, *Sacred Melodies v.I,* 1812
BERA	85A	L.M.	John E. Gould, 1849
BETA	72D	Irregular	Eleanor Hutcheson, 1972
BETHLEHEM	149	C.M.D.	Gottfried W. Fink, 1842; Arr. Arthur S. Sullivan
BEULAH CHURCH	7B	10.10.10.10	Robert M. Copeland, 1972
BEVAN	27D	66.66.88	Sir John Goss, 1853
BINGHAM	54A	C.M.	Anonymous
BIRMINGHAM	18J	10.10.10.10	Francis Cunningham, *Selection of Psalm Tunes,* 1834
BISHOPTHORPE	119S	C.M.	Jeremiah Clark, 1700
BOSTON	27A	C.M.	Uzziah C. Burnap
BOSWELL	119D	C.M.	Lowell Mason
BOVINA	77B	C.M.D.	Laura A. Tate
BOYLSTON	53	S.M.	Lowell Mason
BOYNTON	111A	C.M.	H.A. Cesar Malan
BRADBURY	85B	L.M.	William B. Bradbury, 1843
BRADFORD	104D	10.10.11.11	John K. Robb, 1950
BROCKLESBURY	38C	87.87	Charlotte A. Barnard, 1868
BROOMSGROVE	74B	86.866	Thomas Williams, *Psalmodia Evangelica,* 1789
BROWN	106A	C.M.	William B. Bradbury
BRYN CALFARIA	80B	88.88.88.98	William Owen
BUCHER (See HEATH)			
BUNYAN	141B	C.M.	Adapted from Felix Mendelssohn

Name of Tune	Number	Meter	Composer, Arranger or Source
CALM	141A	C.M.	Adapted from Thomas Hastings
CAMPBELL	32D	C.M.D.	Anonymous
CANAAN	107E	C.M.D.	Thomas E. Perkins
CANONBURY	18C	L.M.	arr. from Robert Schumann
CAPEL	144A	C.M.	Mel. Coll., Lucy Broadwood; harm. & arr. Ralph Vaughan-Williams
CASSELL	109A	87.87.D	Thommen, *Erbaulicher, Musikalischer Christenschatz, 1745*
CHAMPS ELYSEES	34A	C.M.D.	French Air
CHANT A	19C	Single	Frederick A.G. Ouseley
CHANT B	19D	Single	William H. Havergal
CHANT C	19E	Single	Edwin G. Monk
CHANT D	47B	Double	Sir John Goss
CHANT E	84C	Double	Thomas Jackson
CHANT F	93B	Single	John Stainer
CHANT G	127B	Single	James Nares
CHARLESTOWN	119G	87.87	Amos Pilsbury, *U.S. Sacred Harmony,* 1799; harm. by Robert M. Copeland, 1972
CHERITH (See SPOHR)			
CHIMES	119J	C.M.	Lowell Mason
CHRISTINE	119A	88.88.88	Ernest R. Kroeger
CITY OF OUR GOD	119F	C.M.	C.E. Leslie
CLARENDON	66B	C.M.	Isaac Tucker
CLARKSVILLE	19A	66.66.88	William B. Bradbury
CLINTON	57A	C.M.	Joseph P. Holbrook
CLONMEL	105D	C.M.D.	Irish Melody; harm. Robert M. Copeland, 1972
COMMEMORATION	65B	76.76.D.	Bartholomeus Gesius, 1605; arr. Johann S. Bach
COMMUNION (See ROCKINGHAM)			
COMPASSION	103C	87.87	S.A. Sterrett Metheny, 1910
CONFIDENCE	112B	10.10.10.10	Eleanor Hutcheson, 1972
CONSOLATION	56	86.86.86	John Wyeth, *Repository of Sacred Music, II,* 1813 arr. Robert M. Copeland, 1972
CONSOLATION (See EMMANUEL)			
CONSTANCE	136B	87.87.D. (Iambic)	Arthur S. Sullivan
CONTEMPLATION	71A	C.M.	Frederick A.G. Ouseley
CONVERSE	146A	87.87.D.	Charles C. Converse, 1870
CONWELL	86A	11.8.11.8	John K. Robb, 1949
COOLING	63A	C.M.	Alonzo J. Abbey
CORONATION	96A	86.86.86	Oliver Holden, 1793
COVENANTERS	40B,89F	C.M.	Joseph C. Lowry, 1817
COWPER	123	86.866	Lowell Mason
CRASSELIUS	18H	10.10.10.10	George Wittwe, *Musikalisches Handbuch,* 1690
CREATION	22I	88.88.88	Franz J. Haydn; arr. Isaac B. Woodbury
CREDITON	59B	C.M.	Thomas Clark
CRIMOND	23B	C.M.	Jessie S. Irvine; arr. David Grant
CROYDON	68E	C.M.	Arr. from Ludwig van Beethoven
CRUSADER'S HYMN (See ST. ELIZABETH)			
CULROSS	64A	C.M.	*Scottish Psalter,* 1634
CWM RHONDDA	122B	87.87.877	Attributed to John Hughes, 1907
DALEHURST	17C	C.M.	Arthur Cottman
DARWALL'S 148TH	92C	66.66.4444	John Darwall, 1770
DAVIS	119T	11.8.11.8	John Wyeth, *Repository of Sacred Music, II.* 1813 harm. Austin C. Lovelace
DEDEKAM	78E	C.M.D.	Sophie Dedekam
DELPHINE	86B	11.8.11.8	Hart P. Danks
DELTA	106G	Irregular	Eleanor Hutcheson, 1972
DENFIELD (See AZMON)			
DE PROFUNDIS	130B	10.4.10.4	Alt. from George Lomas
DESERT	98A	C.M.	Thomas Jarman
DETROIT(See DETROY)	25B	S.M.	Eurotas P. Hastings
DETROY	140B	C.M.	*Supplement to Kentucky Harmony,* 1820 arr. Robert M. Copeland, 1972
DIADEMATA	45C	S.M.D.	George J. Elvey, 1868
DODD	37E	C.M.	William B. Bradbury
DOMINUS REGIT ME	23D	11.11.11.11	S.A. Sterrett Metheny, 1910
DORRNANCE	132B	87.87	Isaac B. Woodbury

Name of Tune	Number	Meter	Composer, Arranger or Source
OWNS	60A	C.M.	Lowell Mason
UKE STREET	145A	L.M.	John Hatton, 1793
UNDEE	28A	C,M.	*Scottish Psalter,* 1615
UNFERMLINE.	8A	C.M.	*Scottish Psalter,* 1615
UNLAPSCREEK.	137	C.M.	Aaron Chapin, 1813
URHAM (See ST. AGNES)			
BENEZER	54B	87.87.D	Thomas J. Williams, 1890
FFINGHAM	77C	C.M.	Georg Wittwe, *Musikalisches Handbuch,* 1690. Adapted by Thomas Moore, 1750
IN' FESTE BURG	46C	88.88.66.668	Martin Luther, 1529
ISENACH	18F	L.M.	Johann H. Schein, 1627
LIZABETHTOWN	107C	C.M.	George Kingsley, 1838
LLACOMBE	21B,78C	C.M.D.	*Gesangbuch der Herzogl. Wurttemberg. Hofkapelle,* 1784
ELLERS	88B	10.10.10.10	Edward J. Hopkins, 1869
EMMANUEL	89H	C.M.	Ludwig van Beethoven
EMSWORTH	104B	10.10.11.11.	John K. Robb, 1949
ENTER	100C	Irregular.	Eleanor Hutcheson, 1970
EPHRATAH	69C	C.M.D.	Alonza P. Howard
ERNAN	145B	L.M.	Lowell Mason, 1850
EVADNA	130A	C.M.	S.A. Sterrett Metheny, 1911
EVAN	23A	C.M.	William Havergal; arr. Lowell Mason
EVANGEL (See BETHLEHEM)			
EVENING PRAYER	103B	87.87.	George C. Stebbins
EVENTIDE	39B	10.10.10.10	William H. Monk, 1861
EXETER	106C	C.M.	Henry L. Mason, 1923
FAIR HAVEN	79B	86.84	D. Bruce Martin, 1920
FARMER	30B	76.76.D	John Farmer
FARNINGHAM	133B	C.M.	Charles E. Kettle
FEDERAL STREET	119W	L.M.	Henry K. Oliver, 1836
FILLMORE	22F	88.88.88	Jeremiah Ingalls
FINGAL	40E	66.66.D.	Irish traditional melody, arr. Leopold L. Dix, 1933
FOREST GREEN	40C	C.M.D.	English melody, arr. Ralph Vaughan-Williams, 1906
FOUNDATION	16B	11.11.11.11.	American melody, harm. Carlton R. Young
FOUNTAIN	107D	C.M.D.	American melody
FRENCH (See DUNDEE)			
FREUEN WIR UNS	18B	L.M.	Bohemian melody; arr. Michael Weisse
GABRIEL.	31A	C.M.	Charles H. Gabriel
GAINSBOROUGH (See ST. MARTIN'S)			
GALATEA (See NATIVITY)			
GAMMA	89I	Irregular	Eleanor Hutcheson, 1972
GARDINER	91D	L.M.	William Gardiner, *Sacred Melodies, II,* 1815
GENEVA	126A	C.M.	John Cole, 1810
GERARD (See NOEL)			
GERMANY (See Gardiner)			
GIESSEN	1B	88.88.88	*Gauntlett's Comprehensive Tune Book,* 1851
GIVE YE TO JEHOVAH	29B	12.11.12.11.	Horatio R. Palmer
GLASGOW	100B	C.M.	Thomas Moore, 1756
GOD REVERED	89C	C.M.D.	T. Scott Huston, 1972
GOELDEL	18D	L.M.	Johann H. Schein, 1625
GRAEFENBERG	119L	C.M.	Johann Cruger, 1653
GRAFTON	97A	C.M.	Thomas Clark
GREEN HILL	40D	C.M.	Albert L. Peace
GREYFRIARS	24C	11.11.11.11.	S.A. Sterrett Metheny, 1909
GRIGG	78F	C.M.	Joseph Grigg
GUIDE	51F	77.77.77	Marcus M. Wells
HALIFAX	89E	C.M.D.	George F. Handel, 1748; harm. Austin C. Lovelace
HALLELUJAH	146B	87.87	Hugh A. Clarke, 1910
HAMBURG.	35A,119U	L.M.	Gregorian Chant; arr. Lowell Mason, 1824
HARVEY'S CHANT	31C	C.M.	William B. Bradbury
HAYDN	108C	11.86.D.	Franz J. Haydn

Name of Tune	Number	Meter	Composer, Arranger or Source
HEATH	41B	C.M.	Lowell Mason, 1841
HEAVENLY FOLD	37B	C.M.D.	William F. Sherwin
HEBER	105B	C.M.	George Kingsley, c. 1873
HEBER (See MISSIONARY HYMN)			
HELENA	51A	C.M.	William B. Bradbury
HENDON	113A	77.77	H.A. Cesar Malan, 1827
HENRY	97B	C.M.	Sylvanus B. Pond
HERBERT	68C	C.M. Triple	Arr. from John B. Herbert
HESPERUS	119B	L.M.	Henry Baker, 1866
HETHERTON	46B	C.M.D.	John K. Robb, 1949
HINTZE	2	77.77.D	Jakob Hintze, 1678; harm. Johann S. Bach
HOLLEY	139A,139C	L.M.	George Hews, 1835
HOLY CROSS (See REMEMBER ME)			
HOLY CROSS	79A	86.84	Arthur H. Brown
HOLY TRINITY	18E	L.M.	Nikolaus Hermann, 1560
HOPE	121A	C.M.	D. Bruce Martin, 1920
HOUGHTON	104E	10.10.11.11	Henry J. Gauntlett
HOWARD	119H	C.M.	Elizabeth H. Cuthbert
HOW GOOD THE LORD IS	135A	87.87.D	T. Scott Huston, 1972
HUDSON	118A	C.M.D.	Ralph E. Hudson
HULL	119N	C.M.	Asa Hull
HUMILITY	131	C.M.	S.A. Sterrett Metheny, 1910
HURSLEY	138A	L.M.	*Katholisches Gesangbuch*, Vienna, c. 1774
HYFRYDOL	91A	87.87.D.	Rowland H. Pritchard, c. 1830; harm. Ralph Vaughan-Williams
ILLA	78A	C.M.D.	Louis Spohr
I NEED THEE EVERY HOUR	143B	66.66.D	Adapted from Robert Lowry
INVITATION	143A	66.66.D	Frederick C. Maker, 1881
INVOCATION	34D	10.10.10.10.10.10	Carl W. Landahl
IRISH	83B	C.M.	Irish melody; *A Collection of Hymns and Sacred Poems,* 1749
ISHMAEL	108B	S.M.D.	Charles Vincent
ISHPEMING	41A	C.M.D.	Gerhard T. Alexis, 1924
JACKSON	118C	C.M.	Thomas Jackson
JEHOVAH NISSI	33B	886.886	Edward P. Crawford
JERUSALEM	62A	C.M.	Charles F. Roper
JOANNA	9B	11.11.11.11.	Welsh melody; arr. John Roberts, 1839
JOSEPHINE	61	886.886	Ernest R. Kroeger
JUBILATE	113B	66.66.88	Horatio W. Parker, 1894
KATHRINE	75	C.M.	Charles H. Gabriel
KEOKUK	81B	86.86.86	William B. Bradbury
KILMARNOCK	114	C.M.	Neil Dougall, 1831
KINGDOM	94B	87.87	V. Earle Copes, 1959
KINGSFOLD	22C	C.M.D.	Mel. coll. Lucy Broadwood, harm. Ralph Vaughan-Williams, 1906
KIRKPATRICK	135B	87.87.D	William J. Kirkpatrick
KNOX	106B	C.M.	Temple Melodies
KREMSER	29A	12.11.12.11.	Dutch melody, 1625; arr. Edward Kremser
LABAN	45B	S.M.	Lowell Mason, 1832
LAFAYETTE	69D	C.M.	John B. Herbert
LAIGHT STREET	68A	86.866	Thomas Hastings
LANCASHIRE	31E	76.76.D	Henry Smart, 1836
LANGRAN	39A	10.10.10.10	James Langran, 1861
LATAKIA	21C,21D	12.9.12.9	E.G. Taylor
LAUSANNE	40F	66.66.D	*Lausanne Choral Book*
LEAF	74A	86.866	Anonymous
LEIGHTON	20B	L.M.	William Leighton, c.1614

Name of Tune	Number	Meter	Composer, Arranger or Source
LEOMINSTER	25A	S.M.D.	George W. Martin, arr. Arthur S. Sullivan, 1862
LEONI	99C	66.84.D	Arr. from a Hebrew melody, 1777
LEVEQUE	106E	C.M.D.	Edward Hamilton
LISCHER	144D	66.66.888.	J.C. Friedrich Schneider, 1839
LLANGLOFFAN	31F	76.76.D	Welsh melody
LLOYD	119P	C.M.	Cuthbert Howard
LONGWOOD	7A	10.10.10.10	Sir Joseph Barnby, 1872
LOUISE	27C	C.M.	Robert M. Copeland, 1972
LOUISVILLE	45A	S.M.	John Zundel
LOUVAN	1190	L.M.	Virgil C. Taylor, 1846
LOVE DIVINE (See BEECHER)			
LOWRY	15	64.64.66.64	Robert Lowry
LOZINA	105A	C.M.	Luther O. Emerson
LUX PRIMA	115C	77.77.77	Charles F. Gounod, 1872
LYNTON	27B	C.M.	Arthur J. Jamouneau
LYONS	104A	10.10.11.11	Johann M. Haydn; arr. William Gardiner, *Sacred Melodies, II,* 1815
MAIN	32B	C.M.	Adapted from Johann G. Nageli
MAITLAND	119I	C.M.	George M. Allen, 1846
MANOAH	36A	C.M.	Arr. Henry W. Greatorex, 1851
MARA	44E	11.11.11.11	S.A. Sterrett Metheny, 1911
MARGARET	18G	10.10.10.10	Robert M. Copeland, 1972
MARLOW	119V	C.M.	John Chetham, 1718
MARSELLA	144B	C.M.	William Martin, 1859
MARTYRDOM	90A	C.M.	Hugh Wilson; arr. Robert A. Smith, 1825
MARTYRS	22B	C.M.	*Scottish Psalter,* 1615
MARYTON	139B	L.M.	H. Percy Smith, 1874
MASON'S CHANT	52A	C.M.	William B. Bradbury
MATERNA	46A	C.M.D.	Samuel A. Ward, 1894
McKEE	128A	C.M.	Negro melody adapted by Henry T. Burleigh, 1939
MEAR	24B	C.M.	Aaron Williams
MEDFIELD	16A	C.M.	William Mather
MEDITATION	13	C.M.	John H. Gower, 1890
MELITA	84B	88.88.88	John B. Dykes, 1861
MENDON	35C	L.M.	German melody arr. Lowell Mason, 1832
MERCY	49B	77.77	Louis M. Gottschalk
MERIBAH	33C	886.886	Lowell Mason
MERSINE	88A	10.10.10.10	S.A. Sterrett Metheny, 1910
MILES LANE	66A	C.M.	William Shrubsole, 1779
MILLENIUM	19B	66.66.88	English melody, 1826
MIRIAM	67B	76.76.D	Joseph P. Holbrook
MISSIONARY HYMN	67A	76.76.D	Lowell Mason, 1824
MOBILE	44F	11.11.11.11	John P. Campbell, 1899
MONORA	83A	C.M.D.	William B. Bradbury
MONTGOMERY	50C	S.M.D.	Isaac B. Woodbury, 1852
MORECAMBE	18I	10.10.10.10	Frederick C. Atkinson, 1870
MORNING	115D	77.77.77	William H. Monk
MORNING LIGHT	5A	77.77.D	J.W. Bischoff
MORNING SONG (See CONSOLATION)			
MORNING STAR	119K	11.10.11.10	James P. Harding, 1892
MORWELLHAM	96B	86.86.86	Charles Steggall, 1890
MOUNT VERNON	38D	87.87	Lowell Mason
MYRA	51B	C.M.D.	Paul D. McCracken, 1948
NAOMI	22A	C.M.	Johann G. Nageli; arr. Lowell Mason, 1836
NASHVILLE	42C	888.888	Gregorian Chant; arr. Lowell Mason; rearr. Charles McBurney, 1972
NATIVITY	22E	C.M.	Henry LaHee, 1855
NEANDER	76A	87.87.87	Joachim Neander, 1680
NETTLETON	119Q	87.87.D	American melody; John Wyeth *Repository of Sacred Music, II,* 1813
NEUMARK	76B	98.98.88	Georg Neumark, 1657
NEW BRITAIN	3	C.M.	*Virginia Harmony,* 1831
NEWELL	107A	C.M.	William B. Bradbury

Name of Tune	Number	Meter	Composer, Arranger or Source
NEWINGTON (See ST. STEPHEN)			
NEW JERUSALEM	89A	C.M.	R.S. Tay
NOEL	21A,89B	C.M.D.	English melody, arr. Arthur S. Sullivan, 18
NOMINA	59A	C.M.	Henry Sm
NORWICH	89G	C.M.	Thomas Ravenscro
			The Whole Booke of Psalms, 16
O HEILIGE DREIFALTIGKEIT (See HOLY TRINITY)			
O JESU	81A	86.86.86	J.B. Riemann, *Hirschberger Gesangbuch,* 17
O SALUTARIS	91C	L.M.	Gregorian Chant; arr. S.A. Sterrett Metheny, 19
OLD 38TH	38A	847.847	Louis Bourgeois, 1542; arr. Claude le Jeune, 16
OLD 77TH	52B	88.77.D	Louis Bourgeois, 154
			arr. Robert M. Copeland, 197
OLD 95TH	95C	889.889	Louis Bourgeois; arr. Eleanor Hutcheson, 197
OLD 100TH	100A	L.M.	Louis Bourgeois, 155
OLD 110TH	129	11.10.11.10	Louis Bourgeois, 1551; arr. Lois Schaefer, 197
OLD 124TH	124B	10.10.10.10.10	Louis Bourgeois, 155
OLD 128TH	14C	76.76.D	Louis Bourgeois, 1547
			arr. Robert M. Copeland, 197
OLD 148TH (See DARWALL'S 148TH)			
OLIVE'S BROW	6	L.M.	William B. Bradbury, 185
OLMUTZ	11	S.M.	Gregorian Chant; arr. Lowell Mason, 182
OMEGA	150B	Irregular	Eleanor Hutcheson, 197
OMNI DIE	82	87.87	Corner's *Gesangbuch,* 163
ONWARD	147A	C.M.	W.F. Sherman
OSTEND	116A	C.M.D.	Lowell Mason
PALESTRINA	77A	C.M.	Giovanni P. da Palestrina
PARK STREET	102B	L.M.	Frederic M.A. Venua
			arr. William Gardiner, Sacred Melodies I, 1812
PASCAL (See HURSLEY)			
PATMOS	142	C.M.	Arr. from a Gregorian Chant
PAVANAS	62B	10.8.10.8.12.12	Adapted from Gaspar Sanz
			by Duncan Lowe, 1972
PAX DEI	18L	10.10.10.10.	John B. Dykes
PEACE	36B	C.M.D.	Felix B. Mendelssohn
PENITENCE	4B	11.11.11.11. (Trochaic)	Spencer Lane
PENITENTIA	10A	10.10.10.10.	Edward Dearle, 1874
PERFECT WAY	119M	C.M.D.	John H. Tenney
PETERSBURG	73B	88.88.88	Dmitri S. Bortnianski
PETERSHAM	47A	C.M.D.	Clement W. Poole, 1875
PHUVAH	62C	C.M.	Melchior Vulpius
PILGRIMS	116C	11.10.11.10.9.11.	Henry Smart, 1868
PINNEO	44A	C.M.D.	William B. Bradbury
PISGAH	144C	66.66.888.	Anonymous
POLITZ	71C	C.M.D.	Horatio R. Palmer
PRAYER	51C	C.M.	William U. Butcher
PRINCE	78D	C.M.	Anonymous
PSALM TONE	70C	86.86	Arr. from Joseph Gelineau
PURSUIT	18K	10.10.10.10.	Anonymous
RAKEM	73A	88.88.88.	Isaac B. Woodbury
RATHBUN	132A	87.87.	Ithamar Conkey, 1849
RAVENDALE	33A	886.886.	Walter Stokes
REMEMBER ME	106D	C.M.	Adapted by James C. Wade
RESIGNATION	23C	11.11.11.11.	Anonymous
RESOLUTION	44C	C.M.D.	American melody
REST (See BRADBURY)			
REST	95B	C.M.	Lowell Mason, 1854
RETREAT	119R	L.M.	Thomas Hastings, 1842
REWARD	112A	C.M.D.	D. Bruce Martin, 1929
RIALTO	93A	S.M.	George F. Root
ROBINSON	44D	11.11.11.11	Anonymous
ROCK OF AGES (See TOPLADY)			
ROCKINGHAM	145C	L.M.	Edward Miller
ROCKINGHAM NEW	72B	L.M.	Lowell Mason, 1830

Name of Tune	Number	Meter	Composer, Arranger or Source
ROLLAND	102C	88.888.	William B. Bradbury
RUSSIA	119X	L.M.	Daniel Read, 1786
RUTH	60B	C.M.D.	Adapted from W. Irving Hartshorn
RUTHERFORD	126B	664.66.64.	John K. Robb, 1949
SABBATH EVENING	69E	C.M.	Thomas E. Perkins
ST. AGNES	42A	C.M.	John B. Dykes, 1866
ST. AMBROSE	78H	C.M.	Charles Steggall, 1849
ST. ANDREW	17A	C.M.	William Tans'ur, *New Harmony of Sion, II,* 1764
ST. ANNE	37A	C.M.	William Croft
ST. ASAPH	122A	C.M.D.	Giovanni M. Giornovichi
ST. BRIDE	70A	S.M.	Samuel Howard, 1762
ST. CATHERINE	90C	88.88.88	Henry F. Hemy, 1864; arr. James G. Walton, 1874
ST. CATHERINE'S	148	66.66.4444	Horatio R. Palmer
ST. CHRYSOSTOM	90D	88.88.88.	Joseph Barnby, 1871
ST. DENIO (See JOANNA)			
ST. ELIZABETH	143C	669.668.	Silesian folk song
ST. FLAVIAN	44B	C.M.	John Daye, *The Whole Booke of Psalmes,* 1562
ST. GREGORY	78G	C.M.	Robert Wainwright
ST. HILARY	109C	87.87.D	Anonymous
ST. JOHN	27F	66.66.88	William H. Havergal, 1853
ST. LAWRENCE	99B	C.M.	Robert A. Smith
ST. LEONARD	87	C.M.	Henry Smart, 1867
ST. MAGNUS	89D	C.M.	Jeremiah Clark, 1707
ST. MARTIN'S	117A	C.M.	William Tans'ur, 1740
ST. MATTHEW	55B	C.M.D.	William Croft, 1708
ST. MICHEL'S	37C,58A	C.M.D.	William Gawler, *The Hymns and Psalms,* c.1788
ST. PAUL	140A	C.M.	Chalmer's *Collection,* 1749
ST. PETER	37F	C.M.	Alexander R. Reinagle, c.1836
ST. SAVIOUR	105E	C.M.	Frederick G. Baker
ST. STEPHEN (See ABRIDGE)			
ST. STEPHEN	119C	C.M.	William Jones, 1789
ST. SYLVESTER	38B	87.87	John B. Dykes
ST. THOMAS	50B	S.M.	Aaron Williams, 1770
SAINTS' PRAISE	31G	76.76.D	John K. Robb, 1949
SALVUM FAC.	83C	11.10.11.10.D	Adapted from Andre Campra by Duncan Lowe, 1972
SALZBURG (See HINTZE)			
SALZBURG	115A	C.M.	Johann M. Haydn
SAMUEL	27E	66.66.88	Arthur S. Sullivan, 1874
SANDON	121C	10.4.10.4.10.10	Charles H. Purday, 1860
SANKEY	9A	11.11.11.11.	Ira D. Sankey, 1887
SARAH	55A	C.M.	Charles H. Gabriel, 1901
SAXONY	55C	C.M.	William J. Kirkpatrick
SCHMÜCKE DICH	64B	99.99.D	Johann Cruger, 1649
SCOTT	115B	C.M.D.	Arr. John K. Robb, 1929
SERENITY	26B	C.M.	William V. Wallace; arr. Uzziah C. Burnap
SEYMOUR	49A,49C	77.77	Carl M. von Weber; arr. Henry W. Greatorex, 1851
SHADDICK	107B	C.M.	Bates G. Burt, 1941
SHEFFIELD (See MEDFIELD)			
SHINING SHORE	136A	87.87.D. (Iambic)	George F. Root
SILILIAN HYMN (See SICILIAN MARINERS)			
SICILIAN MARINERS	103D	87.87.	Sicilian melody
SILCHESTER	108A	S.M.	H.A. Cesar Malan
SILOAM	69A	C.M.	Isaac B. Woodbury
SILVER STREET	50A	S.M.	Isaac Smith, c.1770
SOUL'S SURRENDER	116B	C.M.	D. Bruce Martin, 1923
SPENCER	105C	C.M.	Asa B. Everett
SPOHR	26A	C.M.	Adapted from Louis Spohr
STATE STREET	70B	S.M.	Jonathan C. Woodman, 1844
STELLA	84A	88.88.88	English melody, 1894
STOCKTON	20A,34B	C.M.D.	John H. Stockton
STRACATHRO	111B	C.M.	Charles Hutcheson, 1832
STRENGTH AND STAY	12B	11.10.11.10	John B. Dykes, 1875
STROUDWATER	150A	C.M.	Matthew Wilkins, *Psalmody,* c.1730

Name of Tune	Number	Meter	Composer, Arranger or Source
STUTTGART	98B	87.87	Arr. Christian F. Witt, 1715
SUNDERLAND	57B	C.M.	Chester G. Allen, 1869
SURSUM CORDA	10B	10.10.10.10	Alfred M. Smith; arr. Eleanor Hutcheson, 1972
SYRACUSE	127A	C.M.	Arr. John K. Robb, 1929
TABLER	32A	C.M.	E.H. Frost
TALLIS' ORDINAL	48A	C.M.	Thomas Tallis, 1567
TE DEUM	63B	687.687.10.10.87	Adapted from Andre Campra by Duncan Lowe, 1972
THANKSGIVING	92A,92B	C.M.D.	E.O. Butterfield
THE LORD IS NEAR	34E	10.10.10.10.10.10	T. Scott Huston, 1972
THIS ENDRIS NYGHT	71B	C.M.	15th C. English carol, harm. Ralph Vaughan-Williams
THRONE	97C	11.10.11.6.D	Charles McBurney and Eleanor Hutcheson, 1969
TIVERTON	22D	C.M.	John Rippon, *A Selection of Psalms and Hymn Tunes,* c.1791
TOPLADY	51D	77.77.77	Thomas Hastings, 1830
TRIUMPH	135C	87.87	Henry J. Gauntlett
TRENTHAM	25D	S.M.	Robert Jackson, 1888
TRURO	72A	L.M.	Thomas Williams, *Psalmodia Evangelica,* 1789
TRUST	73C	88.88.88	D. Bruce Martin, 1920
TRUST HIM (See STOCKTON)			
ULSTER	128B	87.87.D	Robert Lowry
UNDE ET MEMORES	80A	10.10.10.10.10.10	William H. Monk, 1875
UXBRIDGE	18A	L.M.	Lowell Mason, 1830
VARINA	24A	C.M.D.	George F. Root
VISION	22H	88.88.88.	William H. Doane
VOX DILECTI	32C	C.M.D.	John B. Dykes, 1868
WALLACE	4A	C.M.	Arr. John K. Robb, 1929
WAREHAM	35B	L.M.	William Knapp, 1738
WARRINGTON	35E	L.M.	Ralph Harrison
WARWICK	37D	C.M.	Samuel Stanley
WATCH	134B	Irregular.	Anonymous, arr. Charles McBurney, 1970
WAVERTREE	22G	88.88.88	William Shore
WEBB	65A	76.76.D	George J. Webb, 1837
WELCOME VOICE	25C	S.M.D.	Louis Hartsough
WESLEY	138B	L.M.	Isaac B. Woodbury
WETHERBY	42B	C.M.	Samuel S. Wesley, 1872
WEYMOUTH	68D	C.M.D.	Theodore P. Ferris, 1941
WIE SCHÖN LEUCHTET	66C	887.887.48.48	Philip Nicolai, 1599
WILTSHIRE	71D	C.M.	Sir George T. Smart, c.1795
WINCHESTER OLD	78B	C.M.	Arr. George Kirbye, in Thomas Est, *The Whole Booke of Psalmes,* 1592
WOODWORTH	91B	L.M.	William B. Bradbury, 1849
WORCESTER	58B	C.M.D.	William Billings, 1786
WORSHIP	31B	C.M.D.	Sir Robert P. Stewart
YORKE TUNE	14A	C.M.	*Scottish Psalter,* 1615
YORKE TUNE	14B	C.M.	*Scottish Psalter,* 1615; arr. Thomas Ravenscroft, 1621
YORKSHIRE	34C	10.10.10.10.10.10	John Wainwright, 1750
ZEPHYR	35D	L.M.	William B. Bradbury
ZERAH	48B	C.M.	Lowell Mason
ZION	134A	87.87.47	Thomas Hastings

METRICAL INDEX OF TUNES

SHORT METER (66 86)

SHORT METER DOUBLE

COMMON METER (86 86)

COMMON METER DOUBLE

INDEX OF COMPOSERS, ARRANGERS, AND SOURCE

An asterisk (*) indicates an arrangement or harmonization. References are to selection numbers.

ABBEY, Alonzo Judson (1825-1887) - Cooling, 63A.
ALEXIS, Gerhard Theodore (1889-1927) - Ishpeming, 41A.
ALLEN, Chester G. (1838-1878) - Sunderland, 57B.
ALLEN, George Nelson (1812-1877) - Maitland, 119I.
American Melody - Consolation, 56; Davis, 119T; Detroy, 140B; Foundation, 16B; Fountain, 107D; Nettleton, 119Q; New Britain, 3; Resolution, 44C.
ANONYMOUS - Bingham, 54A; Campbell, 32D; Leaf, 74A; Pisgah, 144C; Prince, 78D ; Pursuit, 18K; Resignation, 23C; Robinson, 44D; St. Hilary, 109C; Watch, 134B.
ARNE, Thomas Augustine (1710-1778) - Arlington, 1A, 40A.
ARNOLD, William (1768-1832) - Alexandria, 95A.
ATKINSON, Frederick Cook (1841-1897) - Morecambe, 18I.
BACH, Johann Sebastian (1685-1750) - *Commemoration, 65B; *Hintze, 2.
BAKER, Frederick George (1840-1876) - St. Saviour, 105E.
BAKER, Henry (1835-1910) - Hesperus, 119B.
BARNARD, Charlotte Alington (1830-1869) - Brocklesbury, 38C.
BARNBY, Joseph (1838-1896) - Longwood, 7A; St. Chrysostom, 90D.
BARTHELEMON, Francois Hippolyte (1741-1808) - Balerma, 17B.
BEETHOVEN, Ludwig van (1770-1827) - Croydon, 68E; Emmanuel, 89H.
BILLINGS, William (1746-1800) - Worcester, 58B.
BEAUMONT, John (1762-1822) - Beaumont, 104C.
BISCHOFF, J.W. - Morning Light, 5A.
Bohemian Melody - Freuen wir uns, 18B.
BORTNIANSKI, Dmitri Stepanovitch (1752-1825) - Petersburg, 73B.
BOURGEOIS, Louis (c. 1510-c.1561) - Old 38th, 38A; Old 77th, 52B; Old 95th, 95C; Old 100th, 100A; Old 110th, 129; Old 124th, 124B; Old 128th, 14C.
BRADBURY, William Batchelder (1816-1868) - Abbeyville, 121B, 125; Agawam, 69B; Andre, 72C; Baca, 102A; Bradbury, 85B; Brown, 106A; Clarksville, 19A; Dodd, 37E; Harvey's Chant, 31C; Helena, 51A; Keokuk, 81B; Mason's Chant, 52A; Monora, 83A; Newell, 107A; Olive's Brow, 6; Pinneo, 44A; Rolland, 102C; Woodworth, 91B; Zephyr, 35D.
BROADWOOD, Lucy (1858-1929) - Capel, 144A; Kingsfold, 22C.
BROWN, Arthur Henry (1830-1926) - Holy Cross, 79A.
BURLEIGH, Henry Thacker (1866-1949) - McKee, 128A.
BURNAP, Uzziah Christopher (1834-1900) - Boston, 27A; *Serenity, 26B.
BURT, Bates Gilbert (1878-1948) - Shaddick, 107B.
BUTCHER, William U. - Prayer, 51C.
BUTTERFIELD, E.O. - Thanksgiving, 92A; 92B.
CAMPBELL, John P. (fl. c. 1900) - Mobile, 44F.
CAMPRA, Andre (1660-1744) - Salvum Fac, 83C; Te Deum, 63B.
CHALMER'S *Collection* - St. Paul, 140A.
CHAPIN, Aaron (1768-18) - Dunlapscreek, 137.
CHETHAM, John (c. 1700-1763) - Marlow, 119V.
CLARK, Jeremiah (c. 1673-1707) - Bishopthorpe, 119S; St. Magnus, 89D.
CLARK, Thomas (1775-1859) - Crediton, 59B; Grafton, 97A.
CLARKE, Hugh Archibald (b. 1839) - Hallelujah, 146B.
COLE, John (1774-1855) - Geneva, 126A.
CONKEY, Ithamar (1815-1867) - Rathbun, 132A.
Collection of Hymns and Sacred Poems, Dublin, 1749 - Irish, 83B.
CONVERSE, Charles Crozat (1832-1918) - Converse, 146A.
COPELAND, Robert Marshall (1945-) - Beulah Church, 7B; *Charlestown, 119G; *Clonmel, 105D; *Consolation, 56; *Detroy, 140B; Louise, 27C; Margaret, 18G; *Old 77th, 52B: *Old 128th, 14C.
COPES, Vicar Earle (1921-) - Kingdom, 94B.
CORNER, David Gregor, *Gesangbuch,* 1631 - Omni Die, 82.
COTTMAN, Arthur (1842-1879) - Dalehurst, 17C.
CRAWFORD, Edward Patrick (1846-1912) - Jehovah Nissi, 33B.
CROFT, William (1678-1727) - St. Anne, 37A; St. Matthew, 55B.
CRUGER, Johann (1598-1662) - Graefenberg, 119L; Schmücke Dich, 64B
CUNNINGHAM, Francis. *Selection of Psalm Tunes,* 1834 - Birmingham, 18J.

CUTHBERT, Elizabeth Howard (c. 1800-1859) - Howard, 119H.
CUTLER, Henry Stephen (1824-1902) - All Saints New, 110.
DANKS, Hart Pease (1834-1903) - Delphine, 86B.
DARWALL, John (1731-1789) - Darwall's 148th, 92C.
DAYE, John. *The Whole Booke of Psalmes,* 1562- St. Flavian, 44B.
DEARLE, Edward (1806-1891) - Penitentia, 10A.
DEDEKAM, Sophie - Dedekam, 78E.
DIX, Leopold L. (1861-1935) - *Fingal, 40E.
DOANE, William Howard (1832-1915) - Vision, 22H.
DOUGALL, Neil (1776-1862) - Kilmarnock, 114.
Dutch Melody - Kremser, 29A.
DYKES, John Bacchus (1823-1876) - Beatitudo, 90B; Melita, 84B; Pax Dei, 18L; St. Agnes, 42A; St. Sylvester, 38B; Strength and Stay, 12B; Vox Dilecti, 32C.
ELVEY, George Job (1816-1893) - Diademata, 45C.
EMERSON, Luther Orlando (1820-1915) - Lozina, 105A.
English Melody - Believe, 68B; Capel, 144A; Forest Green, 40C; Kingsfold, 22C; Millenium, 19B; Noel, 21A, 89B; Stella, 84A; This Endris Night, 71B.
EST, Thomas. *The Whole Booke of Psalmes,* 1592 - Winchester Old, 78B.
EVERETT, Asa Brooks (1828-1875) - Spencer, 105C.
FARMER, John (1836-1901) - Farmer, 30B.
FERRIS, Theodore Parker (1908-) - Weymouth, 68D.
FINK, Gottfried Wilhelm (1783-1846) - Bethlehem, 149.
FINLAY, Kenneth George (1882-) - Ayrshire, 120.
FRECH, Johann Georg (1790-1864) - Aspurg, 118B.
French Psalter, adapted - Barnabas, 28B. Cf. *Genevan Psalter.*
French Air - Champs Elysees, 34A.
FREYLINGHAUSEN, Johann Anastasius. *Geistreiches Gesangbuch,* 1704 - Amsterdam, 8B.
FROST, E.H. - Tabler, 32A.
GABRIEL, Charles H. (1856-1932) - Gabriel, 31A; Kathrine, 75; Sarah, 55A.
GARDINER, William, *Sacred Melodies,* v. 1, 1812 - Belmont, 12A; *Park Street, 102B; v. 2, 1815 - Gardiner, 91D; *Lyons, 104A.
GAUNTLETT, Henry John (1805-1876) - Houghton, 104E; Triumph, 135C.
GAUNTLETT, Henry John. *Comprehensive Tune Book.* 1851 - Giessen, 1B.
GAWLER, William. *The Hymns and Psalms,* c. 1788 - St. Michel's, 37C; 58A.
GELINEAU, Joseph, *S.J.* - Psalm Tone, 70C.
Genevan Psalter (various dates, 1542-1562) - Old 38th, 38A; Old 77th, 52B; Old 95th, 95C; Old 100th, 100A; Old 124th, 124B; Old 128th, 14C.
German Melody - Cassell, 109A; Mendon, 35C.
Gesangbuch der Herzogl. Wurttemberg. Hofkapelle. 1784 - Ellacombe, 21B, 78C.
GESIUS, Bartholomaeus (1555-1613) - Commemoration, 65B.
GIORNOVICHI, Giovanni Marie (1745-1804) - St. Asaph, 122A.
GLASER, Carl Gotthelf (1784-1829) - Azmon, 43, 133A.
GOSS, Sir John (1800-1880) - Bevan, 27D; Chant D, 47B.
GOTTSCHALK, Louis Moreau (1829-1869) - Mercy, 49B.
GOULD, John Edgar (1822-1875) - Bera, 85A.
GOUNOD, Charles Francois (1818-1893) - Lux Prima, 115C.
GOWER, John Henry (1855-1922) - Meditation, 13.
GRANT, David (1833-1893) - *Crimond, 23B.
GREATOREX, Henry Wellington (1813-1858) - *Manoah, 36A; *Seymour, 49A, 49C.
Gregorian Chant - Hamburg, 35A, 119U; Nashville, 42C; O Salutaris, 91C; Olmutz, 11; Patmos, 142.
GRIGG, Joseph (d. 1768) - Grigg, 78F.
GRIGG, Thomas - Tiverton, 22D.
HAMILTON, Edward (1812-1870) - Leveque, 106E.
HANDEL, George Friedrich (1685-1759) - Halifax, 89E.
HARDING, James P. (c. 1860-1911) - Morning Star, 119K.
HARRISON, Ralph (1748-1810) - *Arlington, 1A, 40A; Warrington, 35E.
HARTSHORN, W. Irving - Ruth, 60B.
HARTSOUGH, Louis (1820-1872) - Welcome Voice, 25C.
HASTINGS, Eurotas P. (1791-1866) - Detroit, 25B.
HASTINGS, Thomas (1784-1872) - Calm, 141A; Laight Street, 68A; Retreat, 119R; Toplady, 51D; Zion, 134A.
HATTON, John C. (d. 1793) - Duke Street, 145A.
HAVERGAL, William Henry (1793-1870) - Chant B, 19D; Evan, 23A; St. John, 27F.
HAYDN, Franz Josef (1732-1809) - Austria, 94A; Creation, 22I; Haydn, 108C.
HAYDN, Johann Michael (1737-1806) - Lyons, 104A; Salzburg, 115A.

Hebrew Melody - Leoni, 99C.
HEMY, Henry Frederick (1818-1888) - St. Catherine, 90C.
HERBERT, John Bunyan - Herbert, 68C; Lafayette, 69D.
HERMANN, Nikolaus (c. 1490-1561) - Holy Trinity, 18E.
HEWS, George (1806-1873) - Holley, 139A, 139C.
HINTZE, Jakob (1622-1702) - Hintze, 2.
Hirschberger Gesangbuch, 1741 - O Jesu, 81A.
HOLBROOK, Joseph Parry (1822-1888) - Clinton, 57A; Miriam, 67B.
HOLDEN, Oliver (1765-1844) - Coronation, 96A.
HOPKINS, Edward John (1818-1901) - Ellers, 88B.
HORSLEY, William (1774-1858) - Belgrave, 124A.
HOWARD, Alonzo Potter (1838-1902) - Ephratah, 69C.
HOWARD, Cuthbert (1856-1927) - Lloyd, 119P.
HOWARD, Samuel (1710-1782) - St. Bride, 70A.
HUDSON, Ralph E. (1843-1901) - Hudson, 118A.
HUGHES, John (1873-1932) - Cwm Rhondda, 122B.
HULL, Asa (b. 1828) - Hull, 119N.
HUSTON, T. Scott (1916-) - God Revered, 89C; How Good the Lord Is, 135A; The Lord is Near, 34E.
HUTCHESON, Charles (1792-1860) - Stracathro, 111B.
HUTCHESON, Eleanor McLam (1920-) - Alpha, 41C; Barnet, 117B; Beta, 72D; Confidence, 112B; Delta, 106G; Enter, 100C; Gamma, 89I; *Old 95th, 95C; Omega, 150B; *Sursum Corda, 10B; Throne, 97C.
INGALLS, Jeremiah (1764-1828) - Fillmore, 22F.
Irish Melody - Clonmel, 105D; Fingal, 40E; Irish, 83B.
IRVINE, Jessie Seymour (1836-1887) - Crimond, 23B.
JACKSON, Robert (1842-1914) - Trentham, 25D.
JACKSON, Thomas (c. 1715-1781) - Chant E, 84C; Jackson, 118C.
JAMOUNEAU, Arthur J. - Lynton, 27B.
JARMAN, Thomas (1782-1862) - Desert, 98A.
JONES, William (1726-1800) - St. Stephen, 119C.
Katholisches Gesangbuch, Vienna, c. 1774 - Hursley, 138A.
Kentucky Harmony, 1817 - Covenanters, 40B, 89F. Cf. *Supplement to the Kentucky Harmony.*
KETTLE, Charles E. (1833-1895) - Farningham, 133B.
KINGSLEY, George (1811-1884) - Elizabethtown, 107C; Heber, 105B.
KIRBYE, George (d. 1634) - *Winchester Old, 78B.
KIRKPATRICK, William James (1838-1921) - Kirkpatrick, 135B; Saxony, 55C.
KNAPP, William (1698-1768) - Wareham, 35B.
KREMSER, Edward (1838-1914) - *Kremser, 39A.
KROEGER, Ernest Richard (1862-1934) - Christine, 119A; Josephine, 61.
LAHEE, Henry (1826-1912) - Nativity, 22E.
LANDAHL, Carl Wilfred (b. 1908) - Invocation, 34D.
LANE, Spencer (1843-1903) - Penitence, 4B.
LANGRAN, James (1835-1909) - Langran, 39A.
Lausanne Choral Book - Lausanne, 40F.
LEIGHTON, William (d. before 1614) - Leighton, 20B.
LE JEUNE, Claude (1528-1600) - *Old 38th, 38A.
LESLIE, C.E. City of Our God, 119F.
LOMAS, George, (1834-1884) - De Profundis, 130B.
LOVELACE, Austin C. (b. 1919) - *Davis, 119T; *Halifax, 89E.
LOWE, George Duncan (1935-) - *Pavanas, 62B; *Salvum Fac, 83C; *Te Deum, 63B.
LOWRY, Joseph C. - Covenanters, 40B, 89F.
LOWRY, Robert (1826-1899) - I Need Thee Every Hour, 143B; Lowry, 15; Ulster, 128B.
LUTHER, Martin (1483-1546) - Ein' Feste Burg, 46C.
MAKER, Frederick Charles (1844-1927) - Invitation, 143A.
MALAN, Henri Abraham Cesar (1787-1864)-Boynton, 111A; Hendon, 113A; Silchester, 108A.
MANN, Arthur Henry (1850-1929) - Angel's Story, 30A.
MARTIN, Donald Bruce (1880-1941) - Fair Haven, 79B; Hope, 121A; Reward, 112A; Soul's Surrender, 116B; Trust, 73C.
MARTIN, George William (1828-1881) - Leominster, 25A.
MARTIN, William - Marsella, 144B.
MASON, Henry Lowell (b. 1864) - Exeter, 106C.
MASON, Lowell (1792-1872) - Apheka, 147B; Boswell, 119D; Boylston, 53; Chimes, 119J; Cowper, 123; Downs, 60A; Ernan, 145B; *Evan, 23A; *Hamburg, 35A, 119U; Heath, 41B; Laban, 45B; *Mendon, 35C; Meribah, 33C; Missionary Hymn, 67A; Mount Vernon, 38D; *Naomi, 22A; *Nashville, 42C; *Olmutz, 11; Ostend, 116A; Rest, 95B; Rockingham New, 72B; Uxbridge, 18A; Zerah, 48B.

ATHER, William (1756-1808) - Medfield, 16A.
CBURNEY, Charles Reed (1914-) - *Nashville, 42; Throne, 97C; *Watch, 134B.
CCRACKEN, Paul DeLo (1898-) - Myra, 51B.
ENDELSSOHN, Felix (1809-1847) - Bunyan, 141B; Peace, 36B.
ETHENY, Samuel Alexander Sterrett (1869-1921) - Compassion, 103C; Dominus Regit Me, 23D; Evadna, 130A; Greyfriars, 24C; Humility, 131; Mara, 44E; Mersine, 88A; *O Salutaris, 91C.
ILLER, Edward (1731-1807) - Rockingham, 145C.
IONK, Edwin George (1819-1900) - Chant C, 19E.
ONK, William Henry (1823-1889)-Eventide, 39B; Morning, 115D; Unde et Memores, 80A.
IOORE, Thomas (fl. 1750-1792) - *Effingham, 77C; Glasgow, 100B.
AGELI, Johann George (1773-1836) - Main, 32B; Naomi, 22A.
ARES, James (1715-1783) - Amsterdam, 8B; Chant G, 127B.
EANDER, Joachim (1650-1680) - Neander, 76A.
egro Melody - McKee, 128A.
NEUMARK, Georg (1621-1681) - Neumark, 76B.
NICOLAI, Philip (1556-1608) - Wie schon leuchtet, 66C.
OLIVER, Henry Kemble (1800-1885) - Federal Street, 119W.
OUSELEY, Frederick Arthur Gore (1825-1889) - Chant A, 19C; Contemplation, 71A.
OWEN, William (1814-1893) - Bryn Calfaria, 80B.
PALESTRINA, Giovanni Pierluigi da (1525-1594) - Palestrina, 77A.
PALMER, Horatio Richmond (1834-1907) - Give Ye to Jehovah, 29B; Politz, 71C; St. Catherine's, 148.
PARKER, Horatio William (1863-1919) - Jubilate, 113B.
PARRY, Joseph (1841-1903) - Aberystwyth, 5B.
PEACE, Albert Lister (1844-1912) - Green Hill, 40D.
PERKINS, Theodore Edson (1831-1912) - Canaan, 107E; Sabbath Evening, 69E.
PILSBURY, Amos. *U.S. Sacred Harmony,* 1799 - Charlestown, 119G.
POND, Sylvanus B. (1792-1871) - Henry, 97B.
POOLE, Clement William (1828-1924) - Petersham, 47A.
PRITCHARD, Rowland Hugh (1811-1887) - Hyfrydol, 91A.
PURDAY, Charles Henry (1799-1885) - Sandon, 121C.
RAVENSCROFT, Thomas. *The Whole Booke of Psalmes,* 1621 - Norwich, 89G; *Yorke Tune, 14B.
READ, Daniel (1757-1836) - Russia, 119X.
REDHEAD, Richard (1820-1901) - Ajalon, 51E.
REINAGLE, Alexander Robert (1799-1877) - St. Peter, 37F.
RIEMANN, J.B. *Hirschberger Gesangbuch,* 1741 - O Jesu, 81A.
RIPPON, John. *A Selection of Psalms and Hymn Tunes,* c. 1791 - Tiverton, 22D.
ROBB, John Knox (1868-1960) - Bradford, 104D; Conwell, 86A; Emsworth, 104B; Hetherton, 46B; Rutherford, 126B; Saints' Praise, 31G; *Scott, 115B; *Syracuse, 127A; *Wallace, 4A.
ROBERTS, John, ed., *Caniadou y Cyssegr,* 1839 - *Joanna, 9B.
ROOT, George Frederick (1820-1895) - Alpena, 106F; Rialto, 93A; Shining Shore, 136A; Varina, 24A.
ROPER, Charles F. (fl. late 19th C.) - Jerusalem, 62A.
SANKEY, Ira David (1840-1908) - Sankey, 9A.
SANZ, Gaspar (17th century) - Pavanas, 62B.
SCHAEFER, Lois Hinman (1933-) - *Old 110th, 129.
SCHEIN, Johann Hermann (1586-1630) - Eisenach, 18F; Goeldel, 18D.
SCHNEIDER, Johann Christian Friedrich (1786-1853) - Lischer, 144D.
SCHUMANN, Robert (1810-1856) - Canonbury, 18C.
Scottish Psalter of: 1615 - Dundee, 28A; Dunfermline, 8A; Martyrs, 22B; Yorke Tune, 14A, 14B
1634 - Culross, 64A.
SHERMAN, W.F. - Onward, 147A.
SHERWIN, William Fishe (1826-1888) - Heavenly Fold, 37B.
SHORE, William (fl. mid 19th C.) - Wavertree, 22G.
SHRUBSOLE, William (1760-1806) - Miles Lane, 66A.
Sicilian Melody - Sicilian Mariners, 103D.
Silesian Folk Song - St. Elizabeth, 143C.
SIMPSON, Robert (1790-1832) - *Balerma, 17B.
SMART, George Thomas (1776-1867) - Wiltshire, 71D.
SMART, Henry Thomas (1813-1879) - Lancashire, 31E; Nomina, 59A; Pilgrims, 116C; St. Leonard, 87A.
SMITH, Alfred Morton (1879-19) - Sursum Corda, 10B.
SMITH, Henry Percy (1825-1898) - Maryton, 139B.
SMITH, Isaac (c. 1725-c.1800) - Abridge, 99A; Silver Street, 50A.

SMITH, Robert Archibald (1780-1829) - *Martyrdom, 90A; St. Lawrence, 99B.
SPOHR, Louis (1784-1859) - Illa, 78A; Spohr, 26A.
STAINER, John (1840-1901) - Chant F, 93B.
STANLEY, Samuel (1767-1822) - Warwick, 37D.
STEBBINS, George Cole (1846-1945) - Evening Prayer, 103B.
STEGGALL, Charles H. (1826-1905) - Morwellham, 96B; St. Ambrose, 78H.
STEWART, Robert Prescott (1825-1894) - Worship, 31B.
STOCKTON, John Hart (1813-1877) - Stockton, 20A, 34B.
STOKES, Walter - Ravendale, 33A.
SULLIVAN, Arthur Seymour (1842-1900) - *Bethlehem, 149; Constance, 136B; *Leominster, 25A; *Noel, 21A, 89B; Samuel, 27E.
Supplement to Kentucky Harmony, 1820 - Detroy, 140B.
TALLIS, Thomas (c. 1520-1585) - Tallis' Ordinal, 48A.
TAN'SUR, William (1706-1783) - St. Andrew, 17A; St. Martin's, 117A.
TATE, Laura A. - Bovina, 77B.
TAYLOR, E.G. - Latakia, 21C, 21D.
TAYLOR, R.S. - New Jerusalem, 89A.
TAYLOR, Virgil Corydon (1817-1891) - Louvan, 119O
Temple Melodies - Knox, 106B.
TENNEY, John Harrison (b. 1840) - Perfect Way, 119M.
THOMMEN, *Erbaulicher, Musikalischer Christenschatz,* 1745 - Batty, 109B; Cassell, 109A.
TUCKER, Isaac - Clarendon, 66B.
UNSELD, Benjamin C. (1843-1923) - Ancyra, 31D.
VAUGHAN-WILLIAMS, Ralph, (1872-1958) - *Capel, 144A; *Forest Green, 40C; *Hyfrydol, 91A; *Kingsfold, 22C; *This Endris Nyght, 71B.
VENUA, Frederic Marc Antoine (1786-1872) - Park Street, 102B.
VINCENT, Charles John (1852-1934) - Ishmael, 108B.
Virginia Harmony, 1831 - New Britain, 3.
VULPIUS, Melchoir (c. 1560-1615) - Phuvah, 62C.
WADE, James C. (b. 1847) - *Remember Me, 106D.
WAINWRIGHT, John (c. 1723-1768) - Yorkshire, 34C.
WAINWRIGHT, Robert (c. 1748-1782) - St. Gregory, 78G.
WALKER, William. *Southern Harmony,* 1835 - Foundation, 16B.
WALLACE, William Vincent (1812-1865) - Serenity, 26B.
WALTON, James George (1821-1905) - *St. Catherine, 90C.
WARD, Samuel Augustus (1848-1903) - Materna, 46A.
WEBB, George James (1803-1887) - Webb, 65A.
WEBER, Carl Maria von (1786-1826) - Seymour, 49A, 49C.
WEISSE, Michael (c. 1480-1534) - *Freuen wir uns, 18B.
WELLS, Marcus Morris (1815-1895) - Guide, 51F.
Welsh Melody - Joanna, 9B; Llangloffan, 31F.
WESLEY, John. *Collection of Tunes as they are sung at the Foundry,* 1742 - *Amsterdam, 8B.
WESLEY, Samuel Sebastian (1810-1876) - Aurelia, 101; Wetherby, 42B.
WHEALL, William (c. 1690-1727) - Bedford, 119E.
WILKINS, Matthew. *A Book of Psalmody,* c. 1730 - Stroudwater, 150A.
WILLIAMS, Aaron (1731-1776) - Mear, 24B; St. Thomas, 50B.
WILLIAMS, Thomas. *Psalmodia Evangelica,* 1789 - Broomsgrove, 74B; Truro, 72A.
WILLIAMS, Thomas John (1869-1944) - Ebenezer, 54B.
WILSON, Hugh (1764-1824) - Martyrdom, 90A.
WITT, Christian Friedrich (1660-1716) - *Stuttgart, 98B.
WITTWE, Georg. *Musikalisches Handbuch,* 1690 - Crasselius, 18H; Effingham, 77C.
WOODBURY, Isaac Baker (1819-1858) - *Creation, 22I; Dorrnance, 132B; Montgomery, 50C; Rakem, 73A; Siloam, 69A; Wesley, 138B.
WOODMAN, Jonathan Call (1813-1894) - State Street, 70B.
Wurttemberg *Gesangbuch,* 1784 - Ellacombe, 21B, 78C.
WYETH, John. *Repository of Sacred Music, Part Second,* 1813 - Consolation, 56; Davis, 119T; Nettleton, 119Q.
YOUNG, Carlton R. (b. 1926) - *Foundation, 16B.
ZUNDEL, John (1815-1882) - Beecher, 103A; Louisville, 45A.

FIRST AND FAMILIAR LINES

TOPICAL INDEX

To aid in the quick location of references which are not characteristic of an entire Psalm or selection, some selections are followed by a colon and a verse number. Note that verse numbers are in small superscript throughout THE BOOK OF PSALMS and frequently do not coincide with stanza numbers.

A related or substitute topic listed after "See" is in capital letters if it is a major heading in the index and in lower case if it is a sub-heading.

PSALMS QUOTED IN THE NEW TESTAMENT

Bold face: direct quotation; Light face: allusion or indirect quotation

Psalm	Stanza	New Test. Ref.
1:6	1A:6-B:3	1 Cor 8:3
2:1,2	2:1	**Acts 4:25,26**; Rev 11:18
2:6	2:2	Rev 14:1
2:7	2:3	**Acts 13:33; Heb 1:5; 5:5**
2:8	2:3	Heb 1:2
3:8	3:5	Rev 7:10
4:4	4A:4-B:2	**Eph 4:26**
5:5	5AB:2	Rom 1:30
5:9	5AB:4	**Rom 3:13**
6:8	6:5	**Matt 7:23; Luke 13:27**
7:9	7A:5	Rev 2:23
7:13	7B:7	Eph 6:16
7:14	7B:8	Jas 1:15
8:2	8A:2-B:1	**Matt 21:16**
8:4/6	8A:4/6-B:2,3	**Heb 2:6,7**
8:6	8A:6-B:3	**1 Cor 15:27; Eph 1:22**
9:8	9A:4	Acts 17:31
10:7	10A:4	**Rom 3:14**
14:1/3	14AB:1/3-C:1,2	**Rom 3:10/12**
16:8/11	16A:7/10-B:4,5	**Acts 2:25/28**
16:10	16A:9-B:4,5	**Acts 13:35**
17:15	17C:13	Rev 22:4
18:2	18A:1-G:1	Luke 1:69
18:49	18F:29-L:25	**Rom 15:9**
19:1/6	19A:1/4-C:1/5	Rom 1:20
19:4	19A:2-C:3	**Rom 10:18**
19:9	19B:6-D:8	Rev 16:7; 19:2
21:3	21AC:2	Rev 14:14
22:1	22AB:1-F:1	**Matt 27:46; Mark 15:34**
22:5	22AB:3-F2	Rom 5:5
22:7	22AB:5-F:3	**Matt 27:39**
22:8	22AB:6-F:3	**Matt 27:43**
22:16,20	22C:9,10-G:7	Phil 3:2
22:18	22C:10-G:7	**Matt 27:35; Mark 15:24; Luke 23:34; John 19:24**
22:21	22D:11-G:8	II Tim 4:17
22:22	22D:11-H:9	**Heb 2:12**
23:1,2	23ABCD:1	John 10:11; Rev 7:17
24:1	24ABC:1	**I Cor 10:26**
24:2	24ABC:1	II Pet 3:5
24:4	24A:2-B:4-C:2	Matt 5:8; I Tim 2:8
25:9,14	25C:7,9	John 7:17
26:2	26A:2	Rev 2:23
26:8	26B:5	Matt 23:21
27:14	27C:16-F:10	I Cor 16:13
28:4	28A:4-B:2	Rev 20:12; 22:12
29:3	29A:2	Acts 7:2; Rev 10:3
31:5	31A:4-F:2	**Luke 23:46**
31:24	31D:16-G:10	I Cor 16:13
32:1,2	32A:1,2-C:1	**Rom 4:7,8**
32:2	32A:3-C:1	Rev 14:5
32:9	32B:11-D:4	Jas 3:3
33:3	33A:1	Rev 5:9; 14:3
33:12	33B:6	Titus 2:14
33:13-15	33B:7	Heb 4:13
34:2	34AC:1	Luke 1:46
34:8	34AC:3	I Pet 2:3
34:12/16	34BD:4,5	**I Pet 3:10/12**
34:14	34BD:4	Rom 12:18; 14:19; Heb 12:14; III John 11
34:15	34BDE:5	John 9:31
34:20	34B:7-DE:6	**John 19:36**
35:9	35B:7	**Luke 1:47**
35:19	35D:15	**John 15:25**
36:1	36A:1	**Rom 3:18**
37:11	37B:8	**Matt 5:5**
37:24	37D:14	II Cor 4:9
37:27	37D:16	III John 11
38:11	38A:5-C:7	Luke 23:49
38:20	38A:9-D:12	I John 3:12
39:1	39A:1	Jas 1:26
39:5	39A:3	Matt 6:27; Luke 12:25; Jas 4:14
39:5,6	39A:3,4	Rom 8:20
39:6	39A:4	Luke 12:20
39:12	39B:8	Heb 11:13; I Pet 2:11
40:3	40AB:3-E:1	Rev 5:9; 14:3
40:6/8	40C:6-E:3,4	**Heb 10:5/9**
41:9	41A:4	**John 13:18**
41:13	41BC:8	**Luke 1:68**
42:2	42A:2-C:1	Rev 22:4
44:2	44AD:1	Acts 7:45
44:22	44C:12-F:11	**Rom 8:36**
45:5,6	45B:6	**Heb 1:8,9**
45:8	45B:8	John 19:39
46:3	46ABC:1	Luke 21:25
46:4	46ABC:2	Rev 22:1
46:6	46AB:3-C:2	Rev 11:18
47:3	47A:1-B:2	Rev 3:9
47:8	47A:3-B:4	Rev 4:2,9,10; 5:1
50:6	50A:6	Heb 12:23
50:12	50B:11	I Cor 10:26
50:15	50B:13	Jas 5:13
51:4	51A:3-D:2	**Rom 3:4**
53:1/3	53:1/3	**Rom 3:10/12**
55:17	55C:9	Acts 10:9
55:22	55C:14	I Pet 5:7
62:10	62B:3-C:8	I Tim 6:17
62:12	62B:3-C:10	**Matt 16:27; Rom 2:6;** Rev 2:23; 20:12,13; 22:12
63:4	63A:3-B:2	I Tim 2:8
63:9	63A:7-B:3	Eph 4:9
65:7	65B:4	Luke 21:25
65:9/13	65B:5,6	Acts 14:17
66:6	66A:5-C:2	I Cor 10:1
66:10,12	66B:8,9-C:3	I Cor 3:15; I Pet 1:7
66:18	66B:13-C:5	John 9:31
67:2	67AB:1	Acts 28:28
68:18	68C:11	**Eph 4:8**
69:4	69A:3	**John 15:25**
69:9	69B:8	**John 2:17;** Rom 15:3
69:11	69B:9	**Rev 11:3**
69:21	69C:14	John 19:28
69:22,23	69D:15	**Rom 11:9,10**
69:25	69D:16	**Acts 1:20**
69:28	69D:19	Luke 10:20
72:10,11,15	72B:5,6,8	Matt 2:11; Rev 21:24
72:18	72C:11-D	**Luke 1:68**
73:1	73A:1	Matt 5:8
74:2	74A:1	Acts 20:28
75:8	75:5	Rev 14:10
76:7	76AB:3	Rev 6:17
78:2	78A:1	**Matt 13:35**
78:4	78A:2	Eph 6:4